EFFLUENT TREATMENT AND DISPOSAL

A three-day symposium organised by the Yorkshire Branch of The Institution of Chemical Engineers and held at the University of Bradford, 15 – 17 April 1986.

Organising Committee

P. J. Heggs (Chairman)	University of Bradford
P. J. Bailes	University of Bradford
D. A. Bailey	Yorkshire Water Authority
R. Bragg	Cambridge Process Engineering Consultants
P. Croft	Allied Colloids Manufacturing Co Ltd
M. F. Edwards	University of Bradford
D. Handley	University of Leeds
B. Mills	Peabody Holmes Ltd
G. P. Noone	Severn Trent Water Authority
M. S. Powell	Unilever Research
T. A. Radford	BP Chemicals
J. B. Rhoades	Yorkshire Water Authority
E. Rothwell	Yorkshire Branch
M. Sane	W. S. Atkins
E. H. Stitt	University of Bradford
D. Wakefield	Peabody Holmes Ltd

The Institution of Chemical Engineers
Symposium Series No. 96

ISBN 0 85295 197 3

PUBLISHED BY THE INSTITUTION OF CHEMICAL ENGINEERS

Copyright © 1986 The Institution of Chemical Engineers

First edition 1986 – ISBN 0 85295 197 3

MEMBERS OF THE INSTITUTION OF CHEMICAL ENGINEERS (Worldwide) SHOULD ORDER DIRECT FROM THE INSTITUTION

Geo. E Davis Building, 165 – 171 Railway Terrace, Rugby, Warks CV21 3HQ.

Australian orders to:

R M Wood, School of Chemical Engineering and Industrial Chemistry, University of New South Wales, PO Box 1, Kensington, NSW, Australia 2033.

Distributed throughout the world (excluding Australia) by Pergamon Press Ltd, except to IChemE members.

U.K.	Pergamon Press Ltd., Headington Hill Hall Oxford OX3 0BW, England.
U.S A.	Pergamon Press Inc., Maxwell House, Fairview Park, Elmsford, New York 10523, U.S.A.
CANADA	Pergamon Press Canada Ltd., Suite 104, 150 Consumers Road, Willowdale, Ontario M2J 1P9, Canada
FEDERAL REPUBLIC OF GERMANY	Pergamon Press GmbH, 6242 Kronberg-Taunus, Hammerweg 6, Federal Republic of Germany
JAPAN	Pergamon Press, 8th Floor, Matsuoka Central Building, 1-7-1 Nishishinjuku, Shinjuku-ku, Tokyo 160, Japan
BRAZIL	Pergamon Editora Ltda, Rua Eça de Quciros, 346, CEP 04011, Sáo Paulo, Brazil
PEOPLE'S REPUBLIC OF CHINA	Pergamon Press, Qianmca Hotel, Beijing, People's Republic of China

British Library Cataloguing in Publication Data

Effluent treatment and disposal : a three-day symposium. – (EFCE event; no. 339) (The Institution of Chemical Engineers symposium series; no. 96)
1. Factory and trade waste
I. Heggs, P.J.   II. Institution of Chemical Engineers. *Yorkshire Branch*   III. Series IV. Series
628.5'4   TD897
ISBN 0-08-032642-0

Library of Congress Cataloging-in-Publication Data

Effluent treatment and disposal.
(The Institution of Chemical Engineers symposium series; no. 96)
"EFCE event no. 339."
Includes bibliographies.
1. Sewage–Purification–Congresses.   2. Refuse and refuse disposal–Congresses.
3. Sewage–Purification–Biological treatment–Congresses.   4. Pollution–Developing countries– –Congresses.   5. Technology transfer–Developing countries–Congresses.
I. Institution of Chemical Engineers (Great Britain). Yorkshire Branch.   II. Series: Symposium series (Institution of Chemical Engineers (Great Britain)); no. 96)
TD745.E439   1986   628.3   86-15116
ISBN 0-08-032642-0

Foreword

It is just eleven years since the Institution of Chemical Engineers and its Yorkshire Branch organised a Symposium on the Application of Chemical Engineering to the Treatment of Sewage and Industrial Liquid Effluents (Symposium Series No. 41, 1975). The objective of that symposium was to provide a forum whereby people from a wide range of disciplines could get together to hear papers presented by acknowledged experts in the field, to engage in stimulating discussions, and to exchange ideas.

In the intervening years it has been apparent that effluent treatment and disposal is a multi-disciplinary topic and it is pleasing to note that this symposium has the cooperation of the other Institutions, Societies and Research Centres involved with the subject. Likewise, the structure of the organising committee reflects the cooperation that exists across the various discipline boundaries. I personally thank all the committee members for their efforts in the preparation of this symposium and of course, the members of the conference section at the Institution of Chemical Engineers.

The underlying theme of this conference is technology transfer and this is not too different from the previous objective. The 'newest' interest is the possible option of biological treatment and this is covered in two sessions. Other sessions cover special methods for water pollution control, gaseous pollution control, pollution control in developing countries and aspects of solids waste disposal.

The authors and their employers are thanked for their interest in the conference, and the material presented in the papers. Last, but not least, the referees are acknowledged for their time in reviewing the original manuscripts and the helpful comments.

The forum has been arranged and I hope the registrants enjoy the conference and also the visit to Bradford University and Yorkshire.

P. J. HEGGS
Conference Chairman

Contents

Biological Treatment Processes for Liquid Effluent — Current Status of Aerobic Systems

Solid Phase and Anaerobic Liquid Effluent Treatment Processes

These papers are numbered out of page sequence

Special Methods for Water Pollution Control: Adsorption and Membrane Treatment Processes and Metal Removal Systems

Aspects of Gaseous Pollution Control

Pollution Control in Developing Countries

Aspects of Solid Waste Disposal

Keynote Paper - "The Water Service and its Impact on Industry"
D A Bailey and J B Rhoades, Yorkshire Water Authority

Introduction

The Water Industry in England and Wales derives most of its powers from the
Water Act of 1973 and these are generally to oversee the use of water
resources, licensing abstractions from surface and underground waters taking
action where appropriate to conserve, re-distribute or otherwise augment these
resources in their area. Coupled with this, along with 29 Statutory Water
Companies in England and Wales and the Regional Councils in Scotland, they are
required to provide a supply of water which is sufficient, wholesome and at a
reasonable cost.

Subsequently the Water Authorities, along with the Regional Councils, arrange
for the collection and treatment of the water after use doing this by the
provision of sewers and treatment plants.

They control the pollution of surface and underground waters, including the
sea within the three mile limit, and are required to maintain, improve and
develop fisheries and to look after matters relating to land drainage and the
avoidance of flooding. Regional Councils in Scotland take on this latter
role, the pollution prevention function being carried out by the River
Purification Boards who also look after river gauging and abstraction
licensing.

Therefore throughout the United Kingdom the Water Service is provided by a
mixture of Private, "Nationalised", and Local Authority organisations.

In doing this they operate within many different pieces of legislation, both
National and International, the interpretation of which brings them into close
contact with Industry, both as supplier of raw material and regulator over the
discharge of waste product.

The Service - Sufficiency

Sufficiency, including security of supplies, is that which industry would
demand of any supplier of raw material. The drought in 1976 highlighted the
vulnerability of industry to the loss of water supplies. Following that
experience a lot of work was done by Water Authorities enabling them to better
augment and redistribute supplies, thus improving flexibility when the 1984
drought occurred.

Table 1 shows the volume of public water supplied during the period 1961 to
1984/5.

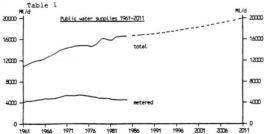

Table 1

1

In Yorkshire two major projects were designed specifically to do just that – the Grimwith scheme and the Yorkshire Grid. In other parts of the Country the Lancashire Conjunctive use scheme was designed to enable supplies to be switched from different sources which involved river, borehole, and reservoir.

It shows a rapid increase in unmetered supplies, whereas the metered supply which includes most industrial supplies shows an increase in the mid 1970s, with a steady fall over the last 10-15 years. This could be accounted for by the industrial recession which is particularly true in those areas of the Country where there used to be traditional large water using industries, for example, textiles. It also follows a trend where industry have become much more efficient in their use of water by using recirculating systems for cooling, etc., and improved housekeeping, a necessity forced upon them by the increase in charges.

It is worth noting that a third factor in "unaccounted for water" has become prominent. This apparently large increase during recent years is more attributable to the Water Authorities more careful measurement of flow and analysis of the data than to the real and sudden increase. Nonetheless many water mains throughout the Country are around 100 years old and approximately 50,000 bursts are attended to each year throughout England and Wales. Not all bursts are as dramatic as the Leeds burst towards the end of 1985, when a 48" water main burst letting 5000 cubic metres of water discharge causing flooding in nearby properties, but how many small leaks go undetected? Such a large volume of lost water must be regarded as a "new resource" notwithstanding money has already been spent on the water to improve its quality and get it to that point.

Authorities are using network analysis to detect and reduce leakage. Better control of pressure in relation to demand through the use of pressure control valves in the distribution system associated with the use of microprocessors to control pumping, saves energy as well as reducing leakage.

Authorities anticipate an increase in demand of unmetered supplies with a steadying of the metered supplies.

Wholesomeness can be defined in a number of ways but generally a wholesome supply would be regarded as one suitable for the use to which it is put.

If this definition is accepted then the dilemma of the Water Industry is clear to try and supply water which at one end of the scale is suitable for drinking purposes and at the other the particular needs of each industrialist and maintain this constantly is an almost impossible task.

A number of traditional industries took root in their present locations because of the suitability of the local water for their purposes. Even then the water may have received further treatment before use but in either event that treatment, as well as the subsequent manufacturing process chemistries had evolved and relied upon a feed supply which was at least consistent in its quality.

Water originating from peaty moorland underlain by millstone grit is likely to be very different to that drawn from a river arising in limestone uplands and receiving later additions from springs draining chalk aquifers.

It is very difficult to say what changes might be expected at particular locations, due to bulk transfers of water, because mixing in transmission

mains and service reservoirs will occur and quality "fronts" will move to and
fro within the distribution network, as a result there can be marked changes
in water quality to consumers. Where such changes are contemplated the
Authorities make every effort to notify the major industrial consumers, but
because of the circumstances some may be unaware of the change before it
happens.

Changes in the legislative framework have come about via European Community
directives, which now influence not only the quality of water abstracted for
drinking water but also the quality of water for human consumption. In the
first case the Directive specifies the physical, chemical and biological
qualities of surface water before being abstracted for drinking water and is
related to the treatment given before being passed into supply. Sources are
divided into three quality categories and the treatment appropriate to each
quality category is specified, Al being simple physical treatment, A2 normal
physical and chemical treatment and disinfection, A3 intensive physical and
chemical treatment and disinfection. Values for the parameters by which the
waters are to be categorised are either mandatory (1 values) or intended as a
guide (G values).

In the case of second directive on the quality of water for human consumption,
the Directive specifies maximum admissible concentrations (MACs) and guide
levels (GLs) for a wide range of parameters in respect of all drinking water
and water used in food and drink manufacture. It applies to the water at the
point where it is made available to the user.

The Directive allows local relaxation from these MACs for toxic and
microbiological parameters, the Water Authorities, Statutory Water Undertakings
and Local Authorities responsible for the supply of water may ask the
Commission for a delay in exceptional local circumstances provided a programme
of improvement is proposed. For organoleptic and physico-chemical parameters
and parameters relating to "undesirable" substances and softened water, the
competent national Authorities may make derogations in certain local
circumstances. There is also provision for temporary derogation from any
parameter in emergencies.

In U.K. decisions have been given on some 750 applications for derogations and
delays from the Directive, roughly a third are for small supplies.

Disposal of Waste Water and Residues

Water Authorities in England and Wales and the Local Authorities in Scotland
have a duty to deal effectively with the contents of public sewers and to do
so without creating a nuisance.

In addition Water Authorities are the regulatory Authority administering the
Control of Pollution Act 1974, Part II, a role carried out in Scotland by the
River Purification Boards. Both Authorities are also statutory consultees in
respect of the licensing of waste disposal sites under part I of the above act.

Existing Controls

Discharges into Sewers

The Public Health Acts 1936 and 1961 and the Public Health (Drainage of Trade
Premises) Act 1937, continue to be the means by which discharges of trade
effluent to sewer are controlled. The Acts permit the discharge of trade

3

effluent to sewer subject to the consent of the Water Authority or the Local Authority in Scotland, who are also permitted to make a charge.

The Conditions of Consent or their need are not always fully understood by the discharger. The Authorities need to be able to treat sewerage effectively and economically and to enable the effluents and residues of the treatment process to be disposed of lawfully and economically.
Acidic discharges to sewer in Yorkshire over the last two years have been responsible for damage to sewers and pumping stations amounting to £0.5m. Sludges arising from the process are disposed of as shown in table 2.

Table 2

Sludge Disposed	000's Tonnes Dry Solids	%
To Grazing land	158	15
To Arable land	275	26
Horticulture, Allotments and Forestry	11	1
Land reclamation	52	5
to land tip	244	23
by incineration	44	4
Sea disposal	256	25
Other	5	1
England and Wales	1,045	100

Source : Water Authorities Association Waterfacts.

The disposal of sludge to land is done in accordance with the Code of Practice produced in conjunction with the Ministry of Agriculture, Fisheries and Food and amongst other things is designed to protect agricultural land from the build up of toxic elements in particular Zinc, Boron, Cadmium, Molybdenum, Lead, Fluorine, Chromium, Selenium Mercury Arsenic. Consents issued to traders for the discharge of effluents containing these elements are controlled. An EC Directive on the use of Sewage Sludge on Agriculture is under consideration.

The disposal of sludges arising from factory premises as a result of these controls can present water authorities with a double problem. They are statutory consultees in the licensing of waste disposal sites by waste disposal authorities under part 1 of the Control of Pollution Act 1974. On consultation they assess the likelihood of water pollution occurring and request provisions in the licence to present this. This is particularly important as compliance with the conditions of a licence is a defence against an offence under section 31 of the Act. Proper consultation is also important as in many cases today the adoption of The Best Practical Environmental Option approach is now becoming increasingly important if the most effective and economic solution to waste disposal problems is to be found.

On 1 January 1986 part 2 of The Food and Environment Protection Act 1985 repealed and replaced The Dumping at Sea Act 1974. This provided and

strengthened provisions on deposits in the sea. The Act is administered by
The Ministry of Agriculture, Fisheries and Food, and water authorities
disposing of sludge to sea will have to obtain the necessary licence subject
to a fee, which will cover administration and technical work. Any controls
will need to be passed back to those influencing the discharge.

Discharges to Relevant Waters

Relevant waters is a term used in part II of the Control of Pollution Act 1974
to describe all inland water, estuaries, tidal rivers, the sea within the
three mile limit and certain cases beyond and specified underground water.
Indirect discharges to underground water via land are also controlled. Under
this Act the Water Authorities in England and Wales and the River Purification
Boards in Scotland have powers to control effluent discharges into the above
waters to help remedy or prevent pollution and by means of regulations made by
the Secretary of State prescribe precautions to be taken with substances
liable to cause water pollution and restrict activities within specific areas
where water pollution might occur.

An important aspect of the Act is the involvement of the public. Two main
areas allow comment by third parties. Before a discharge can be made to
relevant waters the consent of the Water Authority must be obtained. This
applies to discharges of sewage or trade effluent and to matter other than
sewage or trade effluent, provided it is made via a sewer or drain as defined
under the Section 343 of the Public Health Act 1936, or in Scotland by Section
59(1) of the Sewerage (Scotland) Act 1968. All applications for consent must
be advertised, however, if the Authority considers that the discharge in
question will have no appreciable effect on the receiving water, then the
Authority is entitled to waive the requirement.

Water Authorities have a duty to maintain public registers containing
particulars of applications for consent, consents given, analysis of samples
of effluent and receiving water, exemption certificates and notices to abstain
from certain agricultural practices.

The registers provided by Authorities consist of paper records, computerised
data, or a mixture of both. They have been open to the public since August
1985. Some concern was expressed initially that entries from the registers
could be used in prosecutions, this has yet to be tested in the Courts.

Controls on Water Authorities own discharges are by the Secretary of State for
the Environment. Consents for discharge from the Authority's own sewage
works are issued by the Department of the Environment and monitoring of those
discharges is the subject of an agreed sampling programme, details of the
results having to be submitted to the DoE annually.

Influence of European Community Directives

In recent years a number of EC Directives concerning the discharge of certain
dangerous susbstances into the aquatic environment have come into force. The
implementation of the Control of Pollution Act 1974 is the means by which the
United Kingdom Government will be able to fulfil its obligations in respect of
those directives which relate to pollution control.

The Directive on pollution caused by certain dangerous substances discharged
into the aquatic environment of the community (76/464/EEC) provides a
framework for measures to control water pollution caused by the discharge of

dangerous substances. These are grouped into black list (List I) and grey
list (list II) on the basis of their polluting effects. Control is by means
of the "parallel approach" of specifying both limit values and quality
objectives, either of which may be applied by member states.

The Directive does not itself establish limit values or quality objectives for
any of these substances. This is done by separated directives often referred
to as "daughter" directives, five of these so called daughter directives are
as shown in table 3.

Table 3

Directive		Notification	In force	First full year's data to be submitted by
Framework	76/464/EEC	4/05/1976	-	early 1987
Mercury	82/176/EEC	25/03/1982	1/07/1983	1/09/1983 (for 1982)
	84/156/EEC	-	8/03/1986	31/03/1987 (for 1986)
Cadmium	83/513/EEC	28/09/1983	26/09/1985	early 1986 (for 1985)
HCH	84/491/EEC	11/10/1984	1/04/1986	31/03/1987
Groundwater	86/68/EEC	19/12/1979	19/12/1981	Not applicable *

* Data to be submitted on request to DoE on a case by case basis.

Each directive applies in principle to all discharges of the substance with
which it deals, unless otherwise stated and all discharges liable to contain
list II substances require prior authorisation. Authorisations, setting
effluent standards, should be given for all discharges which are regarded as
significant, whether they be untreated discharges, discharges to sewer
(subsequently treated at a sewage works), or discharges from sewage treatment
works. Discharge consents specify effluent standards which must enable the
relevant Environmental Quality Standards (EQS) values to be met. This will
in some cases involve consenting discharges to sewer from certain industrial
premises to enable the Water Authority to comply with the terms of the
directive. There are presently twenty Directives in force affecting water
quality, six proposed and five under consideration by the Commission.

'At a Reasonable Cost'

The Water Act 1973 sets out the provisions by which Water Authorties can
charge for the services they provide, and the level of income to be derived
from charges is determined by the aggregate of operating costs, current cost
depreciation adjustment and the achievement of the financial target specified
by the Secretary of State.

The tariff structures must be devised in such a manner as to satisfy these
requirements. The total costs of performing the services which the
Authorities provide and which has to be recouped from customers can be
broadly analysed over three main headings.

(i) Operating Costs.

(ii) Current Cost Depreciation (based on current asset values, not historic
or marginal cost).

6

(iii) Financial target (calculated by applying a rate of return to current net asset values).

Government controls are applied to the level of operating costs, the Government also determine the level at which the financial target is set; whilst the method of applying current cost accounting within the Industry has been agreed with the Department of the Environment.

Charges for the main services are fixed on a regional basis.   No regard is had, in fixing charges, to differences within the region due to geographic or historic reasons, equally there is no cross-subsidisation between services.

The Water Act 1973 has undergone one major test concerning charging arrangements to date and this involved interpretation of Section 30(1) - charging for services provided. In 1974 the local authorities that were billing on our behalf were obliged for the first time to show sewerage charges separately on the general rate demand note.

This raised a question which had never previously been considered when sewerage and sewage disposal costs were recouped through the general rate on all ratepayers, about the legality of levying a sewerage charge on occupiers of premises which were not connected to the public sewer.   A test case (known as the 'Daymond' case) went eventually on appeal to the House of Lords who upheld that a charge should not be made for a sewerage service not being provided.   As a result of this decision the Water Charges Act 1976 came into being to clarify the position concerning liability for charges.   In this respect it did two things (i) it amended Section 30(1) of the Water Act 1973 to state that charges should only be made for services performed and (ii) it stated that a property can be taken to have a sewerage service if it is connected to the public sewer for foul water, surface water or both.

Allocation of Costs

Water Supply costs are identified for the region as a whole and the costs are shared between two 'classes of persons', the measured group of customers and the unmeasured group of customers, in a way which reflects their respective share of the service.   Having allocated costs to these two classes of persons on a equitable basis it is considered that the requirement concerning 'undue preference' has been satisfied.   It is considered that there is no legal requirement on water authorities to ensure that charges levied on individual customers within groups represent the individual customer's actual use of the service.

Traditionally, costs were allocated between the measured and the unmeasured customers according to a 'parity principle' which meant that the income requirement was allocated between the groups pro-rata to their respective shares of total consumption.   However, further analysis of costs revealed that costs are influenced by three main factors.

1.   The costs of measurement and billing which clearly do not vary with actual consumption, but rather with the kind of measurement and bill provided.   These costs are 'customer related' and can be clearly identified to the two customer groups and allocated directly.

2.   Costs which vary directly with actual consumption or use of the service. The general approach taken by Water Authorities is to classify all the

7

costs from the source to the service reservoir (i.e. the larger proportion of costs) as volume related. These costs are allocated pro-rata to respective consumptions.

3. Other costs which although not varying (except in the long term) with actual use are incurred to make available sufficient capacity to meet a theoretical or potential 'peak' of consumption. These 'peak availability' costs are usually identified as those arising on the customer side of the service reservoir (with the obvious exception of pumping costs which are closely related to total volumes rather than to peak volumes). The basis for this view is that expenditure on what is essentially the distribution system is not predominantly influenced in the medium term by the total annual or daily volume supplied. The distribution system is usually sized to make sufficient capacity available to cope with peak demands and reinforcement of the system to cater for increasing total demands is relatively rare.

The costs of making supplies available, peak availability costs, are allocated by reference to the number and size of connections to the distribution system. Using data available on the number and size of metered connections it is possible to calculate the measured groups share of peak availability costs.

Measured Water Supply Tariff

The measured water supply tariff is in two parts, a standing charge (graduated according to the size of connection) and a volume charge. In Yorkshire the standing charge for a customer with a 13mm ($\frac{1}{2}$ inch) meter in 1986-87 will be £40 made up of a measurement and billing charge of £22 and a peak availability charge of £18. The volume charge will be 28.1 pence per m^3.

Measured Sewerage and Sewage Disposal Tariff (S. & S.D.)

The measured S. and S.D. tariff at present is a two part tariff comprising a volume item and a rateable value item. Generally the volume item is based on the consumption recorded on the water meter, the principle of the charge being that the volume of water into the premises roughly equates to the volume leaving the premises. It is recognised that there is a loss factor and this is based on 95% of the water volume, 5% being assumed not returned to the sewer. It is accepted by most Authorities that if the customer can provide sufficient evidence that there is a higher loss then this will be accepted.

Charges for Trade Effluent

Methods of charging for trade effluent vary slightly from Authority to Authority. Costs taken into account in calculating trade effluent charges are generally based on those works receiving trade effluent only. Some Authorities use total flows, others use foul flows only. The present charging formula used is based on the Mogden type formula

$$C = R + _V + \frac{OtB}{O_s} + \frac{St}{S_s}S$$

Where - C = total charge for trade effluent treatment
R = reception and conveyance charge
V = volumetric and primary treatment costs/m^3
Ot = the chemical oxygen demand (COD) of effluent after one hour
quiescent settlement at pH7
Os = COD of crude sewage after one hour quiescent settlement
B = biological oxidation cost/m^3 of settled sewage
St = total suspended solids (mg/litre) of the trade effluent at pH7
Ss = the total suspended solids (mg/litre) of crude sewage
S = treatment and disposal costs of primary sludges /m^3 of sewage

Some Authorities use suspended solids in the calculations, others use
settleable solids.

The variation in charges and average regional strengths used can be seen from
Table 4.

Table 4

Trade effluent charges 1985/86								
	Average regional strength		Apportionment of charge				total	minimum charge
	Os	SS	R	V	B	S		
	mg/l	mg/l	p/m^3	p/m^3	p/m^3	p/m^3	p/m^3	£
Anglian +	680	400	4.64	5.79	8.47	3.19	22.09	40
Northumbrian	353	178	7.52	4.06	7.15	3.95	22.68	30
North West *	363	258	3.22	2.95	3.74	2.29	12.20	
Severn Trent	331	344	4.33	5.02	5.42	3.13	17.90	50
Southern ++	452	512	4.06	8.51	11.12	6.53	30.22	47
South West	406	343	6.13	5.45	8.73	7.41	27.72	36
Thames +++	442	331	3.24	3.79	5.91	7.46	20.40	30
Welsh	500	350	3.35	3.16	8.26	4.53	19.30	0
Wessex	351	323	1.90	4.76	5.30	4.69	16.65	59
Yorkshire **	927	316	-	7.40	8.08	4.46	19.94	27.50

    * North West charge to satisfactory sea outfalls is
       R + M where M=3.12 p/m3
   ** Yorkshire minimum charge is £5 if no sampling needed
    + Anglian is based upon COD plus 4.5 times the
       total oxidised nitrogen after settlement
   ++ Southern base their charges on foul flows
  +++ Thames has a system of standing charges

Source: Water Authorities Association Waterfacts

Attempts have been made to produce a Standard Code of Practice between the Water Industry and the C.B.I. and this is due for publication shortly.

What of the future

Privatisation of the Water Industry is presently under active discussion. Water Authorities besides being suppliers of raw material, they regulate not only abstractors but also disposers of waste. One of the problems encountered when Water Authorities were first formed in 1974 was that there should be an even handed approach between the Authority and those customers it regulated.   In some cases there has been a very narrow line to walk but generally there have been few problems.   The Secretary of State will continue to monitor the performance of the companies' charges and standards.   The difference in future will be that a private organisation will be regulating another private organisation which may be competing for the same resource.

There will need to be strong safeguards to ensure even handedness.

JBR/6 February 1986

BB 007 34

THE ROLE OF RECENT DEVELOPMENTS IN REDUCING AERATION COSTS

H E Crabtree*

A number of developments have occurred over recent years which have relevance to reducing energy inputs and costs of full scale activated sludge processes and these are briefly reviewed. The extent to which they find application depends on specific site conditions and an analysis of developments in the STWA shows that the speed of implementation is relatively slow due mainly to poor economic return.

1   SIGNIFICANCE OF AERATION COSTS IN WASTE WATER TREATMENT

The treatment of wastewater using the activated sludge process can be a costly exercise and, irrespective of the economic climate, a responsible industrialist will seek to optimise his process to gain maximum benefit from minimum expenditure. In the water services industry where wastewater treatment is a primary function, the energy expended in producing the final product, namely, an effluent of acceptable quality, can be a significant proportion of total costs. By way of example, Fig 1 shows typical cost-breakdowns for sewage works using the activated sludge process. Under pressure from central government to reduce the bill to the consumer, the authorities find that a substantial proportion of the total comprises financing charges. These can only be reduced over the long-term by control of current capital spending. In the elements which are immediately controllable, or apparently so, aeration energy costs figure strongly and in some cases may be a major element (1,2).

For the process industries, costs arising from effluent treatment will constitute a smaller element in the overall cost structure associated with a product. In the textile industry, for example, 3-12% of the total conversion cost is attributable to this source (3). Obviously, on this proportionality basis reduction of aeration cost is of greater significance to the water services industry than to other process industries.

To concentrate on the proportion of revenue expenditure attributable to energy usage on aeration is, however, not entirely realistic. It is the absolute magnitude of the cost element which is often as significant in the mind of the operator as its contribution to the total. So what

* Principal Research and Development Officer, Severn-Trent Water Authority.

developments have been occurring in recent times which might usefully and economically be used to reduce the cost of activated sludge treatment? Because of the relatively greater importance of such costs in the water services industry, these notes will concentrate almost exclusively on developments originating therein, although it should be clear that they will have application throughout the wastewater treatment sector.

2 THE SCOPE OF DEVELOPMENT WORK AND ITS POTENTIAL FOR APPLICATION

The subject of aeration processes and plant has been extensively reviewed in recent years. In 1978 an international conference (4) dealt comprehensively with the theory and practice and this was followed in 1980 by a UK symposium entitled "The Profitable Aeration of Wastewater" (5). A third meeting, "Reducing aeration costs" was held in 1983 (2) at which the present author presented his observations on optimising activated sludge processes. This current report summarises the finding of these earlier meetings and attempts to assess their impact on the operations of, specifically, the STWA.

In 1983 it was clear that

(i)   a large range of aeration and oxygenation devices were available having a wide range of efficiencies.

(ii)   there was a need to test aerator performance on the full scale under standard conditions to determine relative efficiences.

(iii)   it was important to recognise that not only did an aerator oxygenate but that it also performed the integral function of mixing in most cases.

and

(iv)   that adequate control systems were needed to achieve optimum process and economic performance.

In practice, in the water services industry aerator usage was, and continues to be, relatively limited in respect of type of equipment. Broadly, systems fall into subsurface aeration using coarse or fine bubble plant and surface aeration using cones and rotors. The major requirement is to optimise the performance of existing plant to realise cost savings. It is important to understand that in the STWA (where the last major activated sludge plant was commissioned in 1978) loadings have not been increasing and that the exploitation of latest thinking on aeration has been restricted almost exclusively to the uprating situation. In only a few cases has the need to replace old, relatively inefficient (1.4 kgO_2/kWh) mechanical plant at the end of its useful life created a situation where the potential of more efficient plant and new ideas could be considered. Under these circumstances, some of the important developments which have occurred over the few years can be listed as follows.

2.1 Optimisation of fine-bubble aeration plant

An extensive investigation undertaken by WRc (5) has shown how matching the oxygen supply profile to the varying demand profile in aeration basins can lead to substantial energy savings in the case of nitrifying plants. Savings are less marked with non-nitrifying plants, but wastewater can be treated at a higher rate in appropriately modified plants. The modifications include rearrangement of diffuser layout as specified by a mathematical model which predicts the average demand profile from tank shape, flow etc, and installation of automatic air main valves actuated in response to DO signals processed through a plc.

2.2 Dual aeration processes

As a result of a number of investigations (5,6) it is now fully accepted that the high potential efficiency of fine bubble aeration (2.5 kgO_2/kW) is compromised by low -factors during the early phases of purification. Surface aerators suffer much less from this problem (7). It has thus been recommended (8) that for maximum efficiency aeration should be carried out with surface aerators at the front end and fine-bubble aeration at the outlet end.

2.3 Testing of aerators

An aeration system comprises an aerator and a tank both of which can vary independently in size and characteristics. It is not uncommon, therefore, to find (7) that aerator efficiency can deviate from that specified by the manufacturer over the normal range of operation. The effect is particularly marked with surface areators for which a common control method is the use of on/off timers with feedback control. By arranging for the aerator to be deployed at its optimum immersion savings over and above those due to use of timers may be achievable (9).

2.4 Improved variability/flexibility of mechanical plant

For surface aerators input power can be varied by regulating either speed or immersion. Traditionally two speed units with constant freeboard, fixed speed devices with variable, weir-regulated freeboard and fixed speed variable height aerators with fixed weir levels have been used. Similar considerations apply to the blowers used with subsurface aeration. Variability is usually achieved by having a series of blowers cutting in and out in response to demand or by having variable speed (stepped/continuously variable) or constant speed, variable vane units. These alternatives have been more or less acceptable in terms of initial cost, controllability and flexibility in operation. Two recent developments have shown themselves to be of value in overcoming deficiencies in existing plant in relation to total power input or to the relative distributions of power input within an aeration plant containing a number of parallel lanes of treatment.

The first relates to the use of frequency converters (2). They can be readily interposed between existing switchgear and standard squirrel cage motors to regulate motor speeds continuously over the range 0 to 100% rated output.

The second development is of inflatable weirs to provide a simple, cheap method for regulating the water level in an aeration basin (2). One of the problems in large plants is the attainment of satisfactory splitting of sewage flows (and thus of power input) between a number of parallel lanes of treatment despite apparent hydraulic similarity. In addition the maldistribution may be inconsistent and change with flows. The inflatable weir was developed in the STWA (2) to provide a means of increasing or decreasing the head over a dome diffusion system to regulate relative air flows.

2.5 Computer/Plc monitoring and control

A major problem in assessing the potential for improved efficiency in large plants with a multiplicity of lanes is the collection and analysis of base data. The development of computer-based monitoring systems (2) is greatly aiding this task and providing insight into the variability of such control parameters as DO. The use of the computer opens up the possibility of automatic control of energy input given appropriate flexibility in mechanical plant and this major attribute is often cited as a powerful reason for introducing the computer. There can be little doubt that ultimately automatic control will be achieved as demonstrated by the WRc (5). In the short term, however, STWA experience is that the computer, in providing improved monitoring, has mainly served to highlight the deficiencies of control probes and instruments and the need for provision to be made for them to be serviced and calibrated at regular intervals.

3   EXPLOITATION OF AERATION DEVELOPMENTS IN THE STWA

Given the recent history of energy saving developments what has been the effect on aeration process control in the STWA? Table 1 gives the developmental changes which have occurred or are definitely scheduled to take place at the 31 largest activated sludge plants in the Authority. It reveals that there has been little change in control systems over the last

Table 1 - Implementation of DO control strategy in the STWA

Year	1983	1985	1987
Little regular monitoring/control No serviceable permanent DO equipment Inflexible mechanical plant	15	13	7
Permanent DO equipment Flexible mechanical plant Manual control (full/part time)	16	18	12
Full continuous and automatic DO monitoring and control	0	0	12

two years but that significant change will take place in the near future. Even in 1987, however, there will be a number of plants in which little control over energy input will be exercised on a daily basis. Clearly the pace of change is not fast and the reasons for this are manifold.

As illustration reference can be made to a capital project to renovate the line-shaft systems spanning the five outlet-end pockets in a sixteen lane surface aeration plant. The most elegant and potentially most energetically efficient solution was to replace the old plant with fine-bubble aeration as identified under 2.2 above. Detailed consideration revealed, however, that existing works and the operational context imposed constraints which rendered this maximum efficiency solution impossible. The first problem was that using all available plant as is normally the case, the installation of the more efficient oxygen transfer process would lead to mixing deficiencies. This could have been overcome by using, say, half of the aeration volume provided ie, 8 of the 16 lanes. Unfortunately this would then have meant that the relatively new, individual drive inlet-end surface aerators would have become underrated and needed replacement. Additionally, it was demonstrated that modifications to the feed channels would be needed to reduce the head loss developed with partial plant usage. Clearly costs were rising and, given a general reticence by the operator to run intensively and that any energy savings were problematical due to on-site power generation, a more realistic solution had to be found. In fact the expedient and least costly option was to simply refurbish the old inefficient line-shaft system but to build in improvements such as profiling of energy input to simulate the average demand profile and adjustment of overall energy input using frequency converters.

Even with technically feasible and economically sound projects there is still a requirement to budget for tightly-controlled capital funds and typically a lead time for implementation of an energy saving scheme in 1-2 years.

4   CONCLUSIONS

The technology is available for improving the control of aeration processes and for realising energy savings. There is a general move in the water industry to exploiting these developments. The speed of implementation is relatively slow and this is due mainly to poor economic return associated with site specific considerations.

ACKNOWLEDGEMENTS

The author wishes to thank F Earnshaw, Director of Operations, for permission to present this paper. He draws attention to the fact that some of the views expressed herein are his own and do not necessarily constitute STWA policy.

REFERENCES

1   "Cost effective operation at large sewage treatment works"; J Upton, Paper presented at East/West Midlands IWPC Meeting on "Cost effective sewage treatment" Long Eaton, February, 1982.

2   "Some operational aspects of optimising and uprating aeration plant and processes"; H E Crabtree, N E Bastable and J B Watts, Paper No 3, IWPC (South West Branch) Symposium "Reducing aeration costs", (Bristol, October 1983), IWPC, Maidstone, Kent, 1974.

3   "Emission control costs in the textile industry"; H E Crabtree published by OECD, Paris, 1982.

4   "Aeration in aquatic systems"; Proceedings of a conference held in Amsterdam, The Netherlands, September, 1978 Prog. Wat. Tech., 11(3), 1979.

5   "Energy saving by fine-bubble aeration"; B Chambers and G L Jones, Wat. Pollut. Control, 84(1), 70-86, 1985.

6   "Survey and evaluation of fine-bubble dome diffuser aeration equipment"; D H Houck and A G Boon, USEPA, Report No 600/2-81-222, 1981.

7   "Aerator performance"; C F Forster, Paper No 2, IWPC (South West Branch) Symposium "Reducing aeration costs", (Bristol, October, 1983), IWPC, Maidstone, Kent, 1984.

8   Private communication. B Chambers.

9   G A Jones in discussion of ref 2.

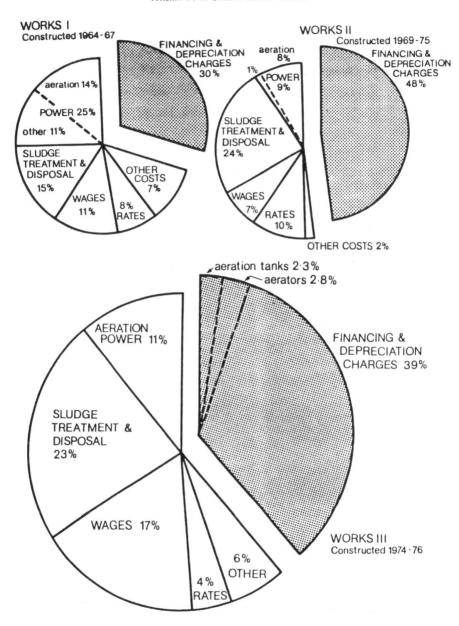

Fig. 1   Breakdown of total annual cost for three works using the activated sludge process

INCOMPATIBILITIES BETWEEN PROCESS BIOLOGY AND PERFORMANCE IN ACTIVATED SLUDGE PROCESSES.

G. Hamer*

Activated sludge processes remain the most widely used sewage and wastewater biotreatment technology for bulk biodegradable carbonaceous pollutant removal. In this contribution the process biology of the completely mixed variant of the activated sludge process is evaluated and a model describing biological processes that occur both in the aeration tank and in the clarifier is presented. It is concluded that short residence time sludge separation processes such as flotation could significantly improve the quality of the discharged effluent with respect to carbonaceous pollutant concentrations.

INTRODUCTION

Biotreatment processes of the activated sludge type are the most widely used secondary biotreatment processes for both municipal sewage and industrial wastewater. Activated sludge technology was originally developed some 70 years ago by Ardern and Lockett[1] and today many variants of the process (2) are in use. Essentially, the process involves two main steps; biooxidation of biodegradable pollutants in an aeration tank and settling of the biomass and other solids(sludge) in a clarifier from whence concentrated sludge is recycled to the aeration tank in order to enhance process intensity. Biooxidation is carried out by dispersed microbial flocs with relatively good settling properties and which can, in many respects, be regarded as pellets of naturally immobilized microbial cells. In general, processes are operated in the continuous flow mode and any excess sludge produced is wasted either continuously or intermittently.

* Institute of Aquatic Sciences, Swiss Federal Institute of Technology Zürich, Ueberlandstrasse 133, CH-8600 Dübendorf, Switzerland

Sewage and many industrial wastewaters contain relatively low
concentrations of biodegradable carbonaceous pollutants in both
solution and suspension, but the number of individual compounds
present will be thousands. Because of the complex mixed nature of
activated sludge process feeds, pollutant concentrations are
measured in terms of "lumped" parameters such as biochemical
oxygen demand (BOD), chemical oxygen demand (COD), total organic
carbon (TOC) and dissolved organic carbon (DOC). Activated sludge
process performance is judged on the basis of removal efficiency
in terms the difference in BOD, COD, TOC or DOC between the
process feed and clarified effluent, but the concentrations of
specific pollutants are largely ignored. Residual pollutants in
the discharged effluent can be either in solution or in suspension. BOD, COD and TOC afford a measure of both pollutant
categories, DOC only the former category. Residual suspended
solids are predominantly descretely dispersed, non-flocculated
microbes, whilst residual soluble pollutants comprize either
compounds present in the feed or compounds produced during the
biotreatment process and can be either biodegradable or recalcitrant. In general, recalcitrant compounds are not removed by
biotreatment, although they might become either sorbed to or
entrapped in the sludge flocs, and hence, separated from the
water undergoing treatment. Biodegradable pollutants should be
almost completely removed during biotreatment, but in fact, degradable DOC in discharged effluents can be several percent of
the influent degradable DOC and it is this aspect of unsatis-
factory process performance that will be addressed in this
contribution.

ACTIVATED SLUDGE PROCESS BIOLOGY

In this evaluation attention will be restricted to only one
variant of the activated sludge process, that in which the
aeration tank is considered to operate as a completely mixed,
continuous flow bioreactor. The hydraulic residence times
employed in such processes are generally between 6 and 10 h and
the sludge residence time, because of sludge recycling, will vary
between 5 and 30 d. The primary objective of the process is, at
high biodegradable pollutant conversions, to minimize the production of microbial biomass (sludge) and maximize the production
of carbon dioxide, i.e., operation under conditions that minimize
the microbial biomass yield coefficient. Extended sludge residence times, in addition to enhancing process intensity, also
contribute to biomass yield coefficient minimization because of
enhancement of endogenous activity. In biotreatment processes,
endogenous activity embraces several distinctly different biological mechanisms; cell lysis and "cryptic" growth(3), sorbed
and entrapped substrate utilization/hydrolysis and cell maintenance energy requirements, which all result in the same overall
effect. In strict microbiological terms, only the latter process
is classified as endogenous activity(4).

20

The major question that arises with respect to endogenous activity in activated sludge plants is whether it occurs only in the
aeration tank or whether a significant, even a predominant, level
of the total endogenous activity actually occurs in the clarifier, where mean sludge residence times are considerable. Hypotheses that assume that the latter situation is a reality provide
plausible explanations for the origin of biodegradable, dissolved, carbonaceous matter that occurs in secondary treatment process effluents. Traditional activated sludge process models
assume that biological activity is restricted to the aeration
tank and that the processes that occur in the clarifier are
exclusively physical in nature(5). Here, an activated sludge
model that considers endogenous biological activities in the
clarifier is presented, but first it is appropriate to examine
the several mechanisms that comprize endogenous activity.

Cell lysis is a process that occurs in any microbial population.
However, it is still a vexed question whether lysis is coincident
with microbial death or occurs subsequent to death. Death and
lysis occur in both growing and in resting populations of microbes. Two distinct mechanisms are responsible for lysis; the first
results the activities of endo-enzymes in the microbial cell
undergoing lysis and is described as autolysis, the second
involves hydrolysis of microbial cells by hydrolytic exo-enzymes
produced by other microbes present in the process environment.

"Cryptic" growth is the process whereby microbes grow on lytic
products resulting from the death and lysis of other microbes
present in the microbial population. It is a widespread phenomenon in mixed cultures, but is thought to be generally less
pronounced in pure mono-cultures. However, Mason(6) has recently
demonstrated the absence of a lag-phase when the bacterium
Klebsiella pneumoniae is grown on disintegrated cells of the same
bacterium as the sole carbon energy substrate, suggesting that
the bacterium is fully adapted for growth on its own cellular
components, i.e. lytic products. When "cryptic" growth occurs,
the maximum theoretical biomass yield coefficient is 0.66(7).

The utilization and/or hydrolysis of sorbed or entrapped carbonaceous pollutants is a most important feature of those
variants of the activated sludge process that have been designed
specifically for the treatment of wastewaters rich in colloidal
and suspended pollutants. It has been shown the colloidal and
suspended pollutants rapidly flocculate when they enter the
aeration tank, such that they are incorporated in the activated
sludge flocs(8). Hence, hydrolysis and/or degradation processes
occur within the microbial flocs. The rates of hydrolysis and/or
degradation of entrapped particulate pollutants are unlikely to
be very rapid and particularly as such processes for many common
particulate pollutants can occur both under aerobic and anaerobic
conditions, it must be assumed, for cases where degradation is
incomplete in the aeration tank, that it will continue to occur
in the clarifier. Negligable data concerning sorbed substrate
degradation exist, but again, depending on rates and concen-

trations, degradation in both the aeration tank and the clarifier can be envisaged.

The maintenance or strictly endogenous requirements of microbial cells involve the energy needed for the turnover of cellular matter, osmotic work to maintain concentration gradients between the cell and the exterior environment and cell motility(9). In many respects, such requirements will tend to be relatively insignificant, but quoted maintenance coefficients are frequently higher than might be expected. In view of the fact that the internal turnover of cellular matter and the external turnover of cellular matter, i.e., lysis and "cryptic" growth are based on idential carbon energy substrates (cellular matter), differentiation between these two distinct mechanisms is not obvious from material balances and as lysis and "cryptic" growth are generally ignored in microbiological investigations, it seems probable that they are erroneously included in estimates of maintenance requirements.

When considering particulate substrate hydrolysis and degradation in microbially mediated processes, two distinct types of particulated matter must be considered, i.e., microbial cells and biodegradable solids of non-microbial origin. In this analysis only the former will be considered. When microbial cells are subjected to either autolysis or exo-enzyme hydrolysis, a complex mixture of biopolymers will first be produced, and subsequently, some of these will be further hydrolyzed to produce simple monomers of the species typically used as carbon energy substrates in microbial growth media. Essentially, one can expect two distinct molecular weight fractions in microbial cell hydrolysates; a high molecular weight fraction which, in spite of its biological origin, might be expected to be essentially recalcitrant, and hence, persistent, and a low molecular weight fraction which will be readily biodegradable. Molecular weight fractionation of a cell free extract of activated sludge has confirmed the existance of two such fractions(10).

The predominant microbes in activated sludge processes are bacteria. A very wide range of bacterial species and strains, with diverse morphological and physiological characteristics, function in concert as the process culture. Because of the aerobic environment that is established in the aeration tank obligate aerobes and facultative anaerobes predominate. However, the clearly heterogeneous nature of the system results in oxygen gradients and anoxic niches where even obligate anaerobes can prosper. In the unaerated clarifier, aerobic bacterial activity will be negligable because of anoxis, but such an environment will promote the activities of both the facultative and obligate anaerobes.

PROCESS MODEL WITH AEROBIC AND ANAEROBIC ACTIVITY

A completely mixed activated sludge process is shown
diagrammatically in Figure 1.

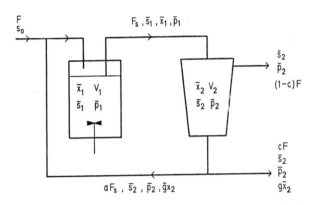

Figure 1   Activated sludge process with completely mixed aeration
tank, clarifier and sludge recycle loop.

The basic assumptions used in developing the process model are:

1) The aeration tank is a completely mixed, continuous flow
steady-state, aerobic bioreactor in which flocculent growth
occurs on carbon energy substrate, s, which enters the
system in the process feed and is also the biodegradable
product produced by anaerobic activity in the clarifier.
Acetate would be such a compound.

2) Physical segregation between the sludge (solid) and liquid
phases occurs in the clarifier, but soluble hydrolysis products are uniformly distributed throughout the clarifier
liquid phase.

3) Microbes are neither present in the process feed nor leave
the clarifier in the liquid overflow.

4) Two soluble products, one biodegradable, the other
essentially recalcitrant, are produced by anaerobic action
in the clarifier.

5) No accumulation of either liquid or sludge occurs in either
the aeration tank or the clarifier, i.e., liquid volumes
and the quantity of sludge in both the aeration tank and
the clarifier are constant.

6) Neither liquid nor solids hold-up occurs in the connecting pipes.

7) The concentration factor for sludge in the clarifier is g, the fraction of the liquid outflow from the aeration tank that is recycled is a and the fraction of the liquid leaving the overall process with waste sludge is c.

8) No soluble substate (product) utilization occurs in the clarifier.

9) The growth of individual microbes is described by Monod type saturation kinetics.

10) The transfer of limiting substate s into the microbial flocs in the aeration tank is diffusion limited.

11) Strict endogenous metabolism, which is dilution rate independent, occurs in the aeration tank and only carbon dioxide is produced.

12) That death/lysis/hydrolysis occurs in the clarifier only.

13) That the combined product yield coefficient from lysed biomass in the clarifier is unity.

14) The mean solid and liquid phase residence times in the clarifier are identical.

Material balances can be established for the microbial biomass (sludge), x, for the biodegradable substrate, s, which enters the overall process in the feed and is produced as a result of lysis in the clarifier, and the refractory product, p, produced as a result of lysis in the clarifier.

For the clarifier, V_2,

$$D_2 = F_s/V_2 \tag{1}$$

$$F = F_s (1-a) \tag{2}$$

$$Y_{p/x} + Y_{s/x} = 1 \tag{3}$$

The biomass balance is

$$V_2 dx_2 = F_s x_1\ dt - cFgx_2 dt - aF_s gx_2 dt$$
$$-V_2 k_1 x_2 dt \tag{4}$$

For steady-state conditions, $dx_2/dt = 0$, therefore

$$\bar{x}_2 = D_2 \bar{x}_1/K^* \tag{5}$$

where

$$K^* = \left[cD_2g(1-a)+aD_2g+k_1\right] \qquad (6)$$

The refractory lytic product balance is

$$V_2dp_2 = F_sp_1 \, dt - Fp_2dt - aF_sp_2dt$$
$$+V_2k_1x_2Y_{p/x}dt \qquad (7)$$

For steady-state conditions, $dp_2/dt = 0$, therefore

$$\bar{p}_1 D_2 - \bar{p}_2D_2 + k_1\bar{x}_2Y_{p/x} = 0 \qquad (8)$$

The biodegradable substrate (product) balance is

$$V_2ds_2 = F_ss_1dt - Fs_2dt - aF_ss_2dt$$
$$+ V_2k_1x_2 \, (1-Y_{p/x})dt \qquad (9)$$

For steady-state conditions, $ds_2/dt = 0$, therefore

$$\bar{s}_2 = \left[k_1\bar{x}_1 \, (1-Y_{p/x})/K^*\right] + \bar{s}_1 \qquad (10)$$

For the aeration tank, V_1,

$$D_1 = F_s/V_1 \qquad (11)$$

The biomass balance is

$$V_1dx_1 = -F_sx_1dt + aF_sgx_2dt +$$
$$V_1(\mu-k_d)x_1dt \qquad (12)$$

For steady-state conditions, $dx_1/dt = 0$, and substitution for $\bar{x}_2$ from eqn. (5) gives

$$\mu = D_1 - \frac{agD_1D_2}{K^*} + k_d \qquad (13)$$

The refractory product balance is

$$V_1dp_1 = -F_sp_1dt + aF_sp_2dt \qquad (14)$$

For steady-state conditions, $dp_1/dt = 0$, therefore

$$\bar{p}_1 = a\bar{p}_2 \qquad (15)$$

The biodegradable substrate (product) balance is

$$V_1 ds_1 = Fs_0 dt - F_s s_1 dt + aF_s s_2 dt$$

$$- \frac{V_1 \mu x_1 dt}{Y_{x/s}} \qquad (16)$$

For steady-state conditions, $ds_1/dt = 0$, therefore

$$D_1 s_0 (1-a) - D_1 \bar{s}_1 + aD_1 \bar{s}_2 - \frac{\mu \bar{x}_1}{Y_{x/s}} = 0 \qquad (17)$$

Substituting for $\bar{s}_2$ from eqn. (10) and μ from eqn (13) gives

$$\bar{x}_1 = \frac{D_1 (s_0 - \bar{s}_1)(1-a)}{\left[\frac{D_1}{Y_{x/s}} + \frac{k_d}{Y_{x/s}} - \frac{aD_1 k_1 (1-Y_{p7x})}{K^*} - \frac{agD_1 D_2}{Y_{x/s} K^*} \right]} \qquad (18)$$

For processes where flocculent growth occurs, it is necessary to consider the diffusion of the growth limiting substrate to the site of utilization. Characklis (11) has proposed that diffusional resistances in flocs can be accounted for by considering the limiting substrate flux due to diffusion on the basis of unidimensional transfer, followed by application of Monod type saturation kinetics for substrate utilization by the individual bacteria. The limiting substrate concentration in the Monod expression becomes that at the bacterial surface rather than the bulk liquid phase value. Hence, for steady-state conditions in the aeration tank,

$$\mu = \frac{\mu_m \bar{s}_1'}{(K_s + \bar{s}_1')} \qquad (19)$$

or

$$\bar{s}_1' = \frac{\mu K_s}{(\mu_m - \mu)} \qquad (20)$$

Substituting for μ from eqn. (13) gives

$$\bar{s}_1' = \frac{D_1 K_s - (agD_1 D_2 K_s / K^*) + k_d K_s}{\mu_m - \left[D_1 - (agD_1 D_2 / K^*) + k_d \right]} \qquad (21)$$

Considering limiting substrate transport for steady-state conditions in the aeration tank,

$$\bar{s}_1' = \frac{RK_s}{(k' - R)} \qquad (22)$$

26

where

$$k' = \mu_m \bar{x}_1 / Y_{x/s} A \tag{23}$$

However,

$$R = \frac{k' \bar{s}_1}{\left[K_s + (k' \, 5 / \Phi) + \bar{s}_1 \right]} \tag{24}$$

Therefore,

$$\bar{s}_1' = \frac{\bar{s}_1 K_s}{\left[K_s + (k' \, 5 / \Phi) \right]} \tag{25}$$

Substituting for $\bar{s}_1'$ in eqn. (21) gives

$$\bar{s}_1 = \frac{\left[D_1 - (agD_1 D_2 / K^*) + k_d \right] \left[K_s + (k' \, 5 / \Phi) \right]}{\mu_m - \left[D_1 - (agD_1 D_2 / K^*) + k_d \right]} \tag{26}$$

From eqn. (23)

$$k' \, 5 / \Phi = k'' \, \bar{x}_1 \tag{27}$$

where

$$k'' = \mu_m \, 5 / Y_{x/s} A \, \Phi \tag{28}$$

Putting

$$K' = \left[D_1 - (agD_1 D_2 / K^*) + k_d \right] \tag{29}$$

and substituting from eqn. (27) into eqn. (26) gives

$$\bar{s}_1 = K' \, (K_s + k'' \bar{x}_1) / (\mu_m - K') \tag{30}$$

Substituting for $\bar{s}_1$ in eqn. (18) gives

$$\bar{x}_1 = \frac{D_1 (1-a) \left[s_o (\mu_m - K') - K' K_s \right]}{K'' \, (\mu_m - K') + D_1 K' k'' \, (1-a)} \tag{31}$$

where

$$K'' = K' / Y_{x/s} - aD_1 k_1 (1 - Y_{p/x}) / K^* \tag{32}$$

The above equations allow prediction of the microbial biomass (sludge), $\bar{x}_1$, soluble biodegradable substrate/product, $\bar{s}_1$, and refractory product, $\bar{p}_1$, concentrations in the aeration tank and the concentrations of the soluble biodegradable substrate/product, $\bar{s}_2$, and refractory product, $\bar{p}_2$, in the clarifier overflow, provided, appropriate values can be substituted for the numerous

27

constants. For preliminary evaluation, the following arbitrary values were attributed to the constants:

$Y_{x/s} = 0.4,$

$K_s = 0.2 \text{ g l}^{-1},$

$\mu_m = 0.5 \text{ h}^{-1},$

$b = 2 \times 10^{-5} \text{ cm sec}^{-1},$

$Y_{p/x} = 0.25,$

$a = 0.1,$

$s_o = 10 \text{ g l}^{-1},$

$k_d = 0.04 \text{ h}^{-1},$

$\delta = 0.05 \text{ cm},$

$A = 7.5 \text{ cm}^{-1},$

$k_l = 0.14 \text{ h}^{-1},$

$g = 8.$

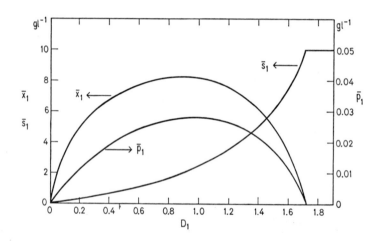

Figure 2   Sludge $\bar{x}_1$, substrate, $\bar{s}_1$, and refractory product, $\bar{p}_1$, concentrations in the aeration tank with respect to hydraulic dilution rate, D_1.

Further, the hydraulic dilution rate for the aeration tank, D_1, was considered to be equal to the hydraulic dilution rate, D_2, for the clarifier. The predictions for $\bar{x}_1$, $\bar{s}_1$ and $\bar{p}_1$, with respect to D_1 are given in Figure 2, and those for $\bar{s}_2$ and $\bar{p}_2$ with respect to D_2, in Figure 3. These results indicate that the value used for the specific lysis/hydrolysis rate constant, k_1, was probably too high, but in spite of this, trends with respect to both biodegradable and refractory soluble matter in the clarifier overflow are clearly evident.

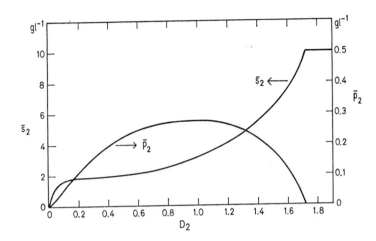

<u>Figure 3</u>   <u>Substrate, $\bar{s}_2$, and refractory product, $\bar{p}_2$,</u>
<u>concentrations in the clarifier overflow with respect</u>
<u>to hydraulic dilution rate, D_2.</u>

<u>DISCUSSION AND CONCLUSIONS</u>

Anaerobiosis in the clarifier of aerobic activated sludge
processes is by no means a newly observed process phenomenon.
More than twenty years ago, Westgarth et al.(12) investigated
this question because, at that time, the currently held belief
was that anaerobiosis in the clarifier was adverse to activated
sludge process performance. However, they concluded that
prolonged periods of anaerobiosis in either conventional or
low-rate activated sludge processes resulted in no detrimental
effects either with respect to the biological activity of the
sludge or overall process performance, whilst in high-rate
activated sludge processes a period of anaerobiosis offered
potential cost savings with respect to waste sludge disposal
because of lower overall sludge production. In more recent work
on the effects of anaerobiosis in aerobic activated sludge
processes(13), the aeration tank was operated in a cyclical

manner, with feeding and aeration for 12 h followed by no feeding and no aeration for the next 12 h. The products produced during the anaerobic portion of the cycle were found to be readily biodegradable during the aerobic portion of the cycle. Aerobic/ anaerobic cycling during the cultivation of facultative anaerobic bacteria has been demonstrated(14) to be effective for overall biomass yield coefficient minimization resulting from uncoupled growth.

In the system discussed in this contribution, most of the anaerobic (hydrolysis/lysis) products produced in the clarifier would only be subjected to aerobic conditions for degradation after discharge from the process, and hence, result in poor process performance. The concept of an essentially recalcitrant fraction in the microbially produced soluble organic pollutant mixture is of particular interest when considering overall pollution control strategies, particularly when this fraction comprizes humic matter, which according to O'Melia(15) would, when discharged into natural receiving waters such as lakes, result in enhanced rates of sedimentation by sorption onto suspended matter present in the lake and thereby result in improved water clarity.

The analysis presented here suggests that, for normal aeration tank residence times, i.e., 6-10 h and for similar clarifier residence times, the disadvantages resulting from anaerobiosis in the clarifier, i.e., significant soluble pollutant concentrations in the process discharge, exceed any advantages resulting the uncoupled growth of facultative anaerobic bacteria with respect to minimization of waste sludge production. Hence, alternative sludge separation process such as short residence time flotation processes, where anaerobiosis can be avoided, seem to offer marked advantages over long residence time gravity sedimentation for activated sludge floc removal from treated sewage and wastewater. The merits of such flotation processes have been discussed in detail by Zlokarnik(16).

NOMENCLATURE

a	=	fraction of aeration tank outflow recycled
A	=	floc surface area per unit aeration tank volume
c	=	fraction of outlet flow in waste sludge stream
D	=	hydraulic dilution rate (reciprocal residence time)
$\mathcal{D}$	=	molecular diffusivity of limiting substrate
F	=	overall process inlet/outlet flow rate
F_s	=	aeration tank outlet flow rate
g	=	concentration factor for sludge in the clarifier

k_d = specific endogenous metabolism rate constant in aeration tank

k_1 = specific endogenous metabolism rate constant in the aeration tank

k' = ⎫

k'' = ⎪

K' = ⎬ constants defined in text

K'' = ⎪

$K*$ = ⎭

K_s = saturation constant

p = recalcitrant product concentrations

R = reaction rate constant per unit floc surface area

s = bulk liquid phase limiting substrate concentration

s_o = process inlet limiting substrate concentration

s' = limiting substrate concentration at microbial surface

t = time

V = operating volume

x = microbial biomass (sludge) concentration

Y = yield coefficient

ς = capsular boundary layer thickness

μ = specific growth rate constant

μ_m = maximum specific growth rate constant

subscript 1 = aeration tank

subscript 2 = clarifier

REFERENCES

1. Lockett, W.T., 1954, J. Proc. Instn. Sewage Purif., 53, 194.

2. Committee on Water Pollution Management, 1980, J. Environ. Engng. Div. ASCE, 106, 473.

3. Drozd, J.W., Linton, J.D., Downs, J., and Stephenson, R.J., 1978, FEMS Microbiol. Letters, 4, 311.

4. Hamer, G., 1985, Acta Biotechnol., 5, 117.

5. Mishra, P.N., Fan, L.T., Erickson, L.E., and Kuo, M.-C.T., 1973, Indian Chem. Engr., 15, 1.

6. Mason, C.A., 1985, Unpublished results.

7. Hamer, G., and Bryers, J.D., 1985, Conservation and Recycling, 8, 267.

8. Gujer, W., 1980, Prog. Water Technol., 12, 79.

9. Pirt, S.J., 1975, Principles of Microbe and Cell Cultivation, Blackwell Scientific, Oxford, GB.

10. Leidner, H.A., Fleischmann T., and Hamer G., 1984, Anal. Chim. Acta, 163, 35.

11. Characklis, kW., 1978, J. Environ. Engng. Div. ASCE, 104, 531.

12. Westgarth, W.C., Sulzer, F.T., and Okun, D.A., 1964, Adv. Water Poll. Res., 2, 43.

13. Gonzalez-Martinez, S., and Norouzian, M., 1984, J. Water Poll. Control Fed., 56, 1173.

14. Harrison, D.E.F., and Loveless, J.E., 1971, J. Gen. Microbiol., 68, 35.

15. O'Melia, C., 1985, Private communication.

16. Zlokarnik, M., 1982, Ger. Chem. Engng., 5, 109.

BIOLOGICAL EFFLUENT TREATMENT USING PURE OXYGEN VIA THE VITOX PROCESS

F J Gould * & P R Stringer *

A comparison is made between oxygen based and air based
wastewater treatment plant, with particular reference to
the activated sludge process. Advantages of using oxygen
are discussed including improved settleability and wide
choice of sludge loading. Measurement of the oxygen being
supplied to the process records the "metabolic-rate" of the
bacteria which is then monitored and linked into an alarm
system to warn of process failure. A typical cost
comparision is given of the activated sludge process
treating sewage using oxygen via mechanical aeration and
liquid oxygen.

INTRODUCTION

As UK legislation has tightened, for controlling the pollution of
the environment, so interest in intensifying existing effluent
treatment processes has increased. In recent years oxygen has become
more accepted as a means of obtaining the maximum capacity from the
biological wastewater treatment process. Furthermore due to the
unpredicability of future loading the financial savings of using pure
oxygen to uprate the existing plant, rather than investing much needed
capital in the effluent plant is becoming increasingly the preferred
option.
      This paper highlights the benefits obtained by using pure oxygen
when supplied as a liquid or directly from a British Oxygen gas
production site via an oxygen pipeline to the activated sludge process.

*   Environmental Processes, British Oxygen Co.,Deer Park Rd.,
     London SW19

THE ROLE OF OXYGEN IN THE ACTIVATED SLUDGE PROCESS

An adequate supply of dissolved oxygen is one of the key factors in obtaining good operating performance in the activated sludge process. Aeration of the activated sludge is one of the major operating cost elements in the overall process and consequently a considerable degree of attention has been devoted to the design of aeration systems, to maximise the efficiency and minimise the power absorbed.

When the activated sludge process is used for the treatment of sewage a better performance in terms of BOD removal is achieved when an element of plug flow is employed through the units. (Ref. 8,9). With plug flow the settled sewage feed and sludge return are both introduced into the first pocket or at the head of the lane if diffused air is being used. At this point the respiratory demand is highest to the extent that it cannot be satisfied immediately by the supply capability of conventional aeration equipment. Two methods are commonly employed to overcome such a limitation:-

1. The size of the aeration tank is enlarged and the mixed liquor solids level is reduced to bring about an effective dilution in the intensity of the respiratory demand of the bacteria to the point where it can be satisfied by the aerators available.

2. As an alternative the settled sewage feed can be distributed over, for example, the first third of the treatment lane to introduce an element of what is termed a stepped feed, but unfortunately this reduces the element of plug flow which is beneficial to the overall plant performance.

The optimum situation, therefore, would be the use of a plug flow or multi-stage aeration system designed without the concern for oxygen transfer limitation problems. There are three factors that hinder the efficient dissolving of oxygen from air:

1. Low solubility.
2. Low partial pressure of oxygen in air.
3. Low diffusion rate in the liquid.

It is this third factor which renders the overall transfer process liquid film controlling resulting in the need for substantial amounts of energy to be expended to enhance the interphase mass transfer rate by creating a large gas-liquid interfacial area and a high degree of turbulence at the interface.

It is not the dissolved oxygen concentration that can be obtained with the use of oxygen that is important, but rather the rate at which oxygen can be transferred to the mixed-liquor. Periods of high oxygen demand can be readily satisified with an oxygen system whereas with conventional aeration it can only be achieved at the expense of efficiency and power consumption. It is normal for a plant to be designed to a given biochemical loading per unit mass of sludge (kg BOD applied per kg sludge per day) therefore designs employing oxygen are no longer limited by the intensity of oxygenation that can be supplied per unit volume of tank. The mixed liquor concentration therefore can be increased and hence a larger influent flowrate can be treated.

THEORETICAL ASPECTS OF THE DISSOLUTION OF PURE OXYGEN

Pure oxygen is attractive as a consequence of Henry's law which states that the saturation concentration of a gas in a liquid is directly proportional to the partial pressure of the gas in the atmosphere in contact with the liquid.

$$c_s = k_s p$$

where c_s saturation concentration of the gas in the liquid in milligrams per litre

     p partial pressure of the gas in the gas phase in atmospheres

     k_s coefficient of absorption or Henry's law constant in milligrams litre^{-1} atm^{-1} (oxygen in water at 15°C is 67 mg.1.$^{-1}$atm.$^{-1}$)

If the partial pressure of oxygen is increased from 0.21 to 1.0 atma (air to oxygen) the equilibrium saturation concentration increases fivefold. Furthermore if introduced via a deep submerged injector (such as VITOX ^{R*}) it will increase by 50% for every 5m of depth; since the saturation concentration is proportional to the absolute pressure.

The rate of gas absorption is proportional to its degree of undersaturation in the absorbing liquid:

$$\frac{dc}{dt} = k_L a \, (c_s - c_t)$$

where

    dc/dt rate of change of concentration
    $k_L a$ proportionality factor (mass transfer coefficient) for the conditions of exposure
    c_s saturation concentration
    c_t concentration in the liquid at time t

The rate of oxygen transfer is therefore greater with oxygen than air provided it can be practically and efficiently dissolved into the mixed-liquor. For example with a given dissolving device in a given tank (ie assuming the value of $k_L a$ is unchanged) changing from air to oxygen will increase the overall transfer rate in preortion to the increase in the driving force. In practice however, other parameters such as tank geometry, aeration device, wastewater constituents etc all have an affect on the actual quantity dissolved.

*Process name of the BOC sub-surface mixer oxygenator

ESTIMATION OF OXYGEN DEMAND

The amount of oxygen required for treatment depends on the total demand of the micro-organisms oxidising the waste. The oxygen is required for substrate oxidation (BOD) and sludge respiration, but the actual amount of oxygen required depends on the sludge loading (1). Fig 1 shows the relationship between sludge loading and oxygen requirement. For example at high sludge loadings the oxygen requirement is low since little oxidation occurs. At low sludge loadings the substrate absorbed on the sludge is retained long enough for a proportion of it to be oxidised and therefore more oxygen is required.

This correlation is often used in selection of oxygenator capacity but, to the operator seeking to optimise performance, it has its limitations and in particular it fails to give any indication of how oxygen is used. As can be seen from Fig 1, any comparison of aeration system should include a reference to the sludge production and the sludge loading.(2) (3) Fig 1 shows the sludge production as a dotted line to indicate the dependence on sludge loading, since in practice it also will be dependent upon the characteristics of the material being treated.

As a result of the high mass transfer rates obtained with pure oxygen the optimum sludge loading ratio can be selected, to produce the preferred balance between the required BOD removal, plant size, specific oxygen consumption and sludge disposal costs.

EFFECT ON SLUDGE SETTLING CHARACTERISTICS

The improved settling velocity of sludge is perhaps the most significant effect of operating oxygen activated sludge systems since poor sludge settlement is frequently the limiting factor in the production of a good quality final effluent. It is our experience that the use of oxygen with the Vitox process (currently operating in the coke-making, textile, paper, food and chemical industries) produces a significant improvement in the settlement characteristics. Virtually all of these plants operate at MLSS concentrations over 3000 mg/l (in some installations higher than 15000 mg/l) and return solids concentrations between 1.5% and 3% are readily achieved at low recycle ratios. The improvements achieved can be attributed partly to the provision of a generally higher level of DO on the plant, but more importantly to the maintenance of a steady DO level at all times against variable loading on the plant. Furthermore the improved mixing due to the Vitox sub-surface jets ensures a more uniform DO level throughout the treatment unit thereby maintaining the best possible conditions for biochemical oxidation.

Although the proportion of sludge produced, relative to the BOD removed, is very variable from industry to industry (with domestic sewage probably having one of the highest rates) in all cases the dewatering and disposal of sludge represents a significant operating cost. As has been indicated in Fig.1, for a given treatment, the larger the plant (ie low Food/Microorganisms ratio) the smaller the quantity of sludge produced. The designer therefore has a choice between a large plant at high capital cost and a smaller plant with high sludge disposal costs.

Oxygen can influence this balance, since with many effluents a higher MLSS can be carried thus reducing the physical dimensions necessary for the activated sludge tank. Furthermore, under certain loading conditions, the bacteria oxidise a larger proportion of the organic material in the feed given a favourable oxygen supply; this leads to a higher oxygen use but in return, less sludge.

VITOX INSTALLATION

The Vitox system (fig 3) has been developed as a high rate aqueous oxygenation technique and has previously been documented in detail (4) and has been used to uprate existing biological treatment plants at numerous municipal and industrial plants, or to meet a higher discharge standard.(5) It consists of a pressurised sidestream where pure oxygen enters the recycle through a venturi injector positioned after the pump discharge and comprises of three distinct dissolving components. Initially oxygen is dissolved at the injection point ie the venturi and then a further part dissolves in the high pressure sidestream. The final dissolution stage occurs at the sparger where the oxygenated liquor (a two phase fluid of mixed liquor and micro-bubbles of oxygen gas) is dispersed as rapidly as possible to avoid the formation of regions of high dissolved oxygen. This is achieved by wide jet dispersion and contributes a major part of the oxygenated dissolution process. Within the sidestream oxygen is dissolved under pressure and DO levels soon reach supersaturation relative to atmospheric pressure.

Figure 2 shows a typical two tonne per day Vitox unit with the associated pipework. The system shown employs a submersible pump but Vitox is equally suitable for both submersible or land based pumps and individual site requirements determine the exact choice. The system in fig 3 shows how the recycle liquor is pumped through the Venturi injector and is sparged out, at the bottom of the tank, through a series of jets. The jet-mixing action of the Vitox process results in a very efficient use of the mixing energy and therefore optimum contact between the bacteria, oxygen and the wastewater pollutants.

PROCESS CONTROL AND ALARM SYSTEM (BIOALARM)

An additional feature of the Vitox oxygenation system is the extra controllability of the process which pure oxygen gives. Since the oxygen is only added to the process when required, the rate at which the bacteria are oxidising the waste water (and therefore consuming oxygen) can also be observed, making it possible to respond quickly to any deterioration in the activity of the bacteria; such as a sudden spillage of biocide.

The Vitox system includes an automatic disolved oxygen (DO) controller connected to the oxygen gas control system. A DO sensor is kept immersed in the activated sludge and continually monitors the DO level such that when it drops below the lower set point the oxygen is switched on. Figure 3 shows a typical DO trace produced on a chart recorder linked into the DO meter/controller. At the lower set point A the oxygen is switched on and the Vitox oxygenator quickly raises the DO level until it reaches the higher set point B. At this point the oxygen is switched off but the Vitox recycle continues to provide the necessary mixing. The DO level then begins to drop (B to C) and the rate at which it decreases is the speed at which the bacteria are removing the oxygen; this oxygen removal rate is usually referred to as the "respiration rate" of the bacteria. At the lower set point C the oxygen is again switched on and the whole cycle is repeated.

Since the rate of oxygen consumption (respiration rate) is directly related to the bioxidation process,(10) the rate of dissolved oxygen removal from the liquor (set point B to C) can be measured and connected to an alarm system. If the respiration rate is low (ie it takes longer than a pre-selected time for the DO to drop to the low set point) an alarm can be activated to indicate a process malfunction. This is the basis of the Bioalarm system fitted to all vitox control systems.

ECONOMIC CONSIDERATIONS

Mechanical aeration devices tend to be operated continuously even when the plant is operating at low loadings (such as at night or weekends), resulting in excessive electricity being consumed. Using Vitox the oxygen is only supplied when required by the process and only the energy for keeping the microorganisms in suspension is used during periods of low loading.

The separation of oxygen from air is a highly efficient process in terms of the energy required per unit of oxygen produced. Typically modern air separation techniques, require only about 0.35 kWh/kg (6), (0.29 - 0.42 kWh/kg (7)) of oxygen generated. This corresponds to approximately one third of the amount of energy required to dissolve oxygen from air (typically 0.7 - 1.0 kWh/kg) into activated sludge mixed-liquor . Therefore, provided the oxygen dissolution process is efficient, the high purity oxygen route can make significant savings in energy requirements.

Further economies can be made if the oxygen is supplied from the nearby British Oxygen production plant especially if the plant is also used to supply the local merchant market. The gas would be supplied from the nearby plant via a pipeline to the associated dissolving plant (Vitox). By using pure oxygen and the Vitox submerged jet mixing it is usual to maintain a much higher MLSS (in some instances higher than 15,000 mg/l, cf 3000 mg/l on most activated sludge plants) and also reduce the effect of any toxins in the feed because of the "buffer capacity" of the large population of bacteria.

COMPARATIVE COSTING OF VITOX OXYGENATION AND A CONVENTIONAL PROCESS

The following costing has been based on a municipal plant operating in the UK (8) which was overloaded and suffering from frequent sludge bulking. Various trials were carried out with the existing plant and during this experimental phase it was found that switching from completely mixed to plug flow reduced the incidence of bulking in the final tanks. However, this did not completely remove the problem and it was decided that the load on the first pockets had to be reduced in order to maintain the plug flow regime.

Two options were selected for detailed consideration, a high rate biofilter (and associated settlement) or Vitox oxygenation of the first pockets. A detailed costing is given in appendix 1 & 2 with Vitox showing an annual saving of £54,000 pa

Option 1 - High Rate Filtration

After primary settlement follows high rate filtration, intermediate settlement and then plug flow aeration.The pilot plant studies indicated that approximately 50% of the BOD could be removed by high rate filtration when dosed at 2 kgBOD.m^{-3}.d^{-1}. The intermediate settlement tanks were designed on a surface loading of 30m^3.m^{-2}.d^{-1}, an upward velocity of 1.25 m/h and a total tank capacity of 2 hours at DWF. The major works required for option 1:-

1) Pumping station and rising main.
2) Two high rate tower filters 17 m dia x 4 m high complete with plastic media.
3) Two intermediate settlement tanks 22 m dia x 1.67 m deep.
4) One final tank 28.6 m dia x 2.44 m deep.
5) Modification of south side of works to plug flow.
6) Interconnecting pipework, channel modifications etc.
7) Centrifugal pumps (3 No) each rated @ l/s.
8) Scraper mechanisms for intermediate and final tanks.
9) Distributors for high rate filters.
4) Control panels and uprating power requirements.

Capital cost of Option 1 is £750,000
Running cost   £ 91,000

Option 2 - BOC Vitox Process

Two 1.2 tonne/day Vitox units are to be installed, one into each of the first two pockets. A mixture of settled sewage and return activated sludge is drawn, by the Vitox submersible pumps, from a common sump. The liquor is then sparged into the first pockets to mix and oxygenate the contents (surface aerators switched off) prior to flowing into the other four pockets (ie plug flow) and final settlement. The Vitox pumps run continuously to maintain mixing, but the oxygen injection into the pumped flow is automatically controlled using a dissolved oxygen controller to maintain DO at a preset level. Each unit operates independently dissolving up to 50 kg of oxygen per hour. The oxygen is stored in a vacuum insulated tank holding approximately 1 weeks supply. The major works required for option 2:-

1) Concrete plinth for oxygen vessel.
2) Mild steel baffle boxes in the corner of pocket 1 of each lane.
3) Mild steel base supports and fixing for submersible pumps.
4) Small prefabricated concrete building to house control panel.

Minor electrical work consisted of supply cable from sludge treatment building to control building and feed cables to pumps and oxygen controllers.

Capital cost of Option 2 is £50,000
Running cost   £37,000

CONCLUSIONS

1. The capacity of organically overloaded plants can be increased without the need for increasing the plant hydraulic capacity.

2. Excessively high aeration rates can be avoided by a reduction in the power required per unit of oxygen transferred.

3. The "bioalarm system" provides a continuous check on the performance of the plant by monitoring the rate at which the process calls for oxygen. The chart record of dissolved oxygen level provides a continuous permanent check on plant performance for future reference.

4. Increased rate of biochemical oxidation through elimination of oxygen transfer limitations.

5. Oxygen availability at high organic loading reduces or eliminates periods of zero dissolved oxygen and improves overall process operating conditions.

6. Reduction in plant size and capital investment.

REFERENCES

1) Vosloo, P.B.B., 1973 Inst. Wat. Pollut. Control, 209

2) Boon, A.G. and Burgess, D.R., 1972, Inst. Wat. Pollut. Control, 493

3) Boon, A.G. and Burgess, D.R., 1974, Inst, Wat. Pollut. Control, 382

4) Crook, Cudby and Jeffries, 1982, Inst. Wat. Pollut. Control, 633

5) Wheatland AB and Boon AG., 1979, Prog. Wat. Technol, 171

6) McWhirter J.R. The use of high purity oxygen in the activated sludge process. Vol 1 Chap 3

7) White J.B. Wastewater Engineering Chap 11, 253-6

8) Cowan J.,Heap M.,Millar A.,Wilson G., Presented to the Scottish Branch,Inst. Wat. Pollut. Control, 17th January 1984

9) Tomlinson E.J. and Chambers B. , 1979, Inst. Wat. Pollut. Control, 524

10) Boon, A.G., 1975, Annual Conference Inst, Wat. Pollut. Control

ACKNOWLEDGEMENT

The views expressed in this paper are those of the authors and not necessarily those of BOC Limited.

APPENDIX 1

OPTION 1 - TWO STAGE PROCESS

CAPITAL COSTS

A. Civil Works   £   £

(i) Reinforced concrete humus tanks
22.0 m dia   (2No)   100,000

(ii) High rate filters 17.0 m dia 4 m
high complete with plastic media
                      (2No)   180,000

(iii)Pumphouse and sump for effluent
pumps   20,000

(iv) Pipework - gravity and rising
mains   80,000

(v) Concrete final tank 28.6m dia   90,000

(vi) Alterations to existing settlement tanks   30,000   500,000

B. Mechanical and Electrical

(i)   Centrifugal pumps (150 1/s, 3No) 30,000
(ii)   Scrapers for humus tanks   (2No) 42,000
(iii)   Scraper for final tank   (1No) 30,000
(iv)   Filter bed distributors   (2No) 40,000
(v)   Electrical installation   25,000   167,000

C Design fees, supervision costs and
Contingencies   83,000

                 Estimated Total Cost   £750,000

ANNUAL RUNNING COSTS

1) Plant Maintenance @ 2% annum   3,300

2) Amortisation £750,000 @ 12% annum   90,000
                               93,000

3) Energy saving - deduct   2,700

                     Estimated Total   £90,600

                            Say   £91,000/annum

APPENDIX 2

OPTION 2 - BOC VITOX PROCESS

CAPITAL COSTS

		£	£
A.	**Civil Works**		
	(i) Channel and pipework modifications, baffle boxes etc	10,000	
	(ii) Plinth for liquid oxygen vessel	2,000	
	(iii) Control kiosk	3,000	15,000
B.	**Mechanical and Electrical**		
	(i) Vitox plant, pumps and ancillaries supplied by BOC Ltd	25,000	
	(ii) Electrical power installations and modifications	4,000	29,000
C.	**Design fees, supervision and process monitoring**		6,000
	Total Cost		£ 50,000

ANNUAL RUNNING COSTS

1)	Plant maintenance @ 2% annum	600
2)	Liquid oxygen - 600 tonnes including service charge	40,000
3)	Amortisation £50,000 @ 12% annum	6,000
		46,600
4)	Energy saving - deduct	9,800
	Net Annual Running Cost	£ 36,800
	Say	37,000/ annum

Assumptions:-

1) Running costs are the net additional costs/annum
2) Sludge production is the same for each option and
3) No additional manpower is required.

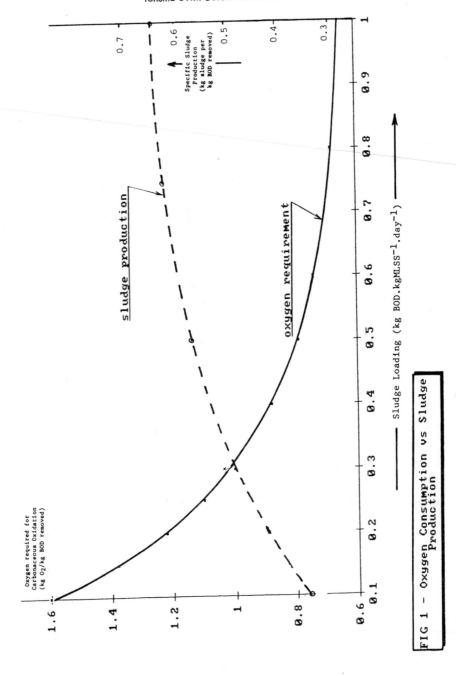

FIG 1 - Oxygen Consumption vs Sludge Production

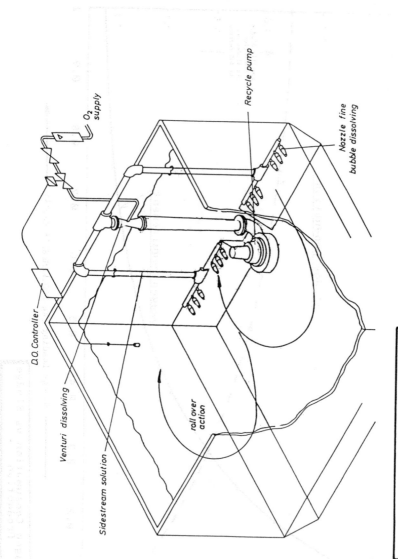

O₂ supply

Recycle pump

Nozzle fine bubble dissolving

D.O. Controller

Venturi dissolving

Sidestream solution

roll over action

FIG 2 GENERAL ARRANGEMENT OF VITOX SYSTEM

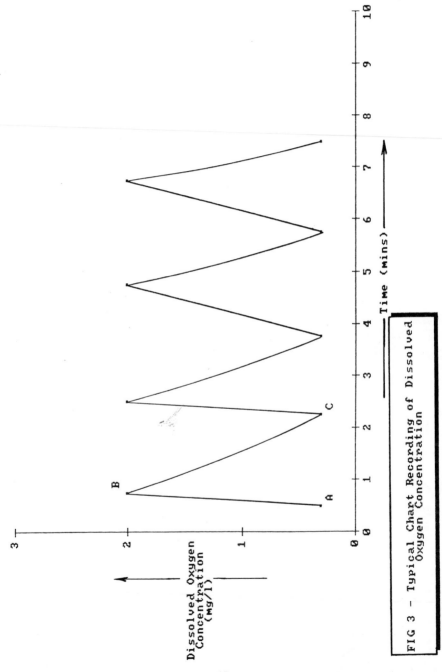

FIG 3 — Typical Chart Recording of Dissolved Oxygen Concentration

PRE-TREATMENT OF ORGANIC WASTES TO SEWER - ECONOMIES AND PLANT EXAMPLES

J. Delaine * Dip Chem Eng, C Eng, FI Chem E, M.Inst.E, MIWES, MIWPC

The majority of organic trade effluents discharged to sewer are produced by the food industry and decisions must be made by industry as to the economic advantage of pre-treatment prior to discharge. The organic chemical industries frequently produce effluent with contaminants unacceptable for direct discharge and pre-treatment is, therefore, a pre-requisite. Whilst the paper concentrates largely on the situation where an effluent is acceptable to sewer without pre-treatment, much of the comment would be applicable to all dischargers. Examples of such pre-treatment plants are given together with the results of a variety of measures which have proved successful. These include improved housekeeping, chemical precipitation to reduce the effluent loading and biological treatment.

INTRODUCTION

It is an inevitable consequence of any process activity that there will be product loss, spillage and waste resulting from that activity. Dependent on the final product, a proportion of the waste may be removed from site as solid or toxic matter not acceptable to the sewer. These are removed by tanker or skip and the remainder discharged to the sewer system.

* Principal John Delaine & Co. First Floor, The Parade, Frimley, Surrey
GU16 5HY

Frequently, when talking to industrialists about effluent waste disposal it is apparent that there is an attitude of mind which regards these as an unavoidable consequence of the activity to be accepted as part of the production overhead!!

Comment that waste is taken away at "so much per load" and that which goes down the drain is charged at "some peculiar formula" is all too often typical of the reaction to the opening of discussions. In consequence, the Trade Effluent account generally goes no further than the Finance Department.

However, with continued financial constraint and budgetary targets, production departments would do well to look at these Trade Effluent Charges for areas of potential overhead reduction. The following comments are intended to assist in the understanding of the system and to illustrate the possibilities for economies.

TRADE EFFLUENT CHARGES

(1)

Trade Effluent Charges are made by Water Authorities on the basis of costs of operation of their system. This includes the sewerage system and the sewage treatment plant. The latter will reduce the level of settleable solids in the sewage and also the biological load which would otherwise lead to pollution of the receiving waters into which the treated sewage is discharged.

Thus the charges are based on a formula including volume, organic load and settleable solids. In general, a formula of the type:-

$$C = R + V + B \frac{Ot}{Os} + S \frac{St}{Ss} \quad \dotsi (i)$$

is used where:

C = the total charge per cu. m of trade effluent discharged.
R = the cost per cu. m of reception into and use of the sewerage system.
V = the cost per cu. m related to volume and primary treatment at the sewage works.
B = the cost per cu. m of biological treatment.
S = the cost of treatment and disposal of primary sludge per cu.m of sewage.
Os = the mean chemical oxygen demand (COD) of settled sewage in the Water Authority's Area.
Ot = the mean COD of the trade effluent after settlement.
Ss, St = the one hour settleable solids of the sewage and trade effluent respectively.

PROCESS WATER COSTS

Trade Effluent Charges, as set out above, are not the end of the matter for the industrialist. Water cannot be discharged until it has first been brought in and paid for. Here again, there is a lack of appreciation of the cost of water purchased. This, like the Trade Effluent Charges, is also frequently considered to be the unavoidable overhead.

In order to provide a true internal picture of the true costs of the use of water in a Water/Effluent Auditing policy, the industrialist is wise to use an extended formula of similar type to that for trade effluent charges alone.

The extended formula includes the initial cost of water purchase to provide the overall cost.

c^1 = water usage cost per cu. m.

where

$$c^1 = (W + R + V) + (B \frac{Ok}{Os}) + (S \frac{St}{Ss}) + Wt \qquad (ii)$$

where W = cost of raw water supply

W + R + V represents a purely volumetric charge for using water in process.

$(B \frac{Oc}{Os})$ is the biological load in effluent, which includes dissolved organics and those organic solids which are not removed by one hour quiescent settlement.

$(S \frac{St}{Ss})$ is the solids load which takes account of settleable solids in one hour quiescent settlement.

Wk   is the treatment cost for water supplied to process. Figure II is prepared using the same data as for Figure I but with water supply cost superimposed. For the purposes of the illustration, it is assumed that raw water is used as received, ie., Wt is zero.

ECONOMICS

When considering the possibility of reduction of effective effluent costs it is essential to evaluate the return from each section of the formula. It is not good enough merely to add more water to reduce the effluent strength.

Tables I and II illustrate the possible avenues for investigation; these are based on a start point of:-

Volume	1000 cum/day
COD	2000 mg/l
Solids	1000 mg/l

using charging data as for Fig I and Fig II.

TABLE I - TRADE EFFLUENT CHARGES 'C' FORMULA (i)

Action Taken	Revised Trade Effluent Data			Costs		Savings
	Flow cu.m	COD mg/l	Solids mg/l	Charge Cp per cu.m	£/day	£/day
None	1000	2000	1000	49.79	497.90	--
Dilute	1500	1333	666	35.59	533.79	(35.89)
Reduce Water use 25%	750	2666	1333	64.00	480.00	17.90
Reduce Water use 50%	500	4000	2000	92.40	462.00	35.90
Reduce COD 25%	1000	1500	1000	42.50	425.00	72.90
Reduce COD 50%	1000	1000	1000	35.20	352.00	145.90
Reduce Solids 25%	1000	2000	750	46.45	464.50	33.40
Reduce Solids 50%	1000	2000	500	43.10	431.00	66.90
Reduce COD 50% and Solids 50%	1000	1000	500	28.50	285.00	212.90
Reduce Water 50%, COD 50% Solids 50%	500	1000	500	28.50	142.50	355.40

From the above, it would appear that the most dramatic savings could be produced by either control of soluble product or by treatment of the effluent to reduce COD and solids discharged. The latter will probably incur the capital and running costs of effluent treatment, in which case, the optimum solution must be to reduce effluent discharged to the minimum volume possible.

TABLE II : PROCESS WATER COST. Cost - C^1 FORMULA (ii)

Action Taken	Revised Trade Effluent Data			Costs		Savings
	Flow cu.m	COD mg/l	Solids mg/l	Cost C^1 per cu.m	£/day	£/day
None	1000	2000	1000	69.79	697.90	--
Dilute	1500	1333	666	55.59	833.85	(135.95)
Reduce Water use 25%	750	2666	1333	84.00	630.00	67.90
Reduce Water use 50%	500	4000	2000	112.40	562.00	135.90
Reduce COD 25%	1000	1500	1000	62.50	625.00	73.90
Reduce COD 50%	1000	1000	1000	55.20	552.00	145.90
Reduce Solids 25%	1000	2000	750	66.45	664.50	33.40
Reduce Solids 50%	1000	2000	500	63.10	631.00	66.90
Reduce COD 50% and Solids 50%	1000	1000	500	48.50	485.00	212.90
Reduce Water 50%, COD 50% Solids 50%	500	1000	500	48.50	242.50	455.40

Examination of Tables I and II will show that dilution is the least attractive option for meeting either discharge consent or to reduce unit costs according to either formula.

The major benefit is obtained by reduced water usage, either by detailed studies in the process areas or by recycle systems which, in some instances, can include effluent recycle to non-strategic areas.

Although it is generally thought that reduction of water use will increase the strength of effluent, indeed as assumed in the Tables above, this is not always the case. Housekeeping improvements in production can minimise spillage and loss which would otherwise be washed away using water purely as a transport medium. Further, if the improved housekeeping does not meet the requirements of, for example, a revised Consent to Discharge, the resulting treatment plant will be of reduced capacity and, therefore, reduced capital cost. Reference to the following paragraphs will demonstrate the potential for improved housekeeping as the first stage of any effluent strategy.

PRE-TREATMENT OPTIONS

The Housekeeping Option

Before embarking on major construction for effluent treatment plant, the
industrial processor should look into his plant housekeeping. By
relatively simple measures or change of routine, considerable savings in
water usage or product loss can be achieved. Three examples will
illustrate the possibilities, albeit the savings may not be as dramatic
as those given, but the first attack on any effluent situation should be
from this direction.

a. Effluent was discharged at 400 - 500 cu.m/day, the COD and solid
    levels were well within consent. However, the process, basically
    rinsing of ethical surgical goods, required hot water at the
    finishing end. The result was that the temperature exceeded that of
    the Consent to Discharge.

    The process was studied and it was proposed that the system of once
    through use of water for multiple rinsing could be converted to a
    counter current system. Clean water was heated for the final rinse
    and with piping modifications it was passed back to the initial
    stages of the process. Heat exchange was used as necessary to
    control the rinse temperatures at each stage.

    The result was a reduction of water usage to 100 - 125 cu.m/day and
    the possibility to reduce steam demand to 50 per cent was obtained
    as a by-product of the exercise.

b. At a food factory (2), hygiene cleaning was carried out at each break
    and a full clean overnight. The major component of the effluent was
    fruit puree, that which was left on the machines was washed to drain
    as well as that unused at the end of the day.

    The housekeeping study showed that no deterioration in standard
    occurred when the hygiene cleaning was reduced to once per shift and
    overnight. Spillage was kept under control, if necessary using
    squeegee cleaning. Further, the use and preparation of the puree was
    put under stricter control. Losses of puree dropped some 30 per cent
    and the effluent volume 25 per cent. Savings in costs amounted to
    £3,000 - £4,000 per week, against an initial effluent bill of £2,500
    per week. The major input being that product savings were costed at
    product cost. Effluent charges fell to £1,340., product not
    discharged was valued at approximately £2,500 per week.

c. A papermill (3), discharging 180 - 200 cu.m per hour had a production
    loss of approximately 2 per cent. By variations in pipework, the use
    of additional internal storage capacity and control of fresh water
    use the effluent volume was reduced to 60 - 65 cu.m per hour. There
    was no reduction in product quality and product loss was reduced to
    0.2 - 0.4 per cent.

Physico-Chemical Treatment

The simplest form of pre-treatment is the installation of a sedimentation
tank. This will allow the settleable material to be removed from the
effluent, generally to approximately 90 per cent dependent on the design

of tank. COD will not be affected in terms of the charging formula.

However, if chemicals are added under controlled conditions, flocculation and precipitation are possible which will remove colloidal suspension and frequently a considerable proportion of the dissolved matter. Thus, both COD and solids are potentially reduced.

In some circumstances, the precipitate can be caused to float rather than settle; this can lead to smaller plant if space is a premium.

a. Abattoir

Untreated Effluent   Cost to discharge C = 60 - 75p per cu.m

Pre-treatment by solids
  removed only   C = 35 - 54p per cu.m

Chemically aided pre-treatment   C = 10 - 20p per cu.m

If chemicaly aided pre-treatment is used, then the cost of chemicals must be considered against the quality of discharge. In the case under examination an evaluation of chemical treatment economics was undertaken and the results are given in Table III.

The effluent was dosed with ferric chloride as coagulant/precipitated and then pH was adjusted to optimum for flocculation using sodium hydroxide.

TABLE III - EFFECT OF CHEMICAL PRE-TREATMENT
(Abattoir Effluent)

$Fe\ Cl_3$ mg/l dosed	0	100	200	300	400	500	600
pH							
Corrected pH	6.7	6.7	6.1	6.7	6.8	6.7	6.7
COD of settled sample	4890	1630	783	434	391	305	298
Settleable Solids in supernatant	420	160	<30	<30	<30	<30	<30

The Water Authority Consent to Discharge required

pH   -   6 to 9
COD   -   not greater than 2000 mg/l
Settleable Solids - not greater than 1000 mg/l

Based on the above, it might be felt that a dose of 100 mg/l ferric chloride was adequate since it meets the Consent to Discharge criteria. However, the data was plotted against costs (as illustrated in Fig III) based on which a dose level of nearer 200 mg/l was recommended to provide a more economic result.

b. Convenience Food

Following the housekeeping study to which previous reference has been made, a variety of possible effluent treatment routes were studied. These showed that chemical pre-treatment prior to discharge to biological effluent treatment either on site or to the sewer showed a benefit of some 35 p per cu.m. The data is presented graphically in Figure IV.

Biological Treatment

Most organic industrial effluents are biodegradeable, those from the chemical industry may require segregation or pre-treatment of some streams and a microbiological population acclimatised to the particular waste. However, in the food and related industries this is not generally so necessary. The options for biological treatment of industrial wastes are the same as for those of sewage treatment, ie., activated sludge or biofiltration. However, there has been a renewed interest in the anaerobic processes for use with high strength discharges. These latter are potentially energy producing whereas the oxidative processes are energy consuming.

Aerobic biological processes generally function without the use of chemicals as are necessary with the physico chemical route. However, where there is a deficiency of nutrient for the biomass, nitrogen and phospherous must be added. There is, however, the necessity of providing air to the process which incurs power costs and, additionally, the biological sludge produced by the processes will require disposal. This can amount to 0.4 - 0.5 Kg per Kg of COD destroyed.

In the anaerobic processes, sludge production is far less because the organic matter is reduced by some 80 - 90 per cent of the organic load applied. In general terms around 0.6 cu.m of biogas is produced per Kg of organic load destroyed.

The anaerobic processes have been discussed in detail by the author[4] in previous publications and the following Table is used to demonstrate the possibilities.

TABLE IV - METHANE PRODUCTION FROM WASTES BY ANAEROBIC TREATMENT

Feed Stock	Digester Yield cu.m gas/Kg COD	% Methane
Sewage Sludge	0.24	75
Pig Slurry	0.30	70
Cow Slurry	0.65	60
Abattoir Waste	0.30	67
Brewery Waste	0.33	65
Molasses	0.52	60

CONCLUSIONS

The paper has attempted to show the possibilities available for reduction of effluent costs and/or process water usage. Regular audits of the system should be included in the financial planning of the industry concerned. It is not sufficient to accept that water is a cheap commodity. Additionally, water usage and effluent disposal when combined are, or should be, an indication of production efficiency. The main area for control must be that of housekeeping, where entrenched practices may be hard to break and where continued attention will be necessary to ensure minimum wastage and thus minimum process water costs.

References: (1)   Trade Effluent Discharged to Sewer : recommended guidelines for control and charging. CBI London 1976.
             (2)   Delaine J. 1981 Food Manufacture Dec. 34-35.
             (3)   Delaine J. 1983 P.I.T.A. Conference Paper Week (8),
                                                            pp.203-216
             (4)   Delaine J. 1981 Food Industry Wastes, Disposal and Recovery.
                   Applied Science Publishers Ltd, London pp.74-84

FIG.I TRADE EFFLUENT CHARGES

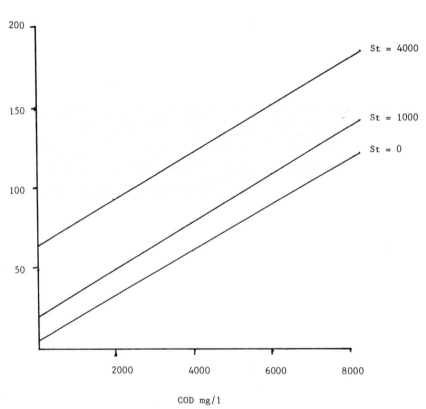

C.
Cost
pence
per cu.m

COD mg/l

FIG. II   EFFECTIVE EFFLUENT COST

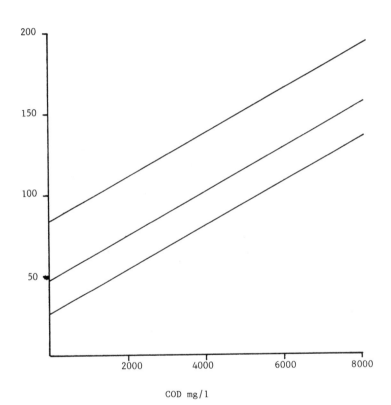

C^1
Cost
pence
per
cu.m

COD mg/l

Data used for FIG.I & FIG.II

R + V = 7.2 p per cu.m.
B   = 5.1 p per cu.m.
S   = 3.9 p per cu.m.
Os = 350 mg/l   Ss = 290 mg/l
Ot = 2000-8000 mg/l St = 0-4000 mg/l
W = 20 p/cu.m.

FIG. III CHEMICAL TREATMENT - ECONOMICS
(abattoir effluent)

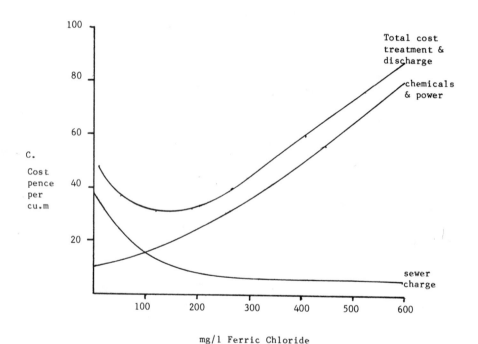

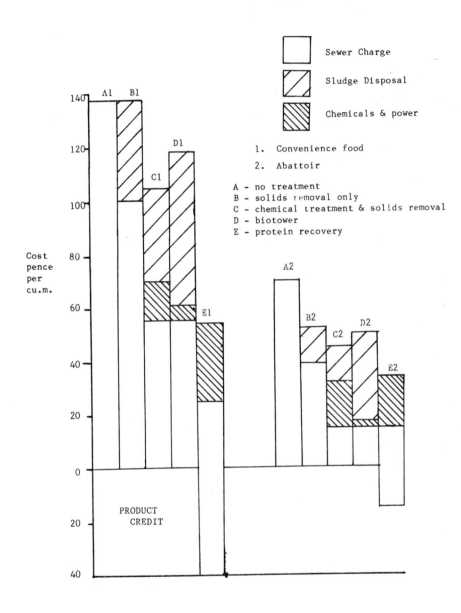

FIG.IV TREATMENT & DISPOSAL COSTS (REVENUE)

BIOLOGICAL TREATMENT OF COKE PLANT EFFLUENT WITH REMOVAL OF NITROGEN COMPOUNDS

R. Fisher*

A three-year investigation involving both laboratory-scale and full-scale studies has been carried out to evaluate the single-sludge pre-denitrification-nitrification process configuration for the control of nitrogen in coke plant effluents. It was established that the organic carbon in the wastewater could be used as energy source and electron donor for the denitrification reaction. Complete denitrification could be achieved in the anoxic reactor, without the need for supplemental organic carbon, provided the ratio of organic carbon-to-total nitrogen in the feed was greater than two. However, the addition of powdered activated carbon or dilution of the feed may be necessary for good process stability.

INTRODUCTION

The production of coke generates large volumes of wastewater containing a variety of contaminants, both organic and inorganic, many of which can have toxic effects on the aquatic environment if discharged without some form of treatment. The purification and disposal of this wastewater have been the subject of extensive research, and many cokemaking plants are now equipped with facilities designed to remove or destroy a proportion of the polluting substances in order to render the wastewater acceptable for discharge. Biological effluent treatment (BET), particularly that based on the activated sludge process, is the most widely adopted approach at the present time.

As usually operated, conventional BET plants comprising an aeration basin, clarifier and sludge recycle system, are capable of destroying most of the oxygen demand of the effluent (as measured, for example, by its chemical oxygen demand - COD - value) along with the bulk of certain toxic substances, eg phenols, cyanides and thiocyanates. Nevertheless, the effluent discharged from such plants can contain a substantial residual COD and there are also substances which are largely unaffected by the treatment process. Important amongst the latter group are nitrogen-containing substances, particularly organo-nitrogen compounds and ammonia.

Legislation within the EEC is becoming more stringent despite the economic recession, and some national legislation now lays down strict limits on the discharge of nitrogen compounds. The bulk of the ammonia in coke plant liquors is removed by steam stripping after liberation of fixed ammonia by the addition of lime or caustic soda. Although low levels of residual ammonia

* British Steel Corporation, Swinden Laboratories, Moorgate, Rotherham.
  S60 3AR

are achievable (ca 50 mg/litre) by this means, operating costs rise quite sharply as the target effluent ammonia concentration is further reduced. Because of the relatively low operating costs of BET plants it is attractive to the carbonisation industry to consider extending the activated sludge process to include the removal of nitrogen compounds as well as carbonaceous contaminants.

The further treatment of coke plant wastewaters by biological nitrification and denitrification was the subject of an earlier ECSC (European Coal and Steel Community)-supported research project conducted[1] at the Centro Sperimentale Metallurgico (CSM) in Rome. The treatment system studied and developed at CSM was essentially a three-stage activated sludge process, with removal of organic carbon, nitrification and denitrification taking place in separate treatment basins, each with separate sludge recycle. However, this approach, involving three separate sludges and an external carbon source for denitrification, is expensive in both capital and operating costs. There is therefore, interest in developing alternative processes which nevertheless retain the inherent advantages of biological treatment.

The primary objective of the work described here was to develop and demonstrate at full-scale a modified biological treatment process for coke plant effluents which utilises a single sludge for the removal of both carbon and nitrogen compounds. The process is based on the pre-denitrification-nitrification (pre-DN-N) flowsheet which has already been successfully experimented with in the laboratory by Bridle et al[2-4] at the Wastewater Technology Centre in Canada using coke plant effluents. Furthermore, it is already applied in full-scale plants for the treatment of chemical industry wastewaters by Dutch State Mines (DSM)[5] in the Netherlands and by Du Pont of Canada[6]. The three year project, which was supported financially by the ECSC, involved both laboratory-scale and full-scale studies.

PROCESS DESCRIPTION

The single sludge pre-DN-N process configuration shown in Figure 1 consists of two stages. The first stage, an anoxic mixed basin, is followed by an extended aeration basin. The raw influent enters the anoxic basin where it is mixed with recycled mixed liquor from the aerated basin and settled sludge returned from the clarifier. Here denitrification occurs with the organic carbon present in the wastewater providing the energy source for the reaction. The denitrified waste passes to the aerobic basin where residual organic carbon is oxidised and ammonia and organo-nitrogen compounds are nitrified. Recycle of mixed liquor from the aeration basin to the anoxic basin allows for partial denitrification of the nitrified waste. Provided complete denitrification occurs in the anoxic reactor the concentration of nitrate in the discharge is determined by the ratio of the recycled mixed liquor to raw influent flow.

LABORATORY-SCALE STUDIES

In their experimental work at the Wastewater Technology Centre, Bridle et al[2-4] found that complete denitrification occurred in the anoxic reactor provided the ratio of degradable organic carbon (measured as filterable organic carbon or FOC) - to - oxidisable nitrogen (expressed as total Kjeldahl nitrogen, or TKN) was in excess of 3.5. They also reported that additions of powdered activated carbon (PAC) to the reactors were necessary to overcome Nitrobacter inhibition in the treatment of high strength wastewater. Bench-scale studies were therefore carried out at BSC Teesside Laboratories to confirm the findings of the Canadian Work using ammonia still effluent from BSC Scunthorpe Works.

The experimental work was carried out in two identical bench scale units. Each system comprised a completely mixed first stage anoxic reactor and a completely mixed second stage aerobic reactor with working volumes of 4.77 and 10 litres respectively. An upflow clarifier was employed for solids separation and mixed liquor and sludge recycle was achieved by returning sludge from the clarifier to the anoxic reactor. The pH and temperature of the aerobic reactors were automatically controlled at 7 ± 0.2 and $25\ ^\circ C \pm 1\ ^\circ C$ respectively. The pH control was effected by means of EIL Model 91B controllers linked to peristaltic pumps for the delivery of sodium hydroxide solution. The temperatures of the anoxic reactors, which were not heated, varied between 21 and 25 $^\circ C$. Generally the recycle ratio was between 6 and 7.

The sludge age in each system was controlled at 50 to 80 days by monitoring the VSS (volatile suspended solids) concentrations in the reactors and treated effluents and wasting sludge from the anoxic and aerobic reactors accordingly. When both systems were fully acclimated PAC (Norit CN 1; Norit U.K. Ltd.) was added to one unit (system B) to give a concentration of 1000 mg/litre in each (ie anoxic and aerobic) reactor; system A was used as a control. Thereafter only the daily maintenance amount of PAC was added to replace that lost from the clarifier and in sludge wasting. Samples of feed and treated effluents were analysed two or three times per week for COD, FOC, SCN^-, NO_2^--N, NO_3^--N, NH_4^+-N, and monohydric phenols. Samples were also taken from the anoxic reactors two or three times per week and analysed for NO_2^--N, NO_3^--N and FOC.

Minimum feed FOC : TKN ratio for denitrification

This aspect was investigated in two ways. Firstly by gradually reducing the FOC : TKN ratio of the feed until unreacted NO_3^- was detected in the anoxic reactors, and secondly from a consideration of the FOC and NO_T-N (total oxidised nitrogen) mass balances around the anoxic reactors. In the first case it was found that residual NO_3^- was detected in the anoxic reactors when the feed FOC : TKN ratio fell to between 1.6 and 1.8. Mass balances carried out around the control stream anoxic reactor showed that on average 2 mg of organic carbon were removed per mg of NO_T-N denitrified. In the PAC-modified stream, however, the consumption of FOC in the anoxic reactor apparently increased from 2 to 3 mg of FOC per mg NO_T-N removed as the feed FOC : TKN ratio was varied from 2 to 4.5. Presumably the excess of FOC over that required for denitrification is adsorbed on the PAC and subsequently degraded in the aerobic reactor. In the control stream the consumptive ratio between FOC and NO_T-N was effectively constant regardless of the FOC : TKN ratio and suggests that physical adsorption of the residual organics on the biomass occurs to a constant and limited extent.

On the basis of these investigations it was concluded that the minimum feed FOC : TKN ratio for complete denitrification was 2. Expressed in terms of COD the critical condition appears to be that the COD : TKN ratio is $\geqslant 7$. The FOC : TKN ratio is dependent on wastewater composition and need not necessarily be as high as the value of 3.5 reported by Bridle et al. This is of considerable importance since it greatly extends the feed liquor composition range within which denitrification can be achieved without the need for supplemental organic carbon. At most coking plants the relative amounts of FOC and TKN in the feed liquor are determined largely by the efficiency of the ammonia stills. This is because the TKN content is independently variable according to the efficiency of stripping whereas the FOC is more or less fixed by other factors. Therefore as the required FOC : TKN ratio increases, so the efficiency of stripping required also increases. Since the operating costs of efficiently operated ammonia stills are directly related to the quality of the effluent discharged from them, a high FOC : TKN ratio would tend to increase stripping costs.

From practical consideration it is preferable to operate as closely as possible to the minimum FOC : TKN ratio for two reasons. Firstly, as already discussed the higher the permissible TKN level (and hence the lower the ratio) the lower the operating costs of the ammonia stills. Secondly, at high FOC : TKN ratios a larger amount of carbonaceous oxidation takes place in the aerobic reactor. This results in increased sludge growth and hence increased sludge disposal costs. Moreover, if the oxygen transfer capacity of the aerators were limited it could lead to loss of nitrification efficiency.

Effects of Adding PAC

In common with the earlier work of Bridle et al[2-4] it was found that the addition of PAC was beneficial in the successful treatment of normal strength liquors. They concluded that the main effect of PAC was in overcoming Nitrobacter inhibition. In the present work, however, it was evident that the addition of PAC was equally important in stabilising the denitrification process. This was most noticeable during periods when the nitrification reaction was being developed (for example, during periods of recovery after partial or complete loss of nitrification or, during acclimation periods). In the control stream the onset of denitrification always lagged well behind the build-up in the nitrification reaction. A typical example is shown in Figure 2. Here it may be seen that there was a build up of NO_3 in the anoxic reactor as the nitrification process developed. From a mass balance around the anoxic reactor it was established that the specific denitrification rate from day 491 onwards was actually at the maximum value of 0.11 eg NO_T-N/g VSS, as predicted by the kinetic studies of Garrasi and Pierucci[1]. However, the apparent nitrogen removal efficiency during this period was only about 50%. As the degree of nitrification increased a high concentration of NO_3 built up within the system because of the lag in establishing the denitrification reaction. The feed FOC : TKN ratio was 2 and there was therefore only sufficient degradable organic carbon available to fully denitrify the input TKN. Because of this organic carbon limitation the reservoir of NO_3 built up in the system could not be reduced hence the high level of NO_3 in the discharge and the apparently poor denitrification efficiency. It should be pointed out that under similar circumstances when the FOC : TKN ratio was above the minimum level rapid reduction of the accumulated NO_3 did not follow immediately. In the PAC-dosed system however, the nitrification and denitrification processes were always re-established in phase with each other and hence there was never any accumulation of NO_3 within the system.

Overall the addition of PAC resulted in better effluent quality as is evident from the performance data shown in Table 1. Typically, COD and FOC removal efficiencies were 83 to 89% and 80 to 86% respectively in the control stream, whilst the corresponding figures for the PAC-modified stream were 87 to 93% and 83 to 92%.

Hydraulic Considerations

The system hydraulic retention time (HRT) has a considerable influence on the capital costs of treatment plants. Bridle et al[2-4] found that there was a significant deterioration in effluent quality at aerobic retention times of 1.1 days (total HRT 1.6 days). Because of its poor stability the control stream was generally operated at an HRT greater than 2.85 days (0.92 anoxic, 1.93 aerobic), except for a period of about 20 days when diluted feed was being used and the total HRT was 2.34 days. Most often the system was operated at 3.5 to 4 days HRT. In the PAC-treated unit it was possible to reduce the HRT from its initial value of 2.85 days to 2.1 days (0.68 days anoxic, 1.42 days aerobic) with no significant reduction in treatment efficiency.

FULL SCALE WORK

The full scale studies were conducted at the BET plant at BSC Scunthorpe Works. The plant was commissioned in 1974 and was originally designed to treat waste liquors from the Appleby Frodingham, Redbourn and Normanby Park coke plants together with wastes from the neighbouring tar distillation plants operated by BSC (Chemicals) Ltd. and Bitmac Ltd. Normanby Park works closed in 1981 before the start of the full scale work, and the Redbourn coke works was replaced by a new plant nearby at Dawes Lane. In the Spring of 1984 the BSC (Chemicals) Ltd. works also closed. The BET plant has nine aeration cells, each of 570 m^3 capacity, arranged in three independent parallel streams, each stream having its own clarifier and sludge return system. Treated effluent is collected in a tidal storage reservoir of 3200 m^3 capacity and subsequently discharged into the River Trent. The discharge takes place only during a period of about 4 hours around each high tide so as to ensure maximum dispersion of the effluent in the tidal reaches of the river.

The Modified BET Plant

The original and modified flowsheets of the experimental stream are shown schematically in Figure 3. Essentially the modifications involved the following changes:

(a)   the first cell R1 was used as the anoxic reactor and the existing sur- face aerator was replaced by a 15 HP turbine mixer. Cells R2 and R3 were aerated as usual using the existing surface aerators. Thus, the nitrification volume was double the denitrification volume;

(b)   feed wastewater was fed only to R1 and the existing feed lines into R2 and R3 were sealed off;

(c)   new flow lines were installed so that all the mixed liquor leaving R1 was fed equally to R2 and R3 in parallel;

(d)   flow lines were also installed to permit the recycling of mixed liquor equally from R2 and R3 back to R1;

(e)   submersible pumps were installed in R1, R2 and R3 to provide the required flows through the system;

(f)   magnetic flow meters were fitted as shown in Figure 3 to monitor the process liquor flows;

(g)   ammonia monitors developed at BSC Teesside Laboratories were installed on site at the BET plant, one to continuously monitor the feed to the plant and one for operation in a batch mode on samples taken from vari- ous parts of the system.

OPERATING EXPERIENCE

Effect of Temperature

Nitrification is reported to be very sensitive[7-10] to both high and low tempera- ture operation, the optimum range is generally quoted as 20 to 30 °C. At BSC Scunthorpe Works' BET plant basin temperatures range from 8 °C in mid-Winter to 23 °C in mid-Summer. During the trials it was established that a high level (>75%) of nitrification could be maintained at temperatures down to 9 °C, albeit at long residence times (4 to 5 days). Care is needed, however, in order to prevent shock loadings especially when operating at low temperatures. During the initial trial, which was held in the period September to December, 1982, the major product of the nitrification reaction was nitrite whereas in subsequent trials nitrate was formed. It is thought that this difference was due to the differing thermal conditions pertaining during the development of the nitrification reaction. In the first trial the nitrifying population was actually being developed in the Autumn as basin temperatures were falling, whereas in subsequent trials nitrification was developed during Summer months when basin temperatures were relatively high and constant. A plausible explanation is that the growth rate of Nitrobacter is inhibited more than that of Nitrosomonas as the temperature is reduced. This would have a more significant impact in the first trial when an initially low population of nitrifying bacteria (Nitrobacter and Nitrosomonas) was being developed as temperatures were falling from 18 °C to 13 °C. Randall and Buth[11] observed that nitrite build-up occurred in the activated sludge process at temperatures below 17 °C. They concluded that there was a critical temperature below which the rate of nitratification is less than the nitritification. This results in the build-up of nitrate in the reactor until the temperature falls to a level where nitrification is completely suppressed.

Effect of pH

Nitrification is generally reported[12] as being very sensitive to pH changes. Despite the regular addition of caustic soda solution the pH in the aerobic basins was generally below 7. Indeed in one six-month trial in 1984 the pH was generally in the range 5.5 to 6 and on two occasions fell to 4.5. However, the depressed pH levels did not have any adverse effects on nitrification efficiency. This leads to the conclusion that the nitrifying bacteria can probably adapt to operation under low pH conditions provided other specific inhibitory effects are absent.

Denitrification Efficiency

The closure of Normanby Park coke works and the BSC (Chemicals) Ltd. plant meant that there was a progressive reduction in the COD of the wastewater during the course of the project. The average COD in 1982 was 1600 mg/litre whilst by 1984 it had fallen to about half this value. The average influent TKN level was about 200 mg/litre throughout most of the period of the investigation. There was therefore a carbon limitation on the denitrification reaction (generally the FOC : TKN ratio was between 1 and 1.5) throughout most of the full scale work. This was less of a problem when nitrite was the dominant product because of its reduced organic carbon requirement. Indeed if the nitrification reaction could be halted at the nitrate stage then this would be beneficial in cases where the feed FOC (or COD) : TKN ratio is low. Essentially three benefits would accrue if this type of operation were possible, namely, reduced oxygen requirement and lower acid production in the aerobic reactor, and a lower carbon requirement in the anoxic reactor. It should be remembered, however, that nitrite is more toxic than nitrate, and would also impose an oxygen demand on the receiving water. High levels of nitrite in the discharge would therefore be very undesirable and some additional treatment would be necessary.

Within the limits set by the FOC (or COD) : TKN ratio of the feed maximum denitrification was generally achieved. For complete denitrification of the recycle mixed liquor, however, a supplemental source of organic carbon would be required. Methanol has been widely used as an external carbon and energy source but its high cost has a very significant impact on plant operating costs. However, Monteith et al[13] and Skrinde and Bhagat[14] have identified a number of industrial wastes that exhibit denitrification rates comparable to that of methanol and which offer a cheaper alternative to methanol. However, before employing another waste as supplemental carbon source it would be necessary to establish that the introduction of the secondary waste did not affect the treatability of the primary waste. Unfortunately it was not possible within the present investigation to explore the feasibility of using a second industrial waste.

CONCLUSIONS

Based on bench-scale and full-scale investigations of the pre-DN-N process configuration for the nitrification and denitrification of coke plant wastewater the following conclusions may be drawn:

1) The process is capable of achieving complete nitrification and denitrification of coke plant wastewater. However, the addition of PAC may be necessary to ensure good process stability.

2) The addition of PAC is particularly beneficial in establishing the denitrification process during recovery of the system after plant upsets, or during initial acclimation.

3) Organic compounds present in coke plant wastewater are a suitable carbon and energy source for the denitrification reaction. No supplemental organic carbon is necessary provided the feed FOC : TKN ratio is $\geqslant 2$ (or at a COD : TKN ratio of $\geqslant 7$).

4) With careful operation a high degree of nitrification can be maintained at temperatures down to 10 $^{\circ}C$, although the residence time is approximately double that at 20 $^{\circ}C$.

5) The effect of pH on the nitrification reaction is not as critical as reported in the literature. Full nitrification could be maintained even when the reactor pH was consistently in the range 5.5 to 6.5.

REFERENCES

1   Garrasi, G. and Pierucci, F., "Further research into the biological treatment of chemical pollutants contained in coke oven wastewater : Biological nitrification and denitrification", Final Report ECSC Project No. 7254-11/279/04, CSM, Rome.

2   Bridle, T.R., Bedford, W.K. and Jank, B.E., "Biological treatment of coke plant wastewaters for control of nitrogen and trace organics", Paper presented at the 53rd Annual Water Pollution Control Federation Conference, Las Vegas, September, 1980.

3   Bridle, T.R., Bedford, W.K. and Jank, B.E., "Biological nitrogen control of coke plant wastewaters", Prog. Wat. Tech., 1980, 12, Toronto, pp 667-680.

4   Bridle, T.R., Bedford, W.K., Jank, B.E. and Melcer, H., "Biological nitrogen and trace organics control of coke plant wastewaters", Paper presented at the 6th Round Table Discussion on Coking Plants, ECSC, Luxembourg, October 6-7, 1980.

5   Dijkstra, F. and Baenens, V.E.A., "Biological treatment of wastewater of
    a chemical industry with complete nitrogen removal", Paper presented at
    the Workshop on Nitrification/Denitrification of Industrial Wastes, held
    at the Environmental Protection Service, Burlington, Canada, October 11,
    1977.

6   Bridle, T.R., Climenhage, D.C. and Stelzig, A., "Operation of a fullscale
    nitrification-denitrification industrial waste treatment plant", Journal
    W.P.C.F., 1979, 51, (1), pp 127-139.

7   Adams, C.E. and Eckenfelder, W.W., "Nitrification design approach for
    high-strength ammonia wastewaters", Journal W.P.C.F., 1977, 49, pp 413
    et seq.

8   Wong-Chong, G.M. and Caruso, S.C., "Biological oxidation of coke plant
    wastewaters for the control of nitrogen compounds in a single-stage
    reactor", Paper presented at the Workshop on Biological Nitrification/
    Denitrification of Industrial Waste, held at the Environmental Protection
    Service, Burlington, Canada, October 11, 1977.

9   Wild, H.E., Sawyer, C.N., McMahon, T.C., "Factors affecting nitrification
    kinetics", Journal W.P.C.F., 1971, 43, 9, pp 1845-1854.

10 Young, J.C., Thompson, L.O., Curtis, D.R., "Control strategy for biologi-
    cal nitrification systems", Journal W.P.C.F., 1979, 51, (1), pp 1824-1840.

11 Randall, C.W., and Buth, D., "Nitrite build-up in activated sludge
    resulting from temperature effects", Journal W.P.C.F., 1984, 56, (9),
    pp 1039-1044.

12 Barnes, D. and Bliss, P.J., "Biological control of nitrogen in waste-
    water treatment", pp 40-42, Published by E. and F.N. Spon, New York.

13 Monteith, H.D., Bridle, T.R. and Sutton, P.M., "Industrial waste carbon
    sources for biological denitrification", Prog. Wat. Tech., 1980, 12,
    Toronto, pp 127-141.

14 Skrinde, J.R. and Bhagat, S.K., "Industrial wastes as carbon sources
    in biological denitrification", Journal W.P.C.F., 1982, 54, (4), pp
    370-377.

ACKNOWLEDGEMENTS

This study was supported financially by the European Coal and Steel Community,
and this paper has been published with their permission and that of Dr. K.J.
Irvine, Director of Research and Development, British Steel Corporation. The
author would also like to express his thanks to BSC Scunthorpe Works for
providing the facilities for the full-scale trials and especially to the
management and staff of the Steam and Water Department for their assistance in
planning and running the trials.

TABLE 1

OVERALL PERFORMANCE OF EXPERIMENTAL PRE-DN-N UNITS

PARAMETER*	FEED		CONTROL STREAM		PAC-STREAM	
	Median	95th** Percentile	Median	95th Percentile	Median	95th Percentile
COD	1430	1840	190	340	140	245
FOC	405	540	64	112	48	74
TKN***	168	240	37	178	12	190
Thiocyanate	172	228	5.6	10.8	3.4	8.0
Monohydric phenols	370	500	2.9	6.8	1.4	4.0
NO_T-N	-	-	20	109	13	39

* all concentrations in mg/litre

** 95% of all observations were equal to or less than the stated
value

*** taken to be the sum of $SCN^- -N$ and $NH_4^+ -N$

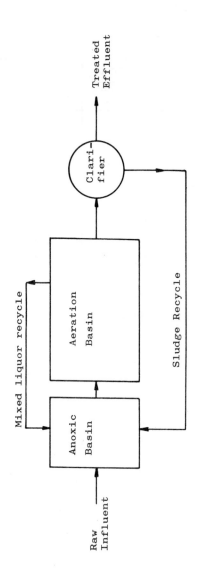

SCHEMATIC ARRANGEMENT OF THE SINGLE SLUDGE
PRE-DENITRIFICATION - NITRIFICATION PROCESS
CONFIGURATION

FIG. 1

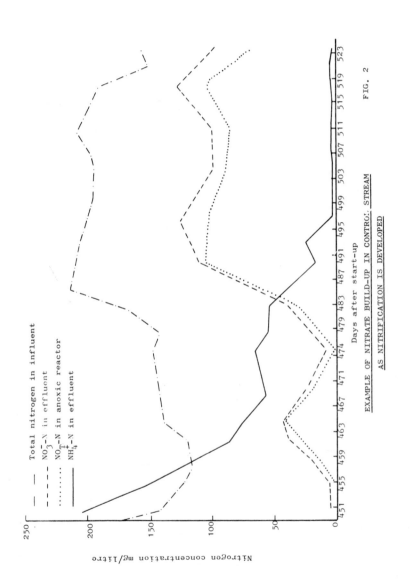

Total nitrogen in influent
NO_3^--N in effluent
NO_3^--N in anoxic reactor
NH_4^+-N in effluent

Nitrogen concentration mg/litre

Days after start-up

EXAMPLE OF NITRATE BUILD-UP IN CONTROL STREAM
AS NITRIFICATION IS DEVELOPED

FIG. 2

71

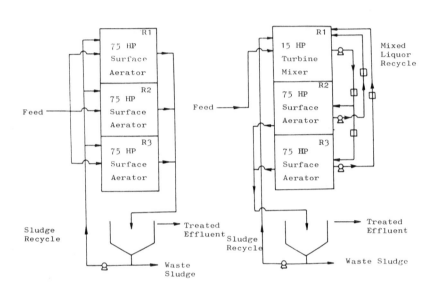

Magnetic flowmeter

Existing Arrangement   Modified Arrangement

FLOW SHEET FOR ONE STREAM AT BSC SCUNTHORPE WORKS
BIOLOGICAL EFFLUENT TREATMENT PLANT   FIG. 3

BIOTREATMENT OF NITROGENOUS REFINERY WASTE WATERS IN A SINGLE SLUDGE
NITRIFICATION-DENITRIFICATION SYSTEM

A.A. Esener*

Effluents from oil-refining and petrochemical industries
often contain nitrogenous in addition to carbonaceous
pollutants. A study of the various available schemes for
biotreating industrial waste water rich in nitrogen compounds has indicated that the "single sludge nitrification-
denitrification" system would offer considerable advantages,
particularly in terms of operating expenditure, over other
possible schemes. In the present study the predicted advantages of this system have been verified experimentally in
the laboratory and the relevant optimal and boundary
operating conditions were established using a synthetic
feed. The recommended design parameters were finally
verified by on-line process demonstration at a refinery.

INTRODUCTION

In the oil-refining and petrochemical industries nitrogen compounds are
undesired substances and are therefore largely removed from the products.
Part of the nitrogen removed during manufacturing operations leaves the
refinery in the waste water effluent streams in the form of ammonia.
Ammonia, in molecular form, is harmful to fish and exerts a high oxygen
demand in the receiving waters. Moreover, if the receiving water is to
be re-used downstream, the presence of ammonia will reduce the efficiency
of disinfection by chlorination since ammonia can react with chlorine or
hypochlorite salts to form chloroamines[1]. In the presence of sufficient
dissolved oxygen the ammonia-nitrogen can be oxidized by bacteria present
in the receiving waters to nitrate. However, a high concentration of nitrate
is not desirable either because this renders the water less suitable for use
as drinking water and may cause uncontrolled development of algae and other
aquatic flora.

Controlled biological nitrification and denitrification - i.e. oxidation of ammonia to nitrate, followed by the reduction of the nitrate to
molecular nitrogen - coupled with carbonaceous waste removal within a treatment plant is now regarded as a cost-effective method of treating ammonia-
rich industrial effluents. This concept is now being used in many domestic
waste water treatment plants and the relevant know-how is available[1-6].
Industrial waste waters, however, are quite different in composition and
nature from domestic waste waters and consequently process requirements
are also different and case and location dependent[7-11]. In view of these
facts, the work reported here dealt with the choice of a process configu-

* Koninklijke/Shell-Laboratorium, Amsterdam (Shell Research B.V.),
  P.O. Box 3003, 1003 AA Amsterdam, The Netherlands

ration suitable for refinery/petrochemical operations. The recommended "single sludge nitrification-denitrification" (SSND) process scheme was then tested experimentally to establish its feasibility and to obtain the required design parameters.

PROCESS CHEMISTRY AND CONFIGURATION

The relevant basic reactions to be considered are listed in Table I. Of these reactions, nitrification is not only intrinsically the slowest but also the most sensitive to environmental factors such as temperature, pH, the amount of dissolved oxygen and the presence of inhibitory substances. Therefore, a long sludge (biomass) residence time must be maintained to achieve the required amount of nitrifiers which can effect nitrification of industrial waste water. As shown by equation (I-2) in Table I nitrification requires a high oxygen input: 4.57 kg of oxygen per kg of ammonium-nitrogen. Moreover, the nitrification reaction produces a significant amount of acidity and hence for high strength industrial waste waters, pH control by alkali addition becomes essential. The denitrification process, on the other hand, takes place in the absence of molecular oxygen (anoxic environment) and produces alkalinity. Moreover organic carbon (electron donor) is required to effect denitrification.

Combining biological processes for nitrification, denitrification and the removal of carbonaceous pollutants presents a considerable number of different process alternatives. Important factors to be considered in the choice of process configurations for biotreatment of industrial waste waters are:

(i)   the degree of nitrogen conversion/removal required;
(ii) COD (available for denitrification)/ammonia-N ratio in the waste water;
(iii) availability (and costs) of external carbon sources;
(iv) availability (and costs) of chemicals required for pH control.

In general separate-stage processes operating in series, for example COD and NH_4^+-N oxidation followed by denitrification with intermittent sludge settling and recycle, offer closer process control and stability. However, for industrial waste water treatment such schemes may be costly due to a high chemicals consumptions for pH control and the required addition of external organic carbon to effect denitrification. In view of these considerations, a combined system "the single sludge nitrification-denitrification" (SSND), was chosen as a cost-effective and versatile route to meet the effluent quality demands. The SSND system (Fig. 1) is based on alternating exposure of the waste water and the biomass to aerobic and anoxic environments. Ammonia-nitrogen is converted to nitrate in the aerobic zone and the recirculated nitrate is subsequently converted to molecular nitrogen by the denitrification process in the anoxic zone. A basic feature of this system is the utilization of the waste water carbonaceous organics as the "electron donor" in the denitrification stage. This has the dual advantage of eliminating the need for an external carbon source, and utilizing the nitrate as an oxygen substitute, thereby reducing the oxygen input requirements in the aerobic reactor. Moreover, particularly for waste waters with a high ammonia content, significant savings in the chemicals used for the pH control are possible due to the improved alkalinity balance of the system. Whenever the SSND process is carried out in a two-reactor configuration as shown in Fig. 1, where nitrified effluent is recycled from the aerobic to the anoxic reactor, the recycle ratio (= return flow/influent flow to the system) becomes a key operational element. The recycle of the treated effluent to the

74

first reactor also effectively dilutes the incoming waste water and enhances the resistance of the system against any inhibitory compounds present in the raw waste water. In view of the advantages offered by the SSND system and the lack of data for refinery application an experimental investigation was initiated to test the viability of the SSND concept.

MATERIALS AND METHODS

All the experiments were carried out in a mobile biotreating unit which consisted of two parallel bench-scale set-ups. During the initial study both the anoxic and aerobic reactors were of 5×10^{-3} m^3 capacity. However, operation with different reactor volume ratios was also possible in the same unit. The pH in the aerobic reactor was controlled at 7.1-7.5 by adding alkali; the amount of alkali dosed was recorded. The synthetic feed used contained five carbon sources: phenol, acetic acid, toluene, glycerol and butanol at approximately equal concentrations on carbon basic (combined feed: TOC; 0.285 kg m^{-3}, theoretical oxygen demand: 0.93 kg m^{-3}, COD: 0.81 kg m^{-3}, BOD-5: 0.62 kg m^{-3}, BOD-15: 0.71 kg m^{-3}). Ammonia was added as ammonium chloride (0.150 kg-N m^{-3}). COD/NH_4^+-N ratio was 5.4 kg kg^{-1}. In some experiments this ratio was varied by using a more concentrated COD feed or NH_4^+-N solution. The operating temperature was 25 $^{\circ}$C.

RESULTS

The influence of recycle ratio on system performance

Operating conditions together with the overall system performance during the first 100 days' period of operation are indicated in Fig. 2. The system hydraulic residence time, based on the combined anoxic and aerobic reactor volumes (i.e. excluding clarifier volume) and the feed flow, varied between 18 and 40 hours while the range of recycle ratios was from 0.5 to 10.6. The actual hydraulic residence time for each reactor based on the combined flow was of course much shorter and varied between 1.5 and 5 hours. The feed composition was kept constant during this period (COD/NH_4-N $\simeq$ 5.4 kg kg^{-1}). The average sludge age weighted for the entire period was estimated at about 50 days.

As shown in Fig. 2, ammonia removal under these conditions was always total (>99 %). The COD removal was also very high: on average 98 $\pm$ 1 (96-99)%. The average effluent COD was about 20(10-30)*10^{-3} kg m^{-3} (spot BOD-5: approx. 2*10^{-3} kg m^{-3}). Under these conditions the system performance was very stable with good sludge settling.

Total percent nitrogen removal (NH_4^+-N plus NO_3^-/NO_2^--N was not influenced by the ammonia loading (0.09-0.20 kg N m^{-3} d^{-1}) of the system, and both nitrification and denitrification per pass in the respective reactors were total. The total system nitrogen removal was then mainly determined by the recycle ratio. In fact, for complete nitrification and denitrification in the respective aerobic and anoxic reactors, and in the absence of significant N assimilation into the biomass, the total N-removal can be theoretically shown to be given by the following expression:

$$\% \text{ N removal} = \frac{R}{1+R} \times 100 \qquad (1)$$

where R is the recycle ratio (return flow/influent flow). Comparison of this relationship with the experimental data shows good agreement (Fig. 3). Experimental N-removal is better at all values of R and this is believed to

75

be due to the removal of a fraction of nitrogen (most likely as ammonium ions) by bacterial assimilation. These results indicate that a recycle ratio of 3-4 will already effect a total N-removal of about 85-90 %. Operation at higher recycle ratios will require a disproportionately large amount of (pumping) energy. If a higher total N-removal is required one must either opt for post-denitrification (after nitrification with the addition of a carbon source in a relatively small third reactor) or for a cascaded system configuration[6], in which the total reactor volume is divided into successive denitrification and nitrification compartments with separate raw waste feed and recirculation flows[10].

Alkali consumption

As mentioned earlier, an advantage of the "single sludge" system is the reduced alkali consumption due to partial internal balancing of the pH. Data obtained during the "recycle study" experiments with total denitrification and nitrification per pass allow the estimation of caustic consumption per mass of ammonium-N removal as a function of the degree of overall nitrogen removal. In Fig. 3 the caustic consumption per NH_4^+-N removed is correlated to the degree of overall N removal (or to nitrate removal since ammonia oxidation to nitrate was always total) as affected by the variation of the recycle ratio. As indicated in Table II, despite complications caused by nitrogen assimilation by biomass and the acidity of the feed, good agreement exists between the theoretical and experimental values. In theory, the caustic consumption curve shown in Fig. 3 may be extrapolated to the no-recycle situation to estimate the equivalent caustic requirement, in case the same quantity of ammonia in the same feed had been converted to nitrate and biomass only, for example, in a conventional activated sludge system or any two sludge system with non-coupled nitrification and denitrification. The extrapolation gives a value which is also very close to the theoretical estimate. Thus under the specified conditions and at a recycle ratio of 3 savings in caustic consumption of up to about 40 % may be attained in comparison to a non-coupled system.

Influence of ammonia and COD loading on system performance

In view of the previous results it was decided to study the overall performance as a function of ammonia and COD loadings at the selected recycle ratio of 3 and hydraulic residence time of 20 hours (based on total system reactor volume). Unsteady state sludge age varied between 20 and 80 days but remained mostly at about 40-50 days. In Fig. 4 the overall system performance is shown as a function of ammonia and COD loadings and their ratio. In the range studied, the overall COD removal efficiency was independent of the system COD (0.14-0.40 kg COD kg^{-1} MLVSS* d^{-1}) and ammonia (0.026-0.11 kg kg^{-1} MLVSS d^{-1}) loadings and the COD/NH_4^+-N ratio (1.5-5.4), and remained high at 97 $\pm$ 2 % (n = 23).

The ammonia-N removal, however, was dependent on the system ammonia loading above 0.065 kg NH_4^+-N kg^{-1} MLVSS d^{-1} and the effluent quality became unacceptable above this level (as shown in Fig. 4 nitrite accumulation started). Below this critical loading ammonia removal efficiency seemed to be independent of the COD/NH_4^+-N ratio of the influent.

Total nitrogen removal at constant recycle ratio and with total ammonia conversion is fixed by the efficiency of denitrification which depends on the COD/NO_3^--N ratio at the anoxic reactor inlet below a critical stoichiometric value, as shown in Fig. 5. Thus, with the synthetic waste water used

76

a COD/NO_3^--N ratio above 4 resulted in total denitrification in the absence of kinetic limitations. The experimental data fitted by a regression line agree well with the theoretical estimate based on feed composition (excluding biosynthesis) and data reported by EPA[1] for methanol (including biosynthesis).

The maximal conversion rates measured during this programme were about 0.25 kg NO_3^--N kg^{-1} MLVSS d^{-1} for denitrification in the anoxic reactor $(COD/NO_3^-$-N$\sim$3 kg $kg^{-1})$ and about 0.13 kg NH_4^+-N kg^{-1} MLVSS d^{-1} for nitrification in the aerobic reactor. These estimates indicate that the volume of the nitrification reactor should be at least twice that of the anoxic reactor. A ratio of 1/2.6 was therefore selected for further on-line process demonstration studies.

Estimation of the bioenergetic parameters

The data collected allowed the formulation of pseudo-steady-state mass balances over the entire system and the estimation – using a conventional unstructured growth model[12] – of bioenergetic parameters for future modelling and design studies.

The yield of biomass (sludge), Y_{sx} (kg sludge produced per kg COD removed), was calculated as a function of the sludge age, θ (days). The bioenergetic parameters, Y_{sx}^{max} (maximum value of Y_{sx}) and b (the decay rate coefficient, day^{-1}) were then estimated by using the following model relationship:

$$Y_{sx} = Y_{sx}^{max} (1 + b\theta)^{-1} \qquad (2)$$

As can be seen from Fig. 6, the data show considerable scatter. This is partly due to the significant variation of the COD/NH_4^+-N ratio during the experimental programme. Moreover, it should be pointed out that this model treats Y_{sx} as a lumped yield factor in that it takes into account all biomass producing processes such as denitrification, nitrification and aerobic COD oxidation. This simplification is made since no sound experimental method is available to differentiate between the various biosynthetic processes. Therefore, the parameters obtained should not be extrapolated to situations with widely different conditions e.g. COD/NH_4^+-N ratios.

On-line process demonstration with actual refinery waste water

Based on the previous results the two parallel bench-scale units were operated on-line with actual refinery waste water (slip stream) at the conditions listed in Table III. Despite large variations in feed COD and NH_4^+-N both units performed well in terms of overall COD and BOD-5 removal: 95% and 98%, respectively (Fig. 7). Ammonia conversion in both units was total most of the time (>99 %), except during shock periods when the feed composition was not representative. Total nitrogen removal performance followed a similar trend for both units and averaged about 60 % (or about 80 % of the theoretical maximum at a recycle ratio of 3). This indicated that the denitrification efficiency was mainly determined by the amount and nature of the carbonaceous pollutants (availability for the denitrification process) present in the waste water (in relation to the ammonia nitrogen in the feed). Periods of high COD/NH_4^+-N ratio in the feed corresponded to periods of high N-removal, as found previously (Figs. 4 & 5). Whenever the COD/NO_3^--N ratio at the anoxic reactor inlet was above 4-5 kg kg^{-1}, almost total denitrification was achieved. As expected, the less loaded unit 2 produced better quality effluent, particularly in terms of BOD-5 and ammonia, and proved to be more resilient towards instabilities. These observations were found to be in good agreement with the previous study carried out with synthetic waste water.

CONCLUDING REMARKS

The predicted advantages of the single sludge nitrification-denitrification system have been experimentally verified for refinery service. Compared to a conventional activated sludge type system, the SSND offers significant savings in the chemicals needed for pH control and as carbon source, and in the total oxygen requirement. Moreover, the system displays good biological stability and in particular the sensitive nitrification process is effectively buffered against shocks of inhibitory substances or excess COD loads because of the dilution of the incoming waste by the recycle flow and substantial COD removal in the denitrification zone. These observations are generally in good agreement with the limited number of industrial waste water studies carried out with with SSND system[7-11].

The main disadvantages of this sytem are the increased pump capacity requirement and the pumping costs for the recycle stream. The recycling costs may be reduced, however, at higher capital costs by staging.

The economics and the eventual choice of the single sludge system will depend not only on the waste water and effluent specifications but also on local conditions and availability of chemicals. An important feature of this configuration is its suitability for revamping the existing and particularly the overdesigned conventional treating plants e.g. by shutting off a number of aerators or partitioning the aeration tank, as already discussed by Argaman[9].

Because of the experimentally verified advantages the single-sludge nitrification-denitrification concept is considered to be a flexible and cost-effective scheme to meet effluent specifications.

ACKNOWLEDGEMENT

Thanks are due to Messrs. A. Heemstra and R. Zaal (student trainee) for carrying out the experimental work.

REFERENCES

1. EPA, U.S. Environmental Protection Agency, Reports Nos. EPA/625/1-75/007 and EPA/625/1-76/00/a.

2. Barnes, D. and Bliss, P.J., 1983, "Biological Control of Nitrogen in Waste Water Treatment", F.N. Spon LTD, London.

3. Van Haandel, A.C., Dold, P.L. and Marais, G.R., 1982, Water Sci. Tech. 14, 443.

4. Argaman, Y.,1981, Water Res. 15, 841.

5. Henze, M. and Bundgaard, E., 1982, gwf-Wasser Abwasser, 123, 240.

6. Mijani, Y., Iwasaki, M. and Sekigawa, Y., 1980, Prog. Water Tech. 12, 193.

7. Monteith, H.D., Bridle, T.R. and Sutton, P.M., 1980, Prog. Water Tech., 12, 127.

8. Bridle, T.R., Climentage, D.C. and Stelzig, A., 1979, J. Water Pollut. Control Fed. 51 (1), 127.

9. Argaman, Y., 1984, Water Res., 18 (12) 1493.

10. Baenens, V.E.A., 1979, Paper presented at the IAWPR Workshop on the Treatment of Domestic and Industrial Waste Waters in Large Plants, Vienna, Austria, September 3-7.

11. Pascik, I., 1982, Hydrocarbon Proces., October, 80.

12. Esener, A.A., Roels, J.A. and Kossen, N.W.F., 1983, Biotechnol. Bioeng, 25, 2803.

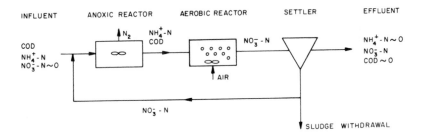

FIG. 1: FLOW SCHEME OF THE SINGLE SLUDGE NITRIFICATION-DENITRIFICATION SYSTEM

TABLE I: BASIC REACTIONS (EXCLUDING BIOSYNTHETIC REACTIONS) TAKING PLACE IN A BIOTREATING SYSTEM FOR THE REMOVAL OF CARBONACEOUS AND NITROGENOUS POLLUTANTS

Aerobic reactions

(i) COD (Chemical oxygen demand) oxidation:

$$COD + O_2 \rightarrow CO_2 + H_2O \tag{I-1}$$

(ii) Nitrification:

$$NH_4^+ + 2\ O_2 \rightarrow NO_3^- + H_2O + 2\ H^+ \tag{I-2}$$

Anoxic reaction

(i) Denitrification with organic carbon (COD):

$$5\ (C\text{-organic}) + 2\ H_2O + 4\ NO_3^- \rightarrow$$
$$2\ N_2 \uparrow + 5\ CO_2 + 4\ OH^- \tag{I-3}$$

TABLE II: ALKALI CONSUMPTION IN THE SINGLE SLUDGE SYSTEM

	equiv. alkali kg^{-1} NH_4-N		kg NaOH kg^{-1} NH_4-N	
	Experiment[†]	Theory*	Experiment	Theory
Single sludge system				
R = 3	85	90	3.40	3.60
R = 0.5	127	119	5.08	4.76
System with no coupled-denitrification i.e. R=0 (extrapolation)	140	143	5.60	5.72

[†] experimental estimates are based on ammonia-N removal
* theoretical estimates are based on data provided by EPA (Environmental Protection Agency of the USA)[1]
: 143 equiv. alkali consumed per kg NH_4-N oxidized &
: 71 equiv. alkali produced per kg NO_3-N reduced to N_2.

TABLE III: ON-LINE OPERATING CONDITIONS OF BENCH-SCALE BIOTREATERS

		UNIT 1	UNIT 2
Recycle ratio	(-)	3	3
Temperature	(°C)	25	25
Target sludge conc.	(kg m^{-3})	3-5	3-5
Target sludge age	(days)	30	50
pH control set point in nitrification tank	(-)	7-7.5	7-7.5
Volume anoxic/volume aerobic	(-)	1/2.6	1/2.6

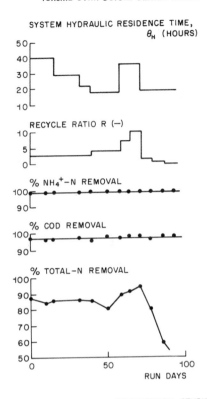

FIG. 2: RECYCLE RATIO OPTIMISATION STUDY:
OPERATING CONDITIONS AND OVERALL SYSTEM PERFORMANCE

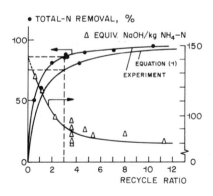

FIG. 3: INFLUENCE OF RECYCLE RATIO ON
TOTAL NITROGEN REMOVAL AND CAUSTIC CONSUMPTION

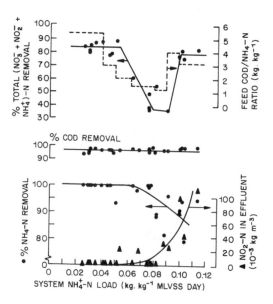

FIG. 4: SYSTEM PERFORMANCE AS INFLUENCED BY
AMMONIA LOADING AND
THE FEED CHARACTERISTIC COD/NH_4^+-N RATIO

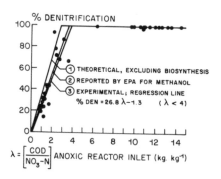

FIG. 5: % DENITRIFICATION AS A FUNCTION OF
THE ANOXIC REACTOR INFLUENT CHARACTERISTIC, λ

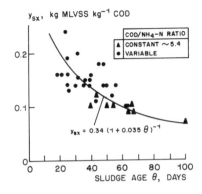

FIG. 6 : YIELD OF BIOMASS ON SUBSTRATE
AS A FUNCTION OF SLUDGE AGE

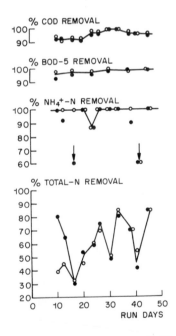

FIG. 7: ON-LINE PERFORMANCE OF
SINGLE SLUDGE BENCH SCALE UNITS
(• UNIT 1; ∘ UNIT 2) WITH REFINERY EFFLUENT
(——▶ SHOCK)

83

AUTOMATED SEWAGE TREATMENT SYSTEM FOR SAFER BATHING BEACHES

D.E. Smith* and W.G. Davies*

A new single stage sewage treatment process has been
devised to pre-treat sewage to a quality suitable for
discharge to coastal waters. The process involves the
physico-chemical treatment of sewage using a newly developed chemical system to flocculate the suspended matter
and establish alkaline pH levels at which viable organisms
are reduced in number. The flocs produced are then
removed in a conical upward flow sludge blanket clarifier.
Initial small scale experimental work led to the construction of a full scale fully automated prototype plant to
further evaluate the potential of the process.

INTRODUCTION

The treatment of sewage before discharge to coastal waters is now becoming
increasingly necessary for several reasons but two major factors stand out
distinctly. Firstly, the need to ensure that bathers do not contract water
borne diseases when swimming in waters where sewage effluent discharge has
taken place, and secondly to ensure that the aesthetic appearance of the
environment is not affected by unpleasant fouling of the beaches. Therefore,
it is necessary to ensure that sewage is treated satisfactorily before final
discharge to short sea outfalls.

Accordingly, a new treatment system has been devised to pre-treat sewage
using specially developed chemical additives to form flocs and removing the
resulting solids in a conical, upward flow sludge blanket clarifier. A one
metre 'Perspex' scale model was manufactured to study the flow patterns and
separation behaviour in the process. This work proved successful and a 6.3
metre diameter prototype process plant was built at Sandown, Isle of Wight,
with the collaboration of the SWA. The Sandown site was particularly per-
tinent as this was one of the designated Euro Beaches in the UK within the
auspices of the SWA.

In order to overcome some of the problems encountered in earlier experimental
work the whole process was automated with full computer control. Variable
speed pumps and automated valves were installed for controlling the process
together with relevant sensors for monitoring the important parameters, as
well as flow and depth, to ensure that the treatment process could be closely
regulated depending upon the variable conditions. Thus, it was possible in a
single stage process to treat a variable flow and strength of sewage and

* Blue Circle Industries PLC, Effluent Treatment Division,
  Newcastle-under-Lyme.

produce an effluent which was of a higher standard suitable for discharge to coastal waters.

THE PROCESS IN OUTLINE

The Upward Flow Sludge Blanket (UFSB) process, is a single stage sewage treatment which produces a quality of final effluent very suitable for direct discharge to estuary or sea without the need for long pipelines. The removal of suspended solids and biochemical oxygen demand is significantly increased in this process over that from primary sedimentation alone due to the formation of a suspended sludge floc blanket. Large scale bacterial removal is also achieved because of the strongly alkaline nature of the coagulant, thus enabling the bacterial level in the receiving sea water to be kept below the standards set by the EEC Directive for Bathing Beaches.

In the process, which is illustrated in Figure 1, an inorganic coagulant is added to raw screened sewage in order to flocculate the suspended and colloidal matter. In the coagulation tank the sewage achieves full flocculation as the flocs are encouraged to develop in size. The flocculated sewage then flows into the upward flow tank where a suspended sludge floc blanket is created. The floc blanket is maintained in position by the velocity of the upward stream counteracting the gravitational forces on the flocculated particles. The blanket level is monitored constantly and various desludging strategies are put into operation dependent upon the position and rate of rise of the blanket. The floc blanket acts as a fluidised filter medium, entrapping additional small flocs and fine suspended matter to clean the effluent further both chemically and biologically. The very heavy flocs and gross suspended matter settle to the bottom of the tank. The final effluent is discharged from the top of the tank. The sludge is removed both from the base of the unit, as a thick sludge, and from the blanket, as a low solids sludge (approximately 0.5-2% solids). The low solids sludge readily settles to higher solids concentrations (up to 15%) and the combined sludge can be easily filtered to a relatively dry (over 40% solids) inoffensive, cake for disposal.

The whole process is computer controlled based on the various quality and process parameters. The quality of the effluent in terms of turbidity, pH and conductivity is measured and recorded at regular intervals and this information, together with other data, such as flow rate, pH, and solids level in the incoming sewage, determines the control strategy.

The treatment tank is of steel construction positioned on a small reinforced concrete base slab. Capital cost is consequently minimised and construction time reduced to weeks.

In order to reduce installation cost further and make the process flexible in application a modular design concept has been adopted. Each module, which is essentially the upward flow tank, has been designed to be capable of dealing with the sewage from 2,000 to 10,000 people. In this manner, the process is suitable for townships in the population range of 2,000 to greater than 100,000. In addition, as the population of the townships increase further modules can be added to deal with the increasing sewage load.

HISTORICAL DEVELOPMENT OF THE PROCESS

Early Development Work

The application of potable water treatment processes to sewage treatment
was studied for several years prior to 1983 by Portsmouth Polytechnic (PP),
in the Department of Civil Engineering. Their work, which was supported by
the Southern Water Authority (SWA), initially investigated the use of
upward flow sludge blanket techniques in secondary and tertiary sewage
treatment processes (1). By injecting low doses of lime into the effluent
arising from biological filters coagulation occurred and loose flocs were
formed. A 10 : 10, TSS : BOD$_5$ standard effluent, low in phosphates and
coliform content, were reported, although there were problems in producing
coherent flocs and in controlling the process under variable rates of flow.

This approach was subsequently extended to the treatment of raw screened
sewage through trials on a converted hopper-bottomed primary settlement
tank. In this instance a stable floc blanket was formed using lime and
polyelectrolyte as flocculant. At those times when the system was under
control a fairly clear supernatant liquor emerged at the surface of the
modified tank, and despite both semi-automatic and manual control, there
were still major problems controlling on a large scale, and in a continuous
manner, the blanket, the chemical dosing, and sludge removal from the
system, as fluctuations in sewage strength, rate of flow and the presence
of air quickly destroyed what appeared to be a stable floc blanket.

The Coagulant

     Blue Circle Industries (BCI) became involved through the introduction
of newly developed stable high solids coagulant slurries. These coagulant
slurries were formulated on technology derived from the experience of BCI
in the use of high solid slurries in the paper industry. These patented
chemical formulations containing lime, a weighting agent and polyelectroly-
tes, generally have 50% solids in suspension, and yet are of low viscosity
for ease of handling, transportation, storage and pumping. These slurries,
now referred to as Clarifloc, can be factory produced and transported to
site without the problem of making up traditional lime slurries at the
Sewage Works. The coagulant can be injected as a thick slurry directly
into raw screened sewage to condition the colloidal and suspended matter by
an auto-flocculation process entrapping the finer material within strong
weighted flocs. Such flocs lead to high rates of sedimentation and
substantial reductions in the polluting load: organics, phosphates and
bacteria.

Initially, these coagulants were aimed solely to improve the performance of
primary sedimentation tanks by physico-chemical treatment (PCT) to relieve
overloaded works, without resorting to major capital expenditure programmes, and significant improvements in performance were achieved over conventional treatment without chemical aids. For example, the removal of
suspended solids improved by 20 to 60% dependent on dose rate, as shown in
Figure 2, with BOD$_5$ typically reduced by 60%, phosphates by 80% and coliforms by 90%. However, as the application of PCT treatment to conventional
processes was not widely accepted in the UK, attention was directed to the
potential of the UFSB process, in combination with the new coagulant
slurries, for the treatment of effluents discharging to estuarine and
coastal waters. The UFSB process was seen as an alternative to the options

of full treatment or long sea outfalls where improvements were necessary
to meet the EEC bathing water quality requirments. An agreement between PP,
SWA and BCI allowed Blue Circle to licence and develop the technology.

PVC Model of UFSB Clarifier

A one metre diameter clear PVC scaled model of a proposed 6.3 m diameter full
scale prototype upward flow clarifier was built in July 1983 to access the
combined UFSB/Clarifloc system. Experimentation on the model enabled the
conditions for establishing and maintaining good stable floc blankets to be
assessed. Blanket stability was maintained at various hydraulic loadings.
The depth of the floc blanket was found to be readily controllable through
careful discharge of blanket sludge via two opposing ports in the cylindrical
side of the UFSB tank. The fluidised flocs in the blanket were observed to
readily redistribute themselves within the blanket and so maintain a
distinct, and level, upper blanket surface and a clear interface with the
final clarified effluent above. Various surface loading rates were investigated and at 0.9 1/sec/m^2, approximately four times that for conventional
primary tanks, an effluent with 50 mg/l TSS was achieved when treating a
screened raw sewage of 350 mg/l TSS with Clarifloc to a pH of 9.

In the clear PVC unit the main reason for blanket failure was identified.
High accumulations of gross solids and heavy sludge in the conical section
created irregular density gradients and hence localised high velocity streams
of influent sewage within the cone. These streams in turn created turbulent
pockets within the blanket and these caused floc disruption, and floc
breakaways from the blanket surface, polluting the final effluent.

The test work on the model clarifier confirmed the potential of using
Clarifloc and the upward flow clarifier to produce, in a single stage once-
through process, a good quality effluent low in TSS, BOD_5 and coliforms, particularly suited to coastal discharge. A full scale prototype unit was
therefore designed and installed at Sandown, Isle of Wight.

THE PROTOTYPE PLANT

The full scale Prototype Plant was designed and built within a six month
period, being commissioned in March 84, and operated 24 hours per day for 12
months. The Upward Flow Tank itself was 6.3 metres diameter and 8.3 metres
high and the plant had the capacity to take total daily flows up to 4000 m^3.

Raw screened sewage was pumped into the Prototype Plant from a temporary
pumping station using a submersible Flygt pump. The pumping station was continuously supplied with bar-screened sewage from a distribution channel
feeding sewage to the Works' primary tanks. Since the need for good control
of the hydraulics, chemical dosing and desludging regimes was very evident
from the experimental phase a fully automated control system was included in
the design.

A flow sheet of the process (Figure 3) shows the control and instrumentation. Two computers, an Apricot and a Micro-Mac 5000 were linked to provide facilities for monitoring, process control and data handling. The I/0
signals consisted 17 analogue and 42 digital inputs and 22 digital outputs.
Throughout the operational period the computerised control system operated
very effectively and allowed the plant to operate continuously and unat-
tended.

PROCESS PERFORMANCE

The upward flow blanket process was extremely good at removing suspended solid matter and final effluent quality tended to exceed initial expectations. The blanket proved to be extremely stable over a wide variety of sewage strengths and flow rates. The information set out graphically in Figures 4 & 5 illustrates the performance under variable flow conditions and the speed with which the blanket forms. The solids removal efficiency was also examined under steady flow conditions equivalent to 1.3 DWF and 3 DWF as shown in Figures 6 & 7.

The biochemical oxygen demand of the sewage was also considerably reduced, the BOD_5 of the effluent being consistently in the region of 70% less than that in the influent sewage, although during the summer the BOD_5 figures were rather high due to high levels of soluble BOD. The phosphate content of the influent sewage was notably reduced by 90%.

Bacterial removal is a particular feature of the process. Investigations were carried out on the effectiveness of the process in removing bacteria, as this was the key parameter requiring improvement to meet the EEC Directive. The investigations conclusively demonstrated that the effect of alkalinity together with that of the blanket filtration, could deactivate (or kill) in excess of 99% of the incoming bacteria. In general terms it is considered that the effluent bacterial level could be reduced over a high proportion of operational time to 2×10^4 bacteria/ml. This concentration of bacteria on dilution into the sea would reduce to below the EEC requirement of 10^4 organisms/100 ml. Data given in Figure 8 illustrates the removal of bacteria (E. coli) during a 24 hour period in summer. Summer levels of bacteria were about ten times higher than those recorded during the winter.

THE NEW FULL SCALE PLANT AT SANDOWN

Following the success of the Prototype at Sandown, the Southern Water Authority commissioned Blue Circle to install a full scale plant based on the upward flow Clariflow Process, which was selected as the most suitable plant for the Sandown situation based on the economic evaluation summarised in Table 1 and other local factors.

The new plant has been designed around four modules to cope with a total flow of three times the dry weather flow (DWF) of 7,000 m^3 per day. The scheme has allowed for future expansion of population to a DWF of 10,000 m^3 per day by the possible incorporation of a further two modules should these be deemed necessary.

REFERENCE

1.   Urwin, R., Winfield B.A. & Stead P.A. Effluent & Water Treatment Journal, May 1980, p.222.

ACKNOWLEDGEMENTS

The authors would like to record the valuable assistance given by members of the Civil and Electrical Engineering Departments of Portsmouth Polytechnic, and of the Isle of Wight Division of the Southern Water Authority, without whose support this investigation would not have been possible.

TABLE 1   COMPARATIVE COST DATA FOR NEW PLANTS FOR SANDOWN

DESIGN FLOW (3 DWF) : 21,000 m^3/day

DESIGN POPULATION : 45,000 (Summer)

22,000 (Winter)

TYPE OF TREATMENT	CAPITAL COST (£)	OPERA-TIONAL COST P.A. (£)	CAPITAL COST PER CAPITA (£)	ANNUAL OPERATIONAL COST	
				PER CAPITA (£)	PER m^3 SEWAGE (p)
UPWARD FLOW PROCESS	2,355,000	80,000*	52	1.7	3.1
LONG SEA OUTFALL	4,500,000	30,000*	100	0.75	1.2
OXIDATION DITCH	4,200,000	100,000*	93	2.2	3.9

* Estimate

1 Screened sewage feed
2 Dilution water
3 Combined chemical/
  water injection
4 Combined overflow
  and scum take off
5 Chemical storage tank
6 Supernatant holding
  tank
7 Grit discharge
8 Coagulation tank
9 Supernatant return
10 Blanket sludge level
  detector unit
11 Scum scraper drive unit
12 Bellmouth weir
  actuator unit
13 Discharge to outfall
14 Bellmouth weir
15 Blanket sludge draw-off
16 Sludge to disposal
17 Bottom sludge draw-off

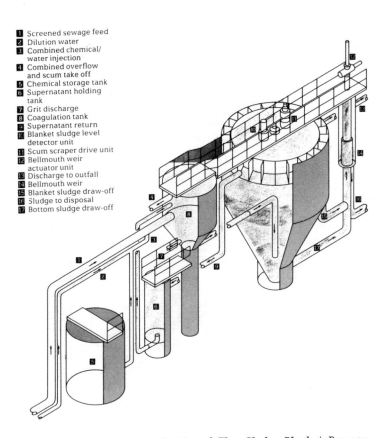

FIGURE 1 - The Upward Flow Sludge Blanket Process

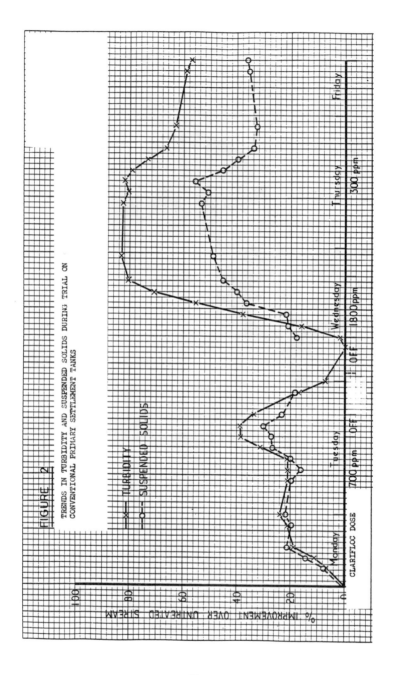

FIGURE 2

TRENDS IN TURBIDITY AND SUSPENDED SOLIDS DURING TRIAL ON
CONVENTIONAL PRIMARY SETTLEMENT TANKS

—x— TURBIDITY
—o— SUSPENDED SOLIDS

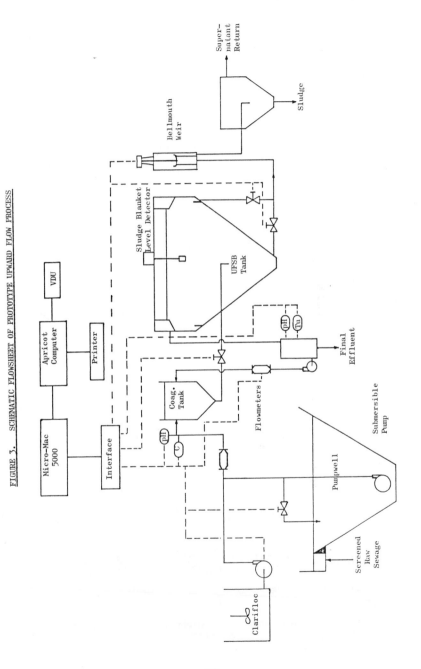

FIGURE 3. SCHEMATIC FLOWSHEET OF PROTOTYPE UPWARD FLOW PROCESS

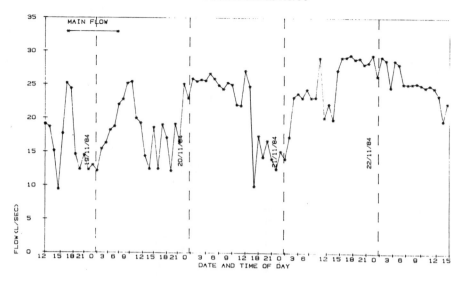

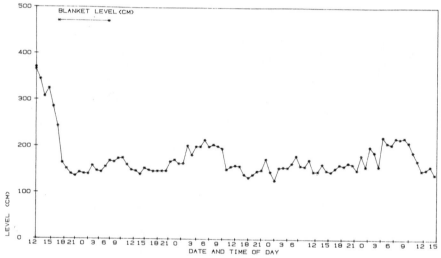

Figure 4 – Performance of Prototype Plant over Four Days
from 19th to 23rd November, 1984 at Various Sewage Flow Rates

(i) Sewage Flow Rate, 1/sec. (Surface loading at 10 1/sec
is 0.32 1/sec/m^2)

(ii) Blanket Level, cm. (Zero height is the supernatant
draw-off level).

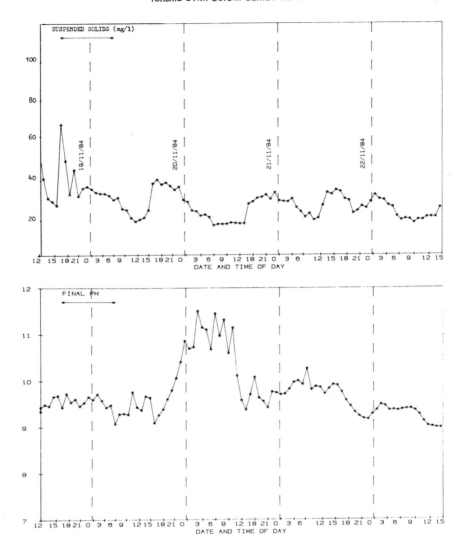

Figure 4 - Performance of Prototype Plant over Four Days
from 19th to 23rd November, 1984 at Various Sewage Flow Rates

(iii) Final Effluent Suspended Solids Content, mg/l

(iv) Final Effluent pH

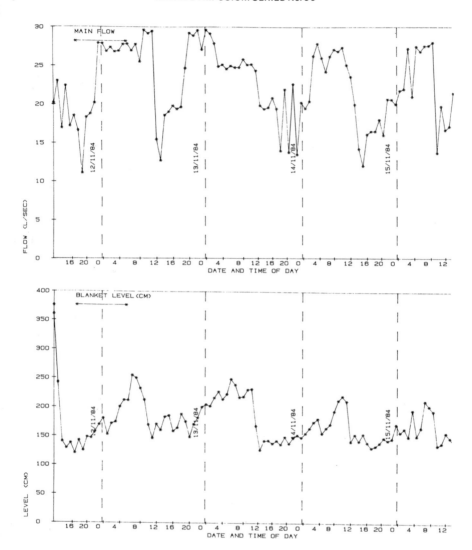

<u>Figure 5 - Performance of Prototype Plant over Four Days</u>
<u>from 12th to 16th November, 1984 at Various Sewage Flow Rates</u>

(i) Sewage Flow Rate, l/sec. (Surface loading at 10 l/sec
is 0.32 l/sec/m^2)

(ii) Blanket Level, cm. (Zero height is the supernatant
draw-off level).

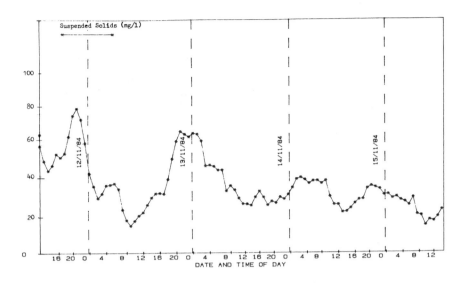

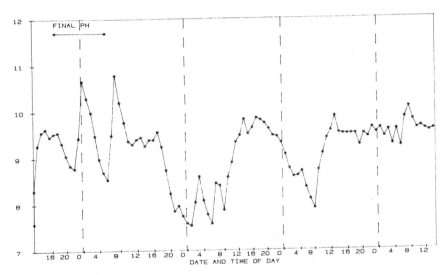

Figure 5 - Performance of Prototype Plant over Four Days
from 12th to 16th November, 1984 at Various Sewage Flow Rates

(iii) Final Effluent Suspended Solids Content, mg/l

(iv) Final Effluent pH

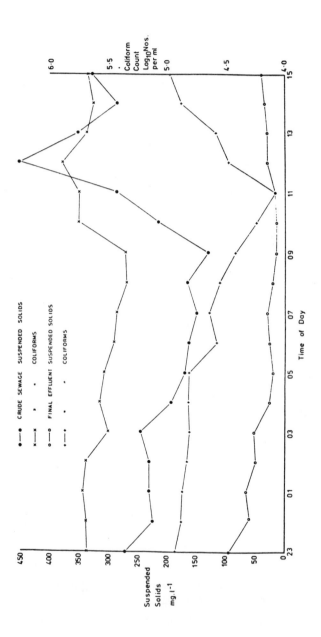

FIGURE 6
Removal of Suspended Solids at 1.3 times DWF,
(16 litres/sec)

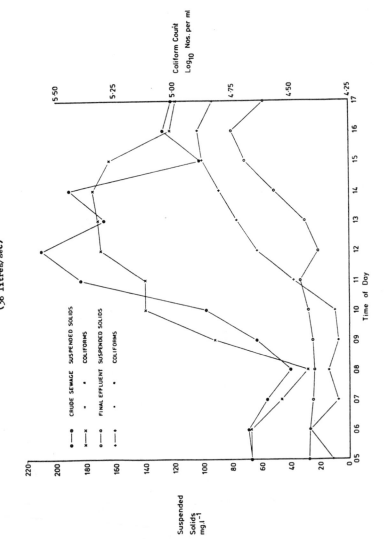

FIGURE 7
Removal of Suspended Solids at 3 DWF,
(36 litres/sec)

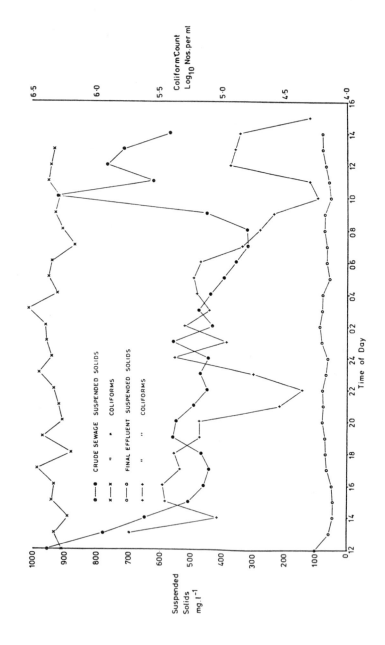

FIGURE 8

Reduction in Bacterial Population at 1.6 DwF
(20 litres/sec)

A REVIEW OF SLUDGE TREATMENT PROCESSES

G P Noone*

Examination of the various options for sludge treatment prior to its disposal has concentrated upon the use of biological systems. From experience in the water industry, these can offer reliable, low-cost processing routes for organic or mixed organic/inorganic sludges. Within this symposium's sub theme of technology transfer, the more usual industrial systems utilising chemical and purely physical processes have not been considered in detail.

INTRODUCTION

The treatment of sludges (the initially solid phase of effluent production) can be achieved by chemical, biological or physical means. The treatment route adopted must consider the sludge type, its ultimate disposal destination and the combined treatment and disposal costs. Chemical sludges derived from physico-chemical processes involving precipitation are already common within the process industries. Such options are not usually cost competitive with biological processes when applied to the organic wastes typical of the food processing, farming and domestic effluent treatment industries. Purely physical processing of waste sludges in the absence of significant chemical additions, eg by gravity consolidation or various mechanical dewatering options such as plate pressing or centrifugation however can be successfully applied to both organic and inorganic sludges. In all cases the ultimate destination of such dewatered, 'untreated', 'organic' sludges must be very carefully matched against a large suite of environmental considerations.

Within an underlying theme of this conference, namely that of technology transfer, the area of widest 'new' interest for most effluent producing industries arises from a possible option to biologically process their liquid and solid effluents, ie the liquors and sludges. This review thus concentrates upon the biological options for solids treatment.

The principal biological processes for solids treatment are those of anaerobic and aerobic digestion. Such 'reactions' are also applied to

* Severn-Trent Water Authority

the liquid effluent phase, indeed for most liquid wastes of low or low
to medium organic strength the aerobic option is usually more
appropriate. Anaerobic processes are more relevant for the higher
strength liquid organic wastes. However, the low influent strengths
of, for example, 'domestic' sewage are such that it is invariably only
the separated organic solids, the sludges, which can usefully be
treated anaerobically, the liquors requiring aerobic treatment. A
simple background consideration of the basic differences between the
aerobic and anaerobic systems is now offered for perspective. Other
papers in this symposium consider those differences in greater detail.

Where a biological treatment system is operating on domestic or
animal wastes, significant populations of bacteria are already present
in the effluent and these can usefully metabolise the 'polluting'
waste to produce more acceptable 'degraded' wastes. Many bacteria can
operate in both an aerobic (in the presence of air/oxygen) or
anaerobic (in the absence of oxygen) mode. For other organic type
wastes an inoculum of a 'digesting' sludge is needed to initiate the
biological reactions. Bacteria which can operate in either régime are
determined to be facultative whilst those specific to either single
regime are termed obligative. The reaction kinetics are such that
both processes are thermodynamically viable although adequately high
reaction rates for economic processing in either regime require a
process energy input.

In the case of aerobic systems, this energy input is achieved by
aeration (oxygenation) devices powered electrically. For aerobic
solids treatment systems, options involving high oxygen inputs can
achieve significant exothermic reaction leading to potentially
thermally stable operation in a wide temperature range as high as
70°C. The overall aerobic process is however effectively endothermic
in purchased energy terms. Anaerobic systems, despite only comparable
or lower kinetics, produce a reaction by-product of methane. This
methane off-gas, although being in admixture with approximately 35%
CO_2, is readily combustible and thus the input energy to raise the
temperature of reaction to an optimum of approx 37°C is readily
available. Despite this optimum anaerobic operation in the mesophilic
range occurs at around blood heat, 37°C, the availability of methane
from simply achievable sludge solids levels (see later paper by
Hoyland[1] in this Symposium) produces a significant availability of
excess methane gas for alternative potentially high grade uses. This
readily results in plants which are net energy exporters. This
surplus (approx 50% methane gas) is often achieved within modestly
loaded reactors utilising only low levels of reactor insulation.

Another paper in this symposium by Anderson and Saw[2] deals with
research areas outlining varied, wider applications of anaerobic
treatment (both liquid and solid phase). For general waste water or
other liquid phase effluent treatments the anaerobic option is however
a relatively new but effective development. To avoid undue repetition
whilst providing a basis for subsequent discussion, it is now proposed
to illustrate the development of the principal biological systems,
anaerobic and aerobic, applied to treatment of the 'solid' phase
materials. In view of its wider application and proven acceptability
it is proposed to begin by considering the history and development of
anaerobic digestion a process already having a developed 'life'
within the sewage treatment industry of some 80 years to date.

REVIEW OF ANAEROBIC DIGESTION

The following account of anaerobic digestion development concentrates upon the recognition of the processing inputs for plant provision. Many of the developments prior to recent work by the author, his many colleagues and other workers had tended to concentrate upon the structural and hydraulic aspects of plant construction.

Anaerobic digestion in the mesophilic temperature range is by far the most popular form of treatment for those sludges which arise from domestic or domestic/industrial waste discharges to sewer. Recently compiled statistics show the proportion of UK Water Industry sludges anaerobically digested to be some 60%[3]. This situation is comparable with or better than that in the vast majority countries of Europe and North America.

In providing details of both the history and recent developments of anaerobic digestion it must be clearly understood that the prime reason behind the processes initial realisation, its development, continued and indeed now more extensive use lies in its virtually unique role as an effective natural odour control and/or elimination system for sewage sludges. This is of course also so for other putrescible organic solids arising from industrial processing.

The need for responsible industrialists, farmers or sludge treatment authorities to have available to them final disposal routes for waste sludges which are both environmentally effective as well as being cost attractive, has significantly widened the application of anaerobic sludge digestion. The 'stabilisation' or odour suppression which occurs by destroying the putrescible (volatile) sludge components. When digestion is considered along with further benefits such as the reduction and/or effective elimination of various relevant pathogenic organisms, the inherent solids disposal of approx 30% of the input solids to CH_4 and CO_2 in the case of sewage sludges, then the reasons for the processes increased popularity become clear.

Anaerobic digestion comprises of essentially three stages of reaction. The initial phase and one which is often ignored is that of partial solids hydrolysis. The resultant 'sugars' then are attacked by acid forming bacteria to produce carboxylic acids. These acid formers are quite a robust strain with short doubling times of the orders of a few hours. A second more sensitive strain of 'methane' formers then carries the reaction to completion. Both strains operate a dynamic balance hinged around a bicarbonate buffer system. Any overload situation can disturb the equilibrium limits and the long doubling time for the methane formers (say up to 9 days) shows the problem of process retrieval if control is lost. This balance is intrinsically robust where process inputs and loading rate remain reasonably constant or change only at a steady rate as like all biological systems high shock loads can offer difficulties.

The process is thus able to reliably and cheaply produce treated materials which are environmentally innocuous and safe for ultimate recycling within agriculture. This ability to facilitate recycle is of course subject to absence of conservative contaminants such as excess levels of heavy metals in the 'raw' waste sludges. It should however also be stressed that this agricultural disposal aspect merely serves as an additional attraction to digestion's historical and abiding principal benefit of stabilisation or odour control. For example, digestion allows environmentally acceptable on-site sludge storage within the flow sheet to accommodate processing variations or breakdowns between other process units. Further, digestion allows mechanical dewatering without malodour production thus providing a more general acceptability amongst both plant operators and sludge recipients. This is particularly relevant to industrial and Water Authority processors alike due to their need to eliminate or minimise any nuisance to their neighbours.

HISTORICAL DEVELOPMENT OF ANAEROBIC DIGESTION

This short section illustrates the development of large scale anaerobic reactors within their 'birthplace', the sewage treatment industry. During the last century or so, in keeping with the majority of developments both in sewage treatment and the wider areas of public health engineering, sludge treatment has followed a progression from its initial 'Hydraulic' emphasis through a period of dominance by 'structural' designers until the more recent recognition of the need for the 'process' design to establish a more prominent role. An anaerobic digester must now be regarded as a heated and mixed biological reactor:- not merely as a sludge storage tank with various items of mechanical and electrical equipment appended.

The process emphasis has been underlined by a basic need to save capital and operating costs by increased plant throughputs from process intensification. As both anaerobic and aerobic sludge digesters are biological reactors, one is led to the obvious conclusion that this biological reaction component should offer the target rate limiting process stage. The process designer's and process engineer's brief is thus to ensure that the major physical processing inputs such as mixing (to distribute food to organisms), feeding regime (periods, if any, between reaction feeds) mass transfer and heat transfer rates are not limiting the often relatively slow biological process. The most recent process developments in mesophilic anaerobic digestion illustrate the elimination of limiting fundamental processing inputs.

Debate continues about who can truly claim to have developed anaerobic digestion as a predictable, defined process:- the contenders being England and Germany during the 1910-1920 period. Saltley works in Birmingham is claimed to have been operating a deliberate 'process' using steam heating as early as 1908[4]. Process discovery, namely the realisation that anaerobic stabilisation (odour suppression) of sewage solids produces a non-putrid product and a methane by-product is not however any subject of debate. The realisation of methane production from sewage sludge was reported by Dibdin[5] as early as 1885. The collection and useful harnessing of this by-product gas for works lighting was later reported by Cameron at Exeter in 1895[6].

The early 'processes' applied prior to the 1900-1910 period were without identified heating or mixing inputs and could only perhaps be truly considered as variations upon sludge storage systems. In the UK, the first sustained purpose designed attempt at providing equipment to intensify digestion by deliberate provision of such processing inputs as heating and mixing are attributed to Whitehead and O'Shaughnessy in Birmingham in 1931[7]. There have been a number of notable periods of work on digestion, each period having acted as significant turning points. Specific quotes from relevant work are reported elsewhere by the author, Noone[8].

Important work in the US circa 1950[9], the UK circa 1954[10] together with that by Griffiths UK (1959)[11] and Simpson UK (1960)[12] all outlined the need to consider a digester as a reactor. The American work introduced design parameters based on reactor loading or processing intensity, the specific loading parameter used was a volatile (reactable) solids loading per unit volume of reactor per unit time. The UK work of the same period stressed the need to consider detention period to prevent excessive washout of the slower methane forming bacterial strains crucial to process stability. For Water Industry anaerobic digesters, hydraulic detention period is equal to the solids retention period as due to the high levels of intractable materials these cannot be recycle reactors. Where a waste is wholly organic and 'tractable' the recycle reactor or alternate reactor systems then become viable options[2].

The next work of major significance was a WPRL (now WRC) paper by Swanwick et al (1969)[13]. Unfortunately, a number of important conclusions capable of derivation from the data provided within this paper appear to have been overlooked by many of the contemporary and subsequent plant designers. A major area overlooked was that part of the paper reporting process operational difficulties as 'always' being found in long detention (> 30 days) lowly loaded digesters. For those of 'medium' loading say 25 days 'intermittent' difficulties were experienced and it was only in the **short** detention or **highly loaded** plants where any operational difficulties had **not** been experienced. This unheeded observation that **higher** reaction intensities led to **more** stable operation is highly significant, indeed it was used by the author as confirmatory evidence to dispel the widely held belief even by recent plant designers that a 'bigger' digester was a 'safer' digester. Reactor considerations lead one to the contrary conclusion.

In an attempt to add perspective to the reported literature information, a short description of historical design consideration is now given from the previously mentioned work by Noone (1982)[8], see Table 1.

Table 1   HISTORIC DESIGN CRITERIA FOR ANAEROBIC DIGESTERS

Year	Reference	Design Parameter
1925	Baltimore USA	1.05 cu.ft/person
1928	USA (Imhoff type)	1.4 - 2.4 cu.ft/person
1928	USA (Dorr type)	1 - 3.7 cu.ft/person
1928	Germany	0.75 - 2.3 cu.ft/person
1928	Bath, UK	3.1 cu.ft/person
1931	UK (Generally)	3.1 cu.ft/person
1928	New South Wales	3.0 cu.ft/person
1954	UK Informal Working Party	1-2 ft^3/head with 28-30 days detention for mixed, mesophilic
	Early Practice USA	Total solids 1.75 lb/ft^3/month or (0.93 $kg/^3$/day)
1969	UK WPRL (Range of Survey)	16 days detention
1975	CIRIA	Minimum, detention of 12 days

Despite doubts about a firm basis for absolute comparability of the information in Table 1, an examination of its chronological progression enables certain conclusions to be drawn. The change of emphasis in chosen design parameter shows a growing awareness of the 'reactor' function of a digester moving as it does from a solely volume provision to one of implied reactant throughput. The American work does however ignore the fundamental **qualifying** design parameter within practicable conventional digestion namely:- solids detention time. Much development work has been undertaken by the author and a number of his colleagues in which it was concluded that **both loading and detention** (washout) are important in plant design. For practicable purposes however, a loading rate failure situation could not be achieved for sewage sludge digesters.[14] It is similarly unlikely that a purely 'loading' failure would arise with the majority of anticipated industrial sludges.

The reason for the author's input to technical developments of the digestion process came with the realisation, that during his assistance with compilation of Severn-Trent Water Authority design manuals for sewage and sludge treatment processes, any truly definitive process design parameters for anaerobic digestion were conspicuous by their absence. The widespread literature search indicated earlier in Table 1 confirmed the wide international variation and great uncertainty in both loading and detention parameters.

A detailed survey of STWA digesters was carried out in an attempt to answer the basic question of 'WHY' did the same basic feedstock (sludge) apparently require up to at least a five fold variation in the primary design parameter of detention period to effect a comparable reaction. The Severn-Trent Water Authority survey[15] concentrated upon the reactor design together with its associated process equipment. Whilst the process design details are reported in the survey, the most disturbing new feature to emerge was that whilst both the mixing and heating provisions and their associated operational regimes varied so widely, their serious inadequacy was widespread.

For sewage sludges on 'non-wholly volatile'organic wastes, an anaerobic
digester is invariably conceived as a completely mixed, heated reactor
and it was thus alarming that none of the surveyed plants appeared to
offer continuous external mixing. Further, only one plant had any
continuous heating capability. With sludge feeding regimes also
varying from a single slug feed of 20 minutes in a 24 hour period to a
maximum frequency of only five feeds per 24 hours, the basic reactor
needs appeared to have been subjugated by plant designers interests in
the associated non-process considerations. Examination of the reactor
shape again betrayed a previous 'structural' dominance in treatment
provision as virtually all plants were provided with relatively
shallow, large diameter and thus difficult to mix tanks. It is however
a shape which reflects a natural structural and economic choice for
volume storage.

To correct these omissions, especially in the fundamental area of
reactor mixing, full-scale plant development work was commenced to
reassess the process design parameters of anaerobic sludge digestion.
Despite Severn-Trent Water Authority being comparatively well provided
for in respect of existing availability of digestion facilities
(approximately 53% of all sludges then being digested) the Authority's
initial capital expenditure requirement to provide additional sensibly
located anaerobic digestion plant was of the order of £25m at 1980
prices. The backlog in availability of digestion facilities for the
majority of other UK sewage treatment undertakings was significantly
greater.

A resumé of the work initiated to resolve the process aspects - namely
those of mixing, heating and sludge feeding, now follows. The process
objectives of each input are also initially defined.

STWA EXAMINATION OF PRINCIPAL PROCESS INPUTS

Mixing

The principal requirements of mixing within the digestion process
are:-

1)   To effect the dispersion of influent raw sludge within actively
     digesting sludge thereby promoting reaction

2)   To maintain the dispersion and effective volume of the reactor
     thereby eliminating any potential for isolated pockets of raw
     (unreacted) sludge.

3)   To eliminate/prevent any thermal stratification and maintain a
     uniform temperature throughout the reactor.

The level of mixing provision in order to satisfy the above
requirements itself then becomes a combination of a number of
contributing factors namely:-

(a) The external applied mixing power available from the process
     mixing equipment.

(b) Any internal mixing power developed by gas evolution from the
     actively digesting sludge.

(c) 'Effectiveness' of the available mixing power (both external and internal). This is dependent upon aspect ratio of the reactor, mixer type and mixer configuration.

The only recent quantification of the external mixing power requirement for digestion is that of the author and colleagues in Severn-Trent Water Authority namely: Whyley & Rundle (1981)[16], and Noone & Brade (1982)[17]. Whilst previous details of external powers for design purposes, as well as some values found in practice, are available, it is worth reiterating that the range of previous literature reported variations were greater than an order of magnitude. The major problem which exists with the comparability of most reported data is that the requisite criteria of 'satisfactory digester performance' are not quantified in relevant processing terms such as rate of dispersion but are only rather more qualitatively defined. The Severn-Trent Water Authority work has also demonstrated a need for previously unprecedented efforts in the area of sludge sampling to provide a firm basis for mixing input design data[16,18].

Attempts to clarify the theoretical situation in respect of digester mixing, namely consideration of the prime contributions to overall mixing inputs, have resulted in the theoretical family of curves indicated in Figure 1[8].

Fig. 1 NOTIONAL RELATIONSHIP OF ASPECT RATIO VS SOLIDS LEVEL VS EXTERNAL MIXING POWER REQUIREMENTS

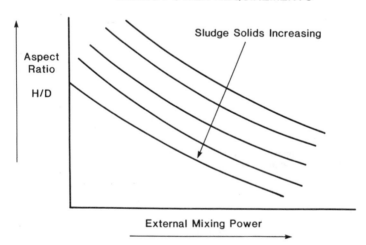

Figure 1 seems destined to remain only a notional representation of mixing requirements with only a few points having been defined[8,16,18] as the efforts to totally optimise mixing input are not justifiable for the potential increase in-process reliability or power savings. Reactor design and operation must thus continue to be based on a limited degree of conservatism by providing a relatively high available external power which is capable of downrating after process start up. Figure 1 also allows explanation of the apparently successful operation of some of the Severn-Trent Water Authority surveyed digesters. Despite their poor available external mixing power, the high sludge solids level and tall narrow shape gave high surface gas flux rates from the internal evolution of methane this then resulting in adequate mixing and digestion.

Heating

This is the other major processing input which affects reactor volume requirements and shape although to a lesser degree. As there is a significantly increased rate of anaerobic reaction at higher temperatures up to the generally accepted mesophilic optimum of approx $37°C$, this then enables smaller reactors to be used. Adequacy of heat transfer capability must have regard to mixing provision within the digester to provide an adequate heat 'sink'.

To avoid sludge heating difficulties and retain temperature levels within the reactor, raw sludge feeding rates must also be considered. Effects of short term 'cooling' arising from large slug feeds will increase as reactor detention time reduces. This aspect underlines the need for more 'continuous' reactor feeding and further illustrates interdependence between the prime processing inputs.

Two conventional basic heating regimes using circulating hot water are currently adopted, namely 'in-tank' and 'external' systems. In view of the sludge velocity requirements to effect adequate heat exchange, the in-tank mixing systems are invariably directly coupled to the mixing system eg jacketed gas lift or hot water coil/mechanical mixer. The more common external heat exchange systems or live steam injection are independent in operation of the mixing system and as such usually offer more simple and flexible methods of providing uprated heating where one wishes to convert to a lower detention period reactor.

As in the case of mixing power provision, there is great variation in the reported exchanger design values and resultant overall heat transfer coefficients. The reported design differences approach two orders of magnitude. This variation clearly has a large impact on performance, exchange area and resultant capital cost.

Whilst the foregoing has dealt with the heating provision for the vast majority of digestion plants, recent Severn-Trent Water Authority work, Noone et al[15,17,18], has evaluated the use of direct steam injection for digester heating. Some eight plants are now operating and it is the author's view that this offers the most promising way of heating future digesters. Details are given elsewhere, but a simple outline of the benefits offered by this option already invariably used in the process industries may prove useful. Direct steam injection is an in-tank heating system and therefore no sludge pumping equipment or recirculating energy is required. Further, the heat exchange surface (the steam itself) is self renewing. Steam equipment is both low cost and reliable resulting from its widespread industrial use. This also applies to the associated steam boiler, the steam application control systems and packaged water softening/conditioning equipment.

Sludge Feeding

The sludge feeding regime is the third input important in its own right, an importance heightened by interrelationships with both the mixing and heating requirements.
The ideal configuration of a continuously fed reactor often referred to in literature had not previously been achieved at full plant scale. The work within Severn-Trent Water Authority on continuous feeding has since demonstrated the benefits of more stable reactor performance together with an elimination of surges in gas production resulting from the alternate periodic large slug basis of sludge feeding. Gas production smoothing alone is a significant benefit as it enable a size reduction in expensive gas storage provision. Gas storage as 'liquid' sludge is clearly both a safer and much less expensive option than storage as the product gas.

Other relevant aspects of the digestion process are worthy of mention, although these cannot be strictly termed as specific processing inputs to the actual digester. Pre and post digestion **thickening** are crucial inputs to the design and cost of the total sludge disposal route as centred on sludge digestion[18]. This is explored later by Hoyland[1].

Further notable areas of digester design interest are:-

1) Digester control systems.

2) Construction materials for use in provision of reactor volume and gas production.

3) Associated energy studies including surplus gas utilisation, reactor insulation and heat recovery techniques.

The above topics have all received closer attention in the author's work referred to elsewhere[19]. These areas are of increased interest for industrial application of anaerobic digestion or the use of anaerobic treatment for strong liquid phase effluents.

Having designed the reactor (digester), one is then faced with its construction. The combined effects of sludge thickening and reduced detention times have now resulted in much smaller reactor volumes being required - typically a reduction down plants to between $1/4$ and $\frac{1}{2}$ of the previously sized plants. This reduction has enabled the application of alternative reactor structural materials with reinforced concrete no longer being the sole or automatic choice.

Fig. 2   UNIT CAPITAL COSTS OF PREFABRICATED
DIGESTION PLANT

(SEPTEMBER 1982)

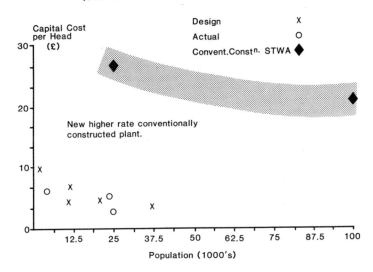

It would be most inappropriate to mention the topic of low cost plant provision which uses prefabricated or 'industrial' tanks without apportioning credit to those persons outside the Water Industry who first applied prefabricated structures to mesophilic anaerobic digestion. Farming and food processing interests, with their high strength wastes, saw the potential of anaerobic processes as options to the more energy intensive aerobic effluent treatment systems previously adopted. Inspired by the fact that these plants require commercial rates of return (equivalent to much shorter financial asset 'lives' than possible in the stable treatment 'market' of Water Authority plants) it is not entirely surprising that plant design born of this necessity should sharply contrast with historical water industry practice in structural provision[20].

Discussion of two aspects of Figure 2 further underline both a cost and technical attractiveness of these prefabricated plants.

(a) The plants initially constructed can also serve much smaller populations than were previously considered feasible (either from cost or heat balance considerations) for anaerobic digestion. Indeed, the smaller plants would have been expected to suffer from severe cost diseconomies of scale. These size and cost aspects are particularly relevant for would be industrial users of the anaerobic digestion process.

(b) Having made it possible to consider thermally self sufficient digestion for much smaller plants, the now more environmentally acceptable product sludge greatly increases the available options for sludge treatment and disposal. This is particularly significant when one considers the high costs of sludge tankering[21].

To conclude consideration of the anaerobic aspect of solid phase treatments, a processing approach (recently completed) to completely mixed reactor provision has enabled definition of effective design criteria for the provision of **RELIABLE LOW-COST REACTORS** utilising mesophilic anaerobic digestion.

Turning to the aerobic digestion option a short review of its development will allow fuller comparison with its anaerobic option.

REVIEW OF AEROBIC DIGESTION

As mentioned earlier, aerobic systems are relatively energy intensive. Historically within the UK Water Industry, aerobic digestion was viewed as a low capital cost but high revenue cost option. This arose from the fact that applied detention periods were low - typically say 6 to 9 days and that equipment requirements were relatively simple - surface aerators or blowers with diffuser systems. The developments in anaerobic digestion have now resulted in plant detention periods between 12 and 15 days compared to the previously practiced 30 day designs. This aspect coupled with simpler, lower cost reactor systems and associated process equipment has revised the historical balance in which anaerobic digestion was viewed. The historic view of anaerobic processes showed it as a high capital/low revenue option namely; the opposite to that of aerobic digestion. Anaerobic systems now offer much lower capital costs whilst retaining their low revenue costs. Whilst the capital costs of anaerobic systems has now approached those of previously found aerobic systems these aerobic plants have themselves been subject to much recent development effort. Prominent in this area of work have been WRC[22], Welsh Water Authority with the Electricity Council[23] together with varied general European interest.

Some early unreported work in STWA showed reaction 'capacity' and efficiency difficulties with raw sludge temperatures below approx 20°C. This compares with an average available sludge temperature of approx 10°C. Whilst this drawback served to underline STWA's efforts in the more popular anaerobic system, other developers began to look at aeration rates and systems which would increase the degree of exothermic reaction to get beyond a minimum 'reaction efficiency' temperature. The general background to this work has been summarised elsewhere[24].

Various temperature regimes and aeration systems have been evaluated including the use of pure oxygen instead of air[25]. Sidestream Venturi induction of oxygen was used and whilst high temperatures were achieved, the process economics and effectiveness of stabilisation were not so clear.

The vast majority of reported literature has shown that aerobically digested sludges invariably produce rather lower reductions in the volatile (odorous) portion of the raw sludge. Whilst this of itself is not a problem, the fact that continuing debate seems to surround whether or not such sludges are truly stabilised, ie do not smell, remains a major water industry concern[26]. Aerobically digested sewage sludges currently experience much tighter restrictions on disposal to farmland than their anaerobic counterparts. This is embodied within both the UK and proposed EC disposal guidelines[27].

A recent thrust in aerobic digestion development has arisen in the area of thermophilic aerobic digestion. This is a high temperature process (typically 50°C) and is aimed at giving high rates of biological activity with a resultant high efficiency of electrical input conversion[25]. Such a process can give the benefit of pasteurisation where a sludge (eg animal or domestic) may contain pathogenic organisms resistant to alternative processes. It is the author's understanding that the thermophilic processes require detention periods of the order of six days. This is a clear benefit over anaerobic systems. However, it is further understood that a significant foam reactor volume is required to achieve adequate efficiency of aeration. At the foam reactor volume levels of approx 50% the detention provision then rises to approximately nine days.

Continued effort in the area of aerobic digestion develoment may yield a significant breakthrough in reactor configuration and efficiency but in view of the more attractive current and potential energy status of its anaerobic counterpart and its recent capital cost reductions it is the author's view that aerobic systems still face a difficult task in achieving significant market penetration. Where a capital aspect is particularly significant and particularly short payback periods are required then this may justify an industrial application where there is willingness to pay the high revenue costs. Whilst developments in aerobic systems rightfully continue, other papers at this symposium seem to however indicate a trend away from aerobic to anaerobic systems for both liquid and solids phase effluents.

Where an effluent treatment flow sheet embodies an activated sludge aerobic stage and anaerobic treatment for solids, it is invariably prudent to maximise sludge production for its treatment in the anaerobic phase. This minimises the cost of energy purchase which would have been needed to aerobically remove organic material in the activated sludge plant[2].

In concluding this short resumé of aerobic digestion, the process has evolved from liquid phase treatments, perhaps having initially been seen as a low capital option for sludge stabilisation. Concerns about the adequacy of proven stabilisation and reducing capital attractiveness of new anaerobic plant designs may result in reduced degree of its market penetration for other than specially attractive sites. These considerations are likely to be less significant for industrial applications of the process.

Having considered the two biological reactors in some detail, concentrating upon that process most widely applied and fully developed within the Water Industry namely anaerobic digestion, it is useful to note the additional options sometimes applied - albeit for rather limited applications.

ADDITIONAL SLUDGE TREATMENT OPTIONS

Lime Stabilisation

This process is used to stabilise domestic sludges for agricultural use. Lime is added to pH 11-12 and maintained for approx three days at this pH level. The product sludge is effectively disinfected and its odour stabilised. Difficulties of cost and increased sludge levels for disposal would restrict this possible process to only the smaller remote sewage works.

Lagoon Treatment

It is doubtful if this can truly be called a process due to the lack of process control afforded in such systems. Cold or so called accelerated cold digestion(28) are adaptations of lagoon treatment. Their application can only be seriously viewed as short term capital deferral options as the longer term environmental difficulties are likely to be severe.

SLUDGE DISPOSAL OPTIONS

Having considered treatment systems, there are however certain disposal options which do not require a treatment stage. This is where environmental factors are not a problem or the nature of the raw sludge permits. Whilst detailed consideration of all disposal options would merely largely rehearse systems already available in most industries, a simple listing of the commonly applied techniques provides a reference for discussion.

Dewatering

Gravity
- Batch
- Continuous
- Drying Bed

Mechanical
- Centrifuge
- Belt Press
- Vacuum Filter
- Plate Press

Final Disposal

Liquid   - Agricultural
              - Tip
              - Sea

Solids   - Agricultural Land
              - Tip
              - Incineration
              - Sale

CONCLUSIONS

1   Recent full-scale process developments within the UK Water
Industry have redefined the design criteria for anaerobic
digestion in completely mixed reactors.

2   Anaerobic digestion systems offer reliable low-cost treatment
for a variety of organic or mixed sludges.

3   Anaerobic systems are also applicable to high strength liquid
organic wastes - fully 'organic' wastes being treatable within a
variety of reactor configurations.

4   Aerobic digestion appears less attractive in purchased energy
terms and the product sludge may not be odour free. However,
capital costs should still be below those of anaerobic plants.

5   Few alternate 'biochemical' treatment systems offer practicable
solutions for most industries or locations.

ACKNOWLEDGEMENTS

The author wishes to express his sincere thanks to his colleagues and
the Severn-Trent Water Authority. Colin Brade his principal
development collaborator is especially thanked. Any views expressed in
this chapter are those of himself and do not necessarily reflect those
of the Severn-Trent Water Authority.

REFERENCES

(1)   Hoyland G, 'A New Approach to the Design of Gravity Thickeners for Sewage Sludges'. This Symposium.

(2)   Anderson G K, Saw C B 'Applications of Anaerobic Biotechnology to Waste Treatment and Energy Production'. This Symposium.

(3)   Noone G P, 'Cost Effective Treatment and Disposal of Sludge to Environmentally Acceptable Standards'. 6th Symposium EWPCA Munich 1984.

(4)   O'Shaughnessy F R, 'The Utilization of the Phenomena of Putrefaction, with Special Reference to the Treatment and Disposal of Sewage Sludge'. Paper presented at a meeting of the Society of Chemical Industry - 15 January 1914.

(5)   Dibdin in 'History of Sewage Treatment in Great Britain - Anaerobic Digestion of Sewage Sludge' by Stanbridge H H 1976 p6.

(6)   Cameron in 'The Practice of Sludge Digestion - Symposium on the Treatment of Waste Waters, University of Durham 1959.

(7)   Whitehead H C, O'Shaughnessy F R 'The Treatment of Sewage Sludge by Bacterial Digestion' Proceedings of the Institution of Civil Engineering November 1931 pp38-135.

(8)   Noone G P, 'Process Design of Anaerobic Sludge Digestion' Effluent and Water Treatment Journal. May 1982 p143.

(9)   Water Pollution Control Federation. Anaerobic Sludge Digestion Manual of practice No. 16 1968.

(10)   Ministry of Housing and Local Government. Report of an Informal Working Party on the Treatment and Disposal of Sewage Sludge 1954 HMSO.

(11)   Griffiths J R, 'The Practice of Sludge Digestion - Symposium on the Treatment of Waste Waters'. University of Durham 1959.

(12)   Simpson J R 'Factors that Effect the Design and Operation of Sludge Digestion Units' Jnl. Inst. Sew. Purification 1960 p330.

(13)   Swanwick J D, Shurbien D G, Jackson S, 'A Survey of the Performance of Sewage Sludge Digestion in Great Britain' Wat. Pollution Control 1969(6) p639.

(14)   Torpey W N, Loading to Failure of a Pilot High Rate Digester. Sewage Industrial Wastes 27 pp 121 1955.

(15)   Brade C E, Noone G P, 'Anaerobic Sludge Digestion - Need It Be Expensive? -I- MAKING MORE OF EXISTING RESOURCES'. Wat. Pollution Control 1981 80(1) p70.

(16)   Rundle H, Whyley J, 'Comparison of Gas Recirculation Systems for Mixing in Anaerobic Digestion'. Wat. Pollution Control 1981 80(4) p463.

(17)   Noone G P, Brade C E, 'Anaerobic Sludge Digestion - Need it be Expensive? II HIGHER RATE AND PREFABRICATED SYSTEMS'. Wat. Pollution Control 1982 p479.

(18)   Noone G P, Brade C E, 'Anaerobic Sludge Digestion - Need it be Expensive? III INTEGRATED AND LOW-COST DIGESTION'. Wat. Pollution Control 1985.

(19)   Noone G P, Bell B, Donaldson M, 'Digestion Gas Package Power Generation - Some Recent Experiences within Severn-Trent Water Authority'. Wat. Pollution Control p91, 1984.

(20)   Noone G P, Boyd A K, 'Prefabricated Systems for Low-Cost Anaerobic Digestion' EEC Symposium on Sludge Treatment Cost by 68 Vienna October 1980.

(21)   Brade C E, Harwood J, 'Tankering Economics - A Fresh Approach' IWES Symposium on Sludge Digestion - Birmingham January 1980.

(22)   Vincent A J, Toogood S J, 'Aerobic Digestion of Sludge At What Cost?'. Paper presented to Welsh and South Western Branches of the Institute of Water Pollution Control January 1983.

(23)   Gunson H G, Morgan S F, 'Aerobic Thermophilic Digestion of Sewage Sludge'. Effluent and Water Treatment Journal August 1982.

(24)   Bruce A M, Fisher W J, 'Sludge Stabilisation - Methods and Measurement in Sewage Sludge Stabilisation and Disinfection (Editor A M Bruce). Ellis Horwood Ltd, Chichester 1984 pp 23-47.

(25)   Wolinski W K, 'Aerobic Thermophilic Sludge Stabilisation Using Air'. Wat. Pollution Control 84 4 pp 433-445 1986.

(26)   Zwiefelhofer H, UTB Buchs Switzerland. In Discussion at 6th EWPCA Symposium Munich 1984.

(27)   Department of the Environment - Report of the Working Party on the Disposal of Sewage Sludge to Land. HMSO London 1977.

(28)   Lowe P, 'Accelerated Cold Digestion' - Discussion to Digestion Paper by Noone et Al. IWPC Conference Harrogate September 1981. Wat. Pollution Control 1982 81(2).

A NEW DESIGN PROCEDURE FOR CONSOLIDATION TANKS

G Hoyland*

Consolidating sludges at sewage works can substantially reduce the cost of downstream treatment and disposal. To date, however, the full benefits of the process have not been realised in practice because an accurate design procedure for consolidation tanks has not been available. The new design procedure described in this report allows consolidation tanks to be designed accurately in accordance with the consolidation characteristics of any particular sludge. Performance charts derived from the procedure show how consolidation performance depends upon the size and height of the consolidation tank and its operational mode. Consolidation tanks have optimum heights and sizes that maximise performance.

INTRODUCTION

Consolidation is one of the simplest processes used at sewage treatment works, and potentially the most cost effective. When properly applied, consolidation can reduce sludge volumes by factors of two and more, and thereby reduce the cost of subsequent disposal by similar factors. The cost of processing the sludge in any downstream digestion or dewatering plant can also be reduced. Given that the total annual cost of dealing with sludge at sewage treatment works in the UK amounts to over £200M, the potential cost benefit of applying consolidation is substantial.

In practice, however, consolidation tanks rarely perform to their full potential and the process often fails completely. It is not uncommon, for example, to find sludge solids floating rather than sinking in consolidation tanks. This poor performance is partly attributable to the absence of a reliable design procedure. Although the principle of the process appears to be simple, the relationship between performance and the design and operation of the plant is not generally understood nor appreciated. As a result, consolidation tanks are rarely designed in accordance with the requirements of the process.

Design procedure

This report describes a new design procedure for consolidation tanks that is reliable and allows the cost and operational benefits of improved sludge thickening to be realised in practice. The basis of the procedure is a mathematical model that is derived from the theory of soil mechanics[1], and attempts to simulate the processes found in consolidating sludges.

* Water Research Centre, Elder Way, Stevenage, Herts SG1 1TH

Consisting of differential equations, the model has to be solved numerically using a computer and solutions cannot be defined in terms of explicit functions.
   The procedure, shown as a series of steps in Figure 1, can be applied to any sewage sludge. A representative sample of the particular sludge is taken and tested in a prescribed way using a centrifuge and a pilot column. Analysis of the test results yields values for the following set of design parameters

(i)   Compression index
(ii) Compression coefficient
(iii) Resistance to consolidation
(iv) Limiting solids-retention time.

   The first three parameters in the list define the consolidation characteristics of the sludge, and are essentially coefficients in the model. The fourth parameter limits the useful size of the consolidation tank thereby determining maximum performance. Given values for the parameters, the model can predict consolidation performance depending on the values of the following set of design variables

(i)   size of consolidation tank relative to loading
(ii) depth of sludge in tank
(iii) concentration of solids in feed sludge

and on

(iv) the operational mode of the consolidation tank.

   Two operational modes can be simulated, namely batch and continuous. Of these, batch mode is more commonly found at sewage works, but continuous mode can produce thicker sludges more cost-effectively.
   The relationship between performance and the design variables, for any particular sludge and operational mode, is presented in the form of performance charts. For example, the performance chart for batch operation shows how sludge retention time and initial depth of sludge affect the average concentration of solids in the thickened sludge. Such charts show that a range of retention times and sludge depths combine to give the same performance.
   Users of the procedure require access to the computer programs that produce the performance charts. These programs are available at WRc for indirect use.

General form of predictions

   The general form of the predictions made by the model is illustrated by the example for batch consolidation in Figure 2. In this operational mode, a batch of sludge is allowed to separate into a clear supernatant and a blanket containing the solids. As shown in Figure 2, the concentration of solids in the blanket increases with time at a decreasing rate until consolidation stops. Most practical consolidations are characterised by an induction period in which the consolidation accelerate from rest. For simplicity, however, the model takes no account of this period which is usually small compared with the total time-scale of the consolidation.
   Consolidations of sewage sludges may proceed to completion, or, more likely, stall prematurely. Stalling occurs because the sludges are usually biological active, and such activity produces biogas which collects as bubbles. The bubbles buoy the solids, and thereby destroy the driving force

of the process before consolidation is complete. In the absence of bubbles, consolidations would proceed to completion, and solids concentration would approach an asymptotic value called the ultimate concentration. Thickening curves are generated by the model using the values of the design parameters. The values of the compression index and compression coefficient determine (for any particular values of the design variables) the value of the ultimate concentration; and the resistance to consolidation determines the consolidation rate. To fix the stalling position, the model assumes that consolidation proceeds only for solids-retention times less than the limiting value. This is a reasonable assumption given that the amount of biogas suspended in the sludge can be expected to be directly related to solids-retention time. Solids can be retained for longer than the limiting value but consolidation performance is assumed not to improve.

Scope of report

The background to the model is described as a means of explaining the basic assumptions and the mathematical significance of the consolidation characteristics. A full description of the model is beyond the scope of this report. Predictions, made by the model, and observations in experimental consolidations are compared to test the model's soundness.

Performance charts are the product of the procedure, and their use in determining the sizes and heights of consolidation tanks and in deriving general design principles is described.

The report also outlines the test procedures used to evaluate the design parameters.

MODEL

The model makes assumptions about the structure of sewage sludges and attempts to simulate the processes that cause water and solids to flow within the structure during consolidation.

Process of consolidation

Solids in sewage and most other types of sludges carry electrostatic charges which cause the solids to conglomerate and attract water to form particles called flocs. The solids can be thought of as forming an infrastructure that is responsible for the strength and integrity of the floc. The water component of the sludge can be differentiated into two major types. That held inside the flocs by the electrostatic forces is referred to as 'bound' water, and that surrounding the flocs is referred to as 'free' water. When a floc in a sewage sludge is in free suspension bound water accounts for about 98% of the floc's volume, the remainder being occupied, of course, by the solids.

Flocs, containing only solids and water, have a density higher than that of water and therefore settle under gravity. In dilute sludges, the flocs settle separately, causing free water to be displaced upwards to the supernatant. This process is called hindered settlement and is used at sewage treatment works for clarification and for thickening activated sludges in secondary sedimentation tanks.

Consolidation starts when settlement has caused the flocs to become contiguous. The transition between hindered settlement and consolidation is known as the compression point and usually occurs in sewage sludges at a solids concentration of about 15 kg/m^3. Thickening beyond this compression point requires bound water as well as free water to be displaced. Because the flocs are contiguous, their apparent weight is transmitted down through the consolidating blanket of sludge, such that flocs submerged in the blanket are subjected to a compressive pressure by the overlying flocs. This pressure causes the flocs to dewater through the expulsion of bound water. As shown in Figure 3, the model depicts that flocs at the top of a consolidating blanket are under no compressive pressure and are 'full' of water. Those in the blanket are squashed by the compressive pressure such that the volume of the flocs and the volume of the pores and channels between the flocs are reduced. Since compressive pressure increases with depth in the blanket, most dewatering occurs at the blanket bottom. The bound water displaced from the flocs and the free water from the pores pass up through the pores at a rate determined by the hydraulic resistance of the blanket. In passing through the pores, the water imposes on the flocs a drag force which acts against the flocs' weight thereby reducing the compressive pressure.

Force balance

The model uses such a mechanism to simulate two operational modes namely batch and continuous. As already described, batch consolidation is an unsteady-state process. In contrast, continuous consolidation is, at least in theory, a steady-state process in which feed sludge is continuously added to the consolidation tank, supernatant and thickened sludge continuously removed from the top and bottom of the tank respectively, and the blanket of sludge in the tank maintained at a constant depth. To handle these different operational modes, the model has two forms; both consisting of differential equations that describe continuity, and the balance of forces that act upon the flocs at any particular elevation. A description of the elements of the force balance serves to explain most of the assumptions made by the model. Such a balance has formed the basis of other models of consolidation[2,3].

On any horizontal plane through the sludge, four forces are acting in equilibrium on the flocs. These forces (N/m^2) are

1. the solids pressure, W, generated by the apparent weight of the flocs above the plane

2. the drag force, D, defined by the friction of the displaced water acting on the flocs above the plane

3. the compressive pressure, P, defined by the difference between the other two forces and countered by the internal pressure of the flocs at the plane

4. the inertia forces which are insignificant and can be ignored.

The balance between the forces is expressed by

$$P = W - D. \tag{1}$$

Clearly, this equation is also valid when the three forces are expressed in terms of unit cross section of blanket rather than unit cross section of flocs, and this is the form used in the model. Expressed as a differential equation the balance becomes

$$\frac{dP}{dh} = \frac{dW}{dh} - \frac{dD}{dh} \tag{2}$$

where h is vertical distance (m) measured, say, from tank bottom.

Solids pressure

Solids pressure can be defined in accordance with Archimede's Principle as follows:

$$\frac{dW}{dh} = -C(1 - \frac{1}{S})G \qquad (3)$$

where C is the concentration of solids (kg/m^3) at any particular elevation in blanket

S is the specific gravity of the non-aqueous phase

and G is the acceleration (m/s^2).

The specific gravity pertains to the non-aqueous phase rather than the solids phase because the flocs may contain bubbles as well as solids and water. Any bubbles will, of course, buoy the solids and thereby reduce the specific gravity of the composite.

Internal pressure of flocs

The internal pressure of the flocs at any elevation can be assumed to be directly related to the concentration of solids in the flocs. Since solids concentration in the flocs and in the bulk of the sludge are directly related it follows that the internal pressure can be directly related to the bulk concentration of the solids. In the absence of any fundamental relationship to describe internal pressure, one has been derived empirically in the following form

$$\frac{P}{P_*} = \frac{C^n - C_p^n}{C_*^n - C_p^n} \qquad (4)$$

where C_p is concentration of solids (kg/m^3) at the compression point, typically 15 kg/m^3

C_* is the solids concentration (kg/m^3) at a reference pressure, P_* (N/m^2)

and n is a constant for any particular sludge.

The relationship accords with the physical constraint that $C = C_p$ at the compression point, that is, when $P = 0$.

The constant n is the compression index, one of the three consolidation characteristics. It is a fundamental property of the sludge with values in the range 3 to 6 depending on the type and nature of the sludge.

The differential form of Equation 4 for use in the force balance is

$$\frac{dP}{dh} = \frac{nP_* C^{n-1}}{C_*^n - C_p^n} \frac{dC}{dh}. \qquad (5)$$

At the end of a batch consolidation when the blanket is at steady state, the apparent weight of the flocs and their internal pressure are equal, such that

$$\frac{dW}{dh} = \frac{dP}{dh}. \qquad (6)$$

From Equation 3, 4 and 6, the following approximate relationship can be derived for the average concentration of solids, C_a (kg/m^3), in a blanket consolidated to completion:

$$\left(\frac{C_a}{K}\right)^n \approx \frac{h_0 C_0 G}{P_*} \tag{7}$$

where h_0 is initial height (m) of sludge blanket
and C_0 is initial concentration of sludge solids (kg/m^3).

The parameter, K, defined by

$$K^n = (C_*^n - C_p^n)(1 - \frac{1}{S})(\frac{n-1}{n})^n \tag{8}$$

is another characteristic that features in the design procedure, and is called the compression coefficient. Because the expression for K contains C_*, its value depends on the reference pressure (P_*). A pressure of 1000 N/m^2, typifying the solids' pressures found in operational consolidation tanks, has been chosen as a standard.

Drag force

A calculation of Reynolds' numbers for consolidating flocs shows that the flow in the pores between the flocs is laminar. The drag force acting on the flocs can therefore be taken to be proportional to the differential velocity, U (m/s), between the flocs and the water, as follows

$$\frac{dD}{dh} = \nu UB \tag{9}$$

where ν is the viscosity of water (Ns/m^2)
and B is a hydraulic resistance (m^{-2}).

The variable, B, is essentially the resistance to water flow of unit length of sludge blanket and, its value depends on the porosity of the blanket and pore dimensions. Since consolidation is essentially a form of low-pressure filtration, an expression for B can be derived by drawing an analogy with conventional filtration theory. In this theory, a specific resistance to filtration (m/kg) is defined by dividing the hydraulic resistance (m^{-2}) of a filter cake by the average concentration of solids in the cake. Similarly, the model defines a specific resistance to consolidation, R (m/kg), as follows

$$R = B/C \tag{10}$$

such that, from Equation 9

$$\frac{dD}{dh} = \nu URC. \tag{11}$$

The model borrows a second concept from filtration theory. It is well known that the flowrate of filtrate through a cake derived from sewage sludge is insensitive to the applied pressure, implying that the specific resistance to filtration is directly proportional to pressure. In the terms used in filtration theory, the compressibility of the cake is said to be equal to unity. Similarly, the model assumes that the specific resistance to consolidation is proportional to compressive pressure as follows

$$R = R_* \frac{P}{P_*} \tag{12}$$

where R_* is the specific resistance to consolidation (m/kg) at the reference pressure P_*.

Substituting for P from Equation 4 and assuming that $C^n \gg C_p^n$ gives

$$R = R_* \frac{C^n}{C_*^n} \tag{13}$$

which expresses R in terms of the local concentration of solids in the sludge blanket. It follows from Equation 11 that

$$\frac{dD}{dh} = vUR_* \frac{C^{n+1}}{C_*^n} \tag{14}$$

which is the expression for the drag force used in the force balance.

In theory, the specific-resistance to consolidation, R_*, could serve as the third consolidation characteristic complementing K and n. For practical expediency, however, another parameter called the resistance to consolidation, R_c, is used as the third characteristic. The relationship between the two resistances is given by

$$\frac{R_c}{R_*} \quad \frac{(C_*^n - C_p)}{C_*^n} (\frac{n-1}{n})^n . \tag{15}$$

Solutions of model

Consisting of non-linear differential equations, the model has to be solved numerically using a computer and solutions cannot be expressed in the form of explicit functions. Expressed generally, solutions take the form

$$C_e \wedge f(R_c, K, n, C_0, v, t, h_0, G) \tag{16}$$

where f is a relationship that depends on operational mode,
  C_0 and C_e are the concentrations of solids in the feed and product
    respectively
  R_c, K and n are the consolidation characteristics
  v is the viscosity of water
  t is the retention time of the sludge in the consolidation tank
  h_0 is the height of the sludge blanket in the consolidation tank or
    initial height in the case of batch consolidation
and G is the acceleration.

Comparison between prediction and experiment

A comparison is made between predictions and experimental measurements to illustrate the soundness of the model. Experimental batch consolidations were performed in four pilot columns, 150 mm diameter, having various heights. The columns were transparent allowing the interface between the blanket and the supernatant to be viewed, and each contained a rotating picket fence to assist the consolidation. Four identical samples of a co-settled sludge were pumped into the columns to depths of 1.5 m, 2.5 m, 4.5 m and 5.5 m, and allowed to consolidate. Interface heights were recorded at intervals until the consolidations stopped.

Values for the consolidation characteristics K, n and R_C were estimated from the experimental data and used in the model to simulate the consolidations in the four columns. The comparison in Figure 4, shows excellent agreement between the predicted and experimental concentration profiles.

The average concentration of solids in the blankets can be calculated from blanket height using a simple mass balance. An interesting observation supported by the model, is that, for retention times less than about 1 hour, the highest solids concentration is found in the smallest column. At long times, however, the tallest column contains the highest concentration. Generally, for every retention time, there is an optimum initial blanket height that maximises solids concentration.

PERFORMANCE CHARTS

The purpose of this section is to describe the use of the performance charts and some general design principles that may be derived from them.

Form of charts

A family of individual predictions, each made in accordance with Equation 16, can be assembled to construct charts that show, for any particular sludge, how C_e varies with h_0 and t. Figure 5 is a chart illustrating predictions for a sludge characterised by

$$K = 80 \text{ kg/m}^3$$
$$n = 4$$
$$R_C = 50 \text{ Gm/kg}$$
$$C_0 = 30 \text{ kg/m}^3$$

undergoing batch consolidation in tanks with heights up to 4 m. Such characteristics typify a sludge with poor consolidation properties, such as a mixed sludge containing a high proportion of activated solids. Charts for other sludges and for continuous consolidation show similar performance trends.

As discussed earlier, an assumption in the design procedure is that biogas bubbles cause consolidations to stall when the sludge solids have been retained for the period called the limiting solids retention time, L_t. In practice, the value of L_t depends upon the efficacy of any picket fence[4] used to assist the consolidation as well as the biological activity of the sludge. A typical value of 2 days has been assumed for the sludge characterised in Figure 5. For batch operation, solids and sludge retention times are clearly equal such that the solids concentrations in Figure 5 pertaining to a sludge retention time of 2 days represent maximum concentrations that the sludge can consolidate to depending on tank height. Retaining the solids for longer results in no further consolidation, and, if retained for too long (say more than 5 days), the solids could float indicating the complete breakdown of the consolidation process.

Optimum design

Inspection of the solids concentration at any particular retention time
in Figure 5 shows that concentration is maximised at a particular blanket
height. For example, at the limiting retention time of 2 days, the optimum
height is about 1.20 m, giving a concentration of 57 kg/m3. This particular
concentration therefore represents the maximum that the sludge can be
consolidated to in one-stage batch operation. For the same retention time,
doubling tank height would reduce solids concentration to 49 kg/m3, and
halving height would reduce concentration to about 52 kg/m3. The chart also
shows that optimum height is directly related to retention time.

The reason for the optimum heights can be explained in terms of the
process mechanics. In shallow consolidation tanks, the rate of consolidation
is comparatively high because the path length of the water escaping from the
sludge is low, but the solids concentration to which the sludge can ultimately
thicken is low. Conversely, consolidation in tall tanks proceeds at a
comparatively low rate but to a potentially high concentration. At the
optimum height, the rate and the ultimate concentration compromise to maximise
performance. Generally, sludges with the better consolidation characteristics
require higher optimum heights.

Effect of operational mode on performance

The chart in Figure 5 showing predictions for batch operation may be
compared with that in Figure 6 showing predictions for the same sludge
consolidating continuously. The limiting solids-retention time applies, of
course, to both operational modes. Unlike retention times in batch operation,
the retention time of the solids in continuous operation is greater than the
nominal retention time of the sludge because the fixed volume of sludge in the
tank has an average solids concentration greater than the feed concentration.
Performance charts for continuous operation therefore include solids retention
times, calculated by the model, as a dependent variable complementing solids
concentrations.

A comparison between the modes indicates that continuous consolidation is
the more effective. For example, at a nominal retention time of 1.2 days,
continuous operation could thicken the sludge to a concentration of 66 kg/m3,
whereas batch operation could thicken the sludge to only 53 mg/m3. A
continuous tank with a nominal retention time of 1.2 days and an optimum
height of 0.6 m would hold the sludge solids for 2 days which is the value
assumed for the limiting solids-retention time of this particular sludge. A
solids concentration of 66 kg/m3 therefore represents the maximum performance
obtainable by continuous consolidation. By comparison, the maximum
concentration for batch consolidation of the particular sludge is about 57
kg/m3.

A comparison of optimum heights shows that those for continuous operation
are generally about half those for batch operation. This relationship is
generally true, such that, for the same nominal retention time, continuously-
operated tanks of an optimal design have about twice the plan area of
batch-operated tanks. In spite of this difference, continuously-operated
tanks generally have similar plan areas as batch-operated tanks giving the
same performance.

Effect of feed concentration on performance

In practice, the concentration of solids in sludges fed to consolidation
tanks is, to some extent, an operational variable. For example, the method

and equipment used to desludge primary sedimentation influences the thickness of primary sludge. The relationship between the thickness of the feed sludge and subsequent performance in a consolidation tank is therefore of practical importance.

The relationships between the thickness of a particular feed sludge and the performance and optimum design of batch consolidation tanks can be elucidated by comparing batch performance charts derived for various feed concentrations. Generally for batch consolidation, thicker feed sludges require shallower tanks and thicken in such tanks to higher concentrations.

In contrast, the performance and optimum design of continuous consolidation tanks is insensitive to feed solids concentration, provided the solids loading is constant. Pre-thickening is not only unnecessary but can inhibit performance by ageing the sludge. Feed concentration is, however, limited to a minimum determined by a maximum upward velocity in the clarification zone at the top of the consolidation tank. To prevent a gross loss of solids over the weir, the instantaneous upward velocity should not exceed about 0.5 m/h.

At sewage works, there are major practical implications stemming from the absence of any requirement to thicken before continuous consolidation. Two such implications are

(i) Raw sludges requiring consolidation can be withdrawn in a dilute form from sedimentation tanks such that withdrawal is simplified.
(ii) The process can handle large volumes of dilute activated sludges.

Given that performance in continuous consolidation is primary dependent on solids loading and insensitive to feed concentration, retention time on the performance charts can be expediently replaced with a parameter called the specific plan area (A_S) defined by

$$A_S = \frac{\text{Plan area of tank}}{\text{Loading of sludge solids}} \qquad (17)$$

$$= t/C_o h_o.$$

Presented in this way, one performance chart suffices for each sludge irrespective of its solids concentration.

Figure 7 is such a chart for the same sludge. It shows that, for any particular specific plan area, the concentration of solids in the withdrawn sludge asymptotes to a maximum at large blanket heights. For example, at a specific plan area of 0.03 m^2.day/kg the asymptotic concentration is about 58 kg/m^3. At the assumed limiting solids retention time of 2 days, solids concentration is maximised at a value of 66 kg/m^3, occurring at a blanket height of 0.6 m and a specific plan area of 0.67 kg day/m^2. Converting this area to sludge retention time using Equation 17 gives a value of 1.2 days in accordance with the predictions on the chart in Figure 6.

EVALUATION OF DESIGN PARAMETER

The derivation of interpretation of performance charts requires values of the four design parameters. A simple method of evaluating the parameters requiring a 30 l sample of the particular sludge, a laboratory centrifuge and a pilot column has been developed. The scope of this report allows only the basis of testing procedure to be described, the details being given elsewhere[5].

The compression index is determined by performing a series of small-scale batch consolidations in the centrifuge tubes over a range of G forces, such that the solids pressure in the tubes covers the range found in full-scale consolidation tanks. At each G force (solids pressure) an ultimate solids concentration, C_a, is determined by allowing the consolidations to proceed to completion - a process which takes about 1 hour. It follows from Equation 7 that a plot of $\log(C_a)$ against $\log(h_0 C_0 G)$ gives a straight line, the inverse of the gradient being equal to the index.

Values of the other three parameters are determined from the results of a batch consolidation in the pilot column, which is 150 mm diameter x 2 m high and contains a small picket fence that mimics the action of fences in large tanks. To determine the compression coefficient, the value of the ultimate concentration is estimated from the pilot consolidation and substituted into Equation 7 with values for $h_0 C_0 G$ and P_* (1000 N/m^2). The resistance to consolidation is evaluated by comparing the time-scale of the pilot consolidation with prediction, and the limiting solids retention time is taken to be the time that the pilot consolidation takes to reach the stalling position.

In principle, values of the resistance to consolidation and the compression coefficients, as well as the compression index, could be determined from consolidations in centrifuge tubes. However, values of R determined from centrifuge tests undertaken without the benefits of a picket fence are usually several times higher than those determined from large scale consolidations assisted by fences. Similarly, values of the compression coefficient determined from centrifuge tests can be up to 20% lower. The use of the picket-fence pilot column therefore ensures that the parameter values and hence the predictions are accurate.

CONCLUSIONS

A procedure based on a mathematical model of consolidation has been developed for designing consolidation tanks for sewage sludges. Use of the procedure ensures that the size and height of the tank accords with the consolidation properties of the sludge to obtain maximum performance.

General design principles have been derived from the procedure as follows:

1. For any particular retention time (less than a limiting value) and sludge characteristics, there is an optimum tank height that maximises performance.

2. Continuously-operated tanks generally give a better performance, volume for volume, than batch-operated tanks.

3. Optimum tank heights are lower for continuously-operated tanks than batch-operated tanks.

4. Performance of continuously-operated tanks is insensitive to feed concentration.

REFERENCES

1. TERZAGHI, K. and PECK, R.B. 'Soil Mechanics in Engineering Practice', 2nd Ed. John Wiley & Sons, 1967.

2. SHIRATO, M. et al. 'Analysis of Settling of Thick Slurries Due to Consolidation' J. of Chem. Eng. of Japan, Vol. 3, No. 1, 1970.

3. KOS, P. 'Continuous Gravity Thickening of Sludges', Prog. Wat. Tech. Vol. 9, pp 291-309, 1977.

4. HOYLAND, G. and DAY, M. 'An Evaluation of Picket Fences for Assisting the Consolidation of Sewage Sludges', Paper presented to Metropolitan and Southern Branch of the IWPC, January 1985.

5. HOYLAND, G., DAY, M. and DEE, A. 'Design Procedure for Sewage Sludge Consolidation Tanks', WRc Report 373-S, September 1985.

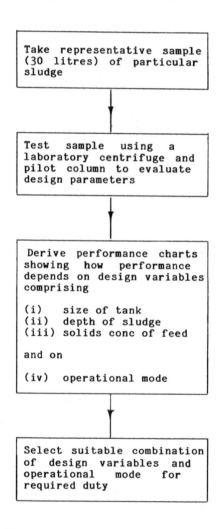

Fig. 1. Steps in design procedure

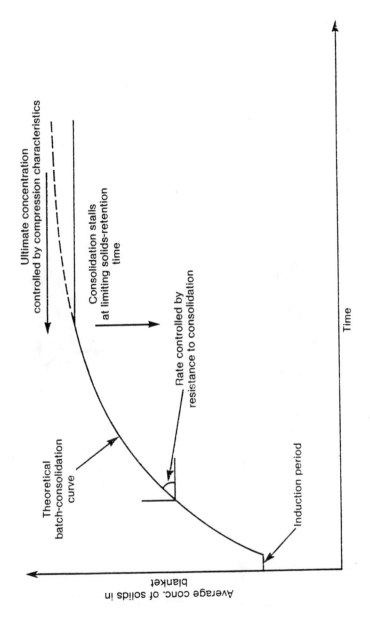

Fig. 2. General form of predictions

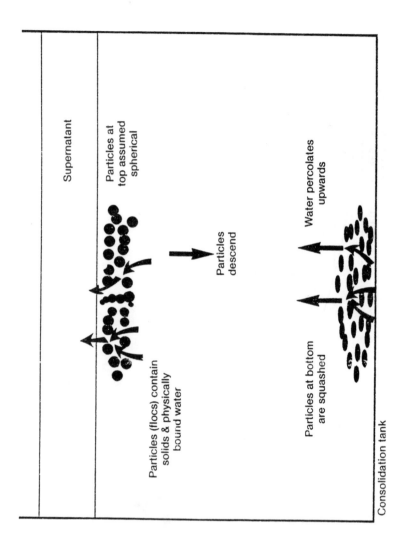

Fig. 3. Process depicted by model

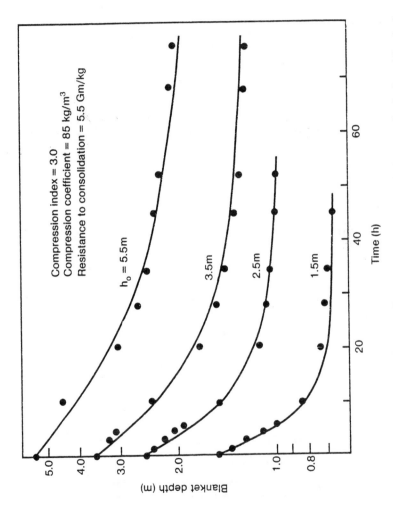

Fig. 4. Comparison between predicted and observed sludge blanket
         Depths in columns of various sizes

         Sludge : Co-settled

FIG 5 : PERFORMANCE CHART FOR BATCH CONSOLIDATION

Solids concentration of feed = 30.0(kg/m3)
Compression coefficient = 80.0(kg/m3)
Compression index =4.0
Resistance to consolidation = 50.00(Gm/kg)

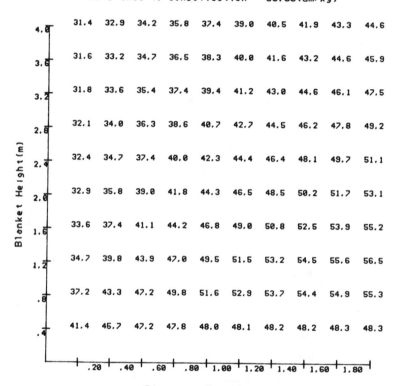

Notes :
1. Numbers on chart represent concentration of solids (kg/m3)
   in withdrawn sludge.
2. Predicted concentrations at limiting solids-retention
   time are maxima.
   Limiting solids-retention time = 2.0Days

FIG6 : PERFORMANCE CHART FOR CONTINUOUS CONSOLIDATION

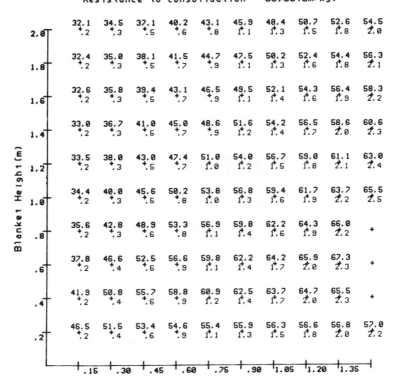

Solids concentration of feed = 30.0(kg/m3)
Compression coefficient = 80.0(kg/m3)
Compression index =4.0
Resistance to consolidation = 50.00(Gm/kg)

Nominal Retention Time (days)

Notes:
1. Upper number in each pair represents concentration of solids (kg/m3) in withdrawn sludge. Lower number represents retention time(days) of solids.
2. Predicted concentrations at the limiting solids-retention time are maxima.
    Limiting solids-retention time = 2.0Days
3. Add 1.5m to blanket height for supernatent and raking zone.

FIG 7 : PERFORMANCE CHART FOR CONTINUOUS CONSOLIDATION

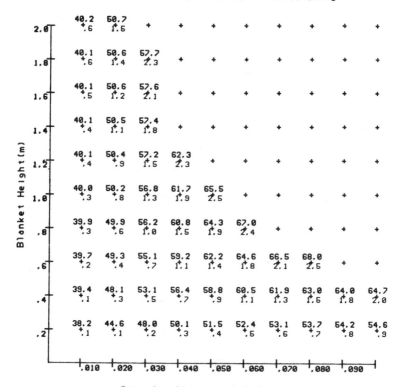

Solids concentration of feed = 30.0(kg/m3)
Compression coefficient = 80.0(kg/m3)
Compression index =4.0
Resistance to consolidation = 50.00(Gm/kg)

Specific Plan Area(m2.day/kg)

Blanket Height (m)

Notes:
1. Upper number in each pair represents concentration of solids (kg/m3) in withdrawn sludge. Lower number represents retention time(days) of solids.
2. Predicted concentrations at the limiting solids-retention time are maxima.
Limiting solids-retention time = 2.0Days
3. Add 1.5m to blanket height for supernatant and raking zone.

136

APPLICATIONS OF ANAEROBIC BIOTECHNOLOGY TO WASTE TREATMENT AND ENERGY PRODUCTION

G.K. Anderson[*] and C.B. Saw[*]

Extensive research has been carried out into the effect of important environmental factors on anaerobic digestion, methods of retaining a sufficient quantity of active biomass in the reactor and methods of optimising the microbial activity. Rapid advances in bioscience and recent developments in biochemical process engineering are having a substantial impact on the applications of anaerobic biotechnology to waste treatment and energy production. This paper outlines the potential beneficial aspects of the anaerobic process for methane production from industrial wastes and describes some recent developments in anaerobic digestion technology.

INTRODUCTION

The objectives of a wastewater treatment system are governed by a number of factors: the nature of the receiving system, i.e. whether the discharge is to sewer, river, lake or marine environment; the legal requirement of meeting any standards imposed by the regulating agency; and the desire to protect the aquatic environment. Treatment objectives are largely related to alleviating adverse effects on the environment and include:
- the removal of organic matter to reduce biochemical oxygen demand (BOD) and chemical oxygen demand (COD);
- the removal of suspended matter;
- the removal of toxic matter;
- the removal of nitrates and phosphates;
- pH control;
- disinfection;
- water reuse.

Some of these objectives are achieved best by a suitable biological process together with any necessary pretreatment. The first two items above form the basis of the most frequently applied consent conditions for discharge - the Royal Commission recommended levels. Most organic substances and a wide variety of inorganic compounds can be removed biologically, provided certain conditions essential for microbial growth are established.

* Department of Civil Engineering
  University of Newcastle upon Tyne, U.K.

All biological treatment processes depend upon the natural selection and growth of the required microorganisms contained in the biomass. In the presence or absence of free oxygen and essential nutrients, they utilise the pollutant for growth and therefore have the ability to remove dissolved and suspended organics from the waste being treated. There are basically two types of biological process, aerobic and anaerobic.

AEROBIC BIOLOGICAL PROCESSES

The basic principle of aerobic treatment involves contact between the organic matter in the industrial wastewater and a biological growth of bacteria and protozoa in the presence of free oxygen. Two methods have evolved for achieving this, namely fixed-film reactors and suspended-growth systems.

(i) Fixed-film reactors:

This method is typified by the conventional biological filter which has been used for some 100 years for treating domestic wastes and many industrial wastes. The biological film develops on an inert medium (e.g. 25-100 mm rock) contained in a bed about 2m deep on which the settled wastewater is distributed. There are various problems associated with this system:
- it is not suitable for high-strength wastes;
- a large land area is required;
- there is a high hydraulic head loss (3-4 m);
- it has a high initial capital cost;
- there is a potential fly nuisance;
- excess sludge is produced and is costly to dispose of;
- toxic wastes may present problems.

In order to overcome some of these problems, a number of process alternatives have been developed (Table 1).

Table 1: Fixed-film aerobic reactors

System	Advantages	Disadvantages
High-rate filters (plastic media)	High loading rates Reduced land costs Inert packing High BOD removal rate	High capital costs High operating costs Difficult sludge Odour often produced during operation
Rotating biological contactors (disc and drum types)	Compact Prefabricated Covered Low operating cost Limited operation and maintenance requirements Flexible loading Infrequent de-sludging	High capital cost Limited total load

(ii) Suspended growth systems:

The most widely used system of this type is the conventional
activated-sludge type process in which the settled wastewater is introduced
to a suspended biomass at a relatively low concentration (about 200 mg/l).
Atmospheric oxygen is used, either by means of surface aeraton or from
compressed-air diffusers. The system is used very widely for domestic and
industrial wastes, and frequently provides an optimum solution to the
problem. However, as with conventional biological filters certain
difficulties are associated with the process:
  - it is not suitable for high-strength wastes;
  - high operating costs (for power) are involved;
  - sophisticated operating technology is necessary;
  - a large volume of high moisture content sludge is produced;
  - there are sludge settling problems (due for example, to
    filamentous microorganisms);
  - sludge dewatering is difficult;
  - the system may be susceptible to toxic wastes;
  - possible bacterial escape from the system in aerosol sprays.
Modifications to this process have been developed to meet some of the
specilised requirements of industry (Table 2).

(iii) Stabilization pond treatment:

If sufficient land area is available it may be possible to treat adequately
an industrial waste in specially designed ponds. In warm climates, the high
temperatures and greater light intensities may result in relatively high
organic load-removal rates and algae oxygen-generation capacity. However, in
the U.K., pond treatment is usually limited to the pre-treatment of
relatively lightly polluting wastes in mechanically aerated ponds or for
balancing shock or seasonal loads.

Table 2: Suspended-growth aerobic systems

System	Advantages	Disadvantages
Extended aeration (e.g. Pasveer Ditch oxidation)	Simple operation Flexible w.r.t. load Low sludge production Low capital cost	High energy cost Large land use Rising sludge
Deep shaft process	High loading rates Low land area High MLSS Covered tanks	High capital cost High energy cost Dissolved gases Sophisticated technology
Pure oxygen systems	Load variations met Relatively high strength waste treated Sludge bulking On-site O_2 generation	Power costs Sophisticated operation

ANAEROBIC WASTE TREATMENT FUNDAMENTALS

Anaerobic digestion is the stepwise conversion of large molecules of organic compounds into methane and carbon dioxide by bacteria in the absence of free oxygen. Three different but related groups of bacteria are involved (Zehnder 1978, Mosey 1982), namely, the hydrolytic fermentative organisms, the acetogenic bacteria and the methane-forming bacteria. The hydrolytic bacteria hydrolyse a wide range of complex polymeric substrates to form simple organic compounds, carbon dioxide and hydrogen. The acetogenic bacteria convert these organic fermentation products into acetate, hydrogen and carbon dioxide. In the methanogenic phase, the acetate and hydrogen will be converted to methane and carbon dioxide.

The methane-forming bacteria are very sensitive to changes in environmental conditions. Optimum environmental conditions are generally temperatures in the mesophilic range of 30 - 35 $^{\circ}$C or the thermophilic range of 50 - 55 $^{\circ}$C, strictly anaerobic conditions, pH 6.6 to 7.6, absence of toxic materials, and sufficient biological nutrients including nitrogen and phosphorus. If the methane-forming bacteria are inhibited by unfavorable environmental conditions, their rate of utilization of volatile acids will decrease to a rate lower than the acid production by the acid-forming bacteria. This will result in an increase in volatile acids concentration which indicates an overall imbalance in the treatment process. Other indicators of imbalanced treatment include an increasing carbon dioxide percentage in the gas, decreasing pH, decreasing total gas production, and a decrease in the waste stabilization taking place as measured by COD reduction.

THE POTENTIAL OF ANAEROBIC DIGESTION FOR TREATING INDUSTRIAL WASTES

An expected question which arises from the proposed anaerobic treatment of waste waters could be "why use anaerobic methods when the technology of aerobic methods is so well developed?". The answer to this question lies in the very limitation of the aerobic system itself. The anaerobic method of treating high strength industrial wastes offers a number of significant advantages over other treatment methods.

Environmentally acceptable

The process, by its very nature, is totally enclosed and does not produce any environmental nuisance (such as offensive odours and bacterial aerosols).

High value by-product recovery for direct factory use

In an anaerobic digester, due to a very long solids retention time and consequent low growth rate, the cell yield (i.e. solids production) is also extremely low, thus most of the carbon in the raw waste is available for methanogenesis and under normal circumstances the yield of methane would, on average, be 0.33 - 0.36 m^3 per kg COD removed.

Biogas ignites at aproximately 690 $^{\circ}$C compared with 645 $^{\circ}$C for natural gas and burns with a flame speed of approximately 43 m/s. Under these circumstances most equipment fitted for natural gas can be operated with biogas after suitable modification. The production of biogas is generally in excess of that needed to operate the anaerobic treatment system, and can be utilised to generate power for other on-site services. Hence, anaerobic digestion is an energy producing process rather than one that demands regular input of energy as in an aerobic system.

Gas production with simultaneous effluent treatment

Removal of organic material occurs by microbial conversion first to hydrogen, carbon dioxide and acetic acid, which then act as precursors to the final by-products of methane and carbon dioxide. Hence it is largely in this last step, through the production of methane and carbon dioxide that the majority of the COD is removed from the raw effluent. Thus gas production and COD removal are inextricably linked in the anaerobic treatment plant.

High organic loading

The anaerobic process is effective at very high loadings, whereas due to the low rate of oxygen transfer from the gas to liquid phase, limited organic loads (BOD, COD) can be applied under aerobic conditions. In addition, the nutrient requirements are low. It requires only about 10% of the nitrogen and phosphorus needed for aerobic systems.

Excess sludge production

Without doubt, a major benefit from the use of anaerobic fermentation for the treatment of industrial effluents is the extremely low biomass yield. Volatile organic material in the form of suspended solids is also dealt with more effectively in the anaerobic system which hydrolyses the volatile solids into soluble organics to allow the eventual conversion into methane and carbon dioxide.

Response to factory operations

The response of the process to stop-start factory operations is important for two reasons :
- the effluent treatment capacity will not be affected.
- in order that financial benefit is gained from the gas, it is clearly desirable that this gas should be produced when the factory has use for it.

The anaerobic process generally has been shown to have the ability to operate successfully under part day loading (i.e. 12 hours per day) and 5 days per week and has also been able to withstand complete shutdown for several months.

The gas production profile resulting from stop-start operation is, again, a common feature of most anaerobic processes. Although anaerobic bacteria have a relatively low growth rate, this must not be confused with their substrate utilization rate. The high rate of substrate utilization is reflected in the response of gas production to load variations. In the case of soluble substrates a sudden increase in load is reflected proportionally by an increase in gas production generally within 15 minutes. Active anaerobic biomass can be preserved unfed for several months and this capability is important when treating wastewaters from seasonal industries.

Cost benefits of anaerobic treatment

It has been shown by many studies that anaerobic digestion becomes economical for wastewaters with a COD in excess of 2000 mg/l. A comparison between the overall costs of aerobic and anaerobic systems for treating high strength industrial wastes has been studied by different investigators (Ragan, 1980; Anderson and Senaratne, 1985; Rantala and Vaananen, 1985), and the major cost differences in operating the treatment plants are energy, chemicals and sludge handling costs in favour of the anaerobic process.

INCREASED RETENTION OF BIOMASS IN THE DIGESTERS

The loading rates permissible in an anaerobic waste treatment process are primarily dictated by the biomass retention in the reactor. A wide variety of anaerobic treatment processes has been evolved to meet the various needs of industrial effluent treatment. Each of these different design configurations has implications for the ratio of solids retention time/hydraulic retention time (SRT/HRT). The solids retention time (SRT) is a measure of the average residence time of microorganisms in the system and is normally defined as:

$$SRT = \frac{\text{Total mass of microorganisms}}{\text{Mass lost from systems/day}}$$

Numerically, the reciprocal of the solids retention time is the net growth rate of the system. For the system to function, the reciprocal of the design SRT of the process must be in excess of the minimum time it takes for the microorganisms to reproduce in the process. Hence there is a minimum SRT, below which the microbial cells will be washed out from the system at a faster rate than they can multiply and the system thereby fails.

SRT is the fundamental design parameter. In anaerobic systems, the microorganisms reproduce less rapidly than in aerobic systems, and a longer minimum SRT is required to accomodate the slower net growth rate. A high SRT is desirable for process stability and minimal sludge production. A short HRT minimises the reactor volume and hence reduces capital costs. Therefore a design configuration which is capable of maintaining a long SRT at a relatively short HRT will allow the system to be operated at high volumetric loading rates.

Figures 1 to 7 illustrate a number of available anaerobic treatment systems. Recent developments in the design of digesters for soluble wastewaters will now be discussed in terms of the retention of elevated levels of bacteria, either as flocs or in films attached to support surfaces.

The Conventional Anaerobic Digester

This is a completely-mixed reactor with no solids recycle, in which the solids retention time equals the hydraulic retention time, i.e. SRT/HRT ratio is one. The slow growth rate of the methane bacteria necessitates maintainance of reactor solids retention times generally for a minimum 12-15 days. This will lead to reactors of a very large volume, and hence unsuitable for most industrial wastes. However it can be used for the digestion of concentrated wastes, particularly those in which the organic matter is predominantly in the form of settleable solids which can be more economically concentrated before anaerobic treatment rather than afterwards, for example sewage sludges. It has limited value for the treatment of liquid effluents because the 'washout' of the micro-organisms will pose a serious problem, particularly if high loading rates were to be obtained. To overcome this problem, a phase separation/solids recycle stage may be incorporated.

The Completely Mixed Anaerobic Contact Digester

This differs from a conventional anaerobic digester system in that a settlement tank is used to concentrate and recycle the biomass to the digester. Anaerobic treatment processes with solids recycle allow the system to have a longer SRT to obtain a high treatment efficiency, low effluent substrate concentration with a short HRT, and consequently a smaller digester. Incorporation of solids recycling increases the SRT/HRT ratio, thereby allowing higher hydraulic loadings than are otherwise possible, while still retaining a long SRT.

The major problem in the practical application of the contact process has always been the separation of the biomass from the effluent for recycle to the digester. The formation of gas tends to continue in the settlement tank and the gas bubbles so formed buoy up the solids, thus preventing efficient sedimentation. Improvements in the performance of the separator have been achieved through the use of process and component design modifications such as the incorporation of inclined plates as part of the settler design (Huss 1982), vacuum degasification (Blade et al. 1974), settling combined with flocculation and thermal shock of the biomass prior to sedimentation (Rippon, 1977).

The Anaerobic Packed Bed Reactor (APBR) / Anaerobic Filter

This type of digester consists of a flooded bed of inert filter medium, up through which the waste water is passed. The packing material provides an inert surface to which bacteria adhere. It also ensures low turbulence and efficient sedimentation, and thus allowed the retention of unattached biomass by entrapment. Anaerobic growth in a quiescent environment allows a relatively large agglomeration of biomass "clumps" to develop. High concentrations of biomass, having long solids retention periods, are achieved by promoting microbial growth on the support medium. Hence it is possible to maintain a long SRT at very high hydraulic loadings, and such fixed-film reactors are an attempt to achieve even higher SRT/HRT ratios.

To prevent accumulation of refractory particulates present in the feed, the packed bed reactor can be operated in a downflow mode. When operated in the upflow mode, the anaerobic filter retains the biological solids by means of film attachment to the surface of the media and entrapment within the elements of the media bed. When operated in the downflow mode, film attachment alone is the retaining mechanism.

Anaerobic Expanded Bed/Fluidised Bed Reactors

In both the anaerobic expanded bed reactor and the anaerobic fluidised bed reactor, the biomass is attached to the surface of small, low specific gravity particles (such as anthracite, high-density plastic beads, sand, etc.) which are kept in suspension by the upward velocity of the liquid flow. These particles provide a very large surface area for biological growth. In addition the particles also increase the settling velocity of the attached biofilm, thereby enhancing efficient biomass retention within the reactor. These digesters readily allow passage of refractory particles that could choke a packed bed reactor and sloughing of biomass may be prevented by controlling the thickness of biofilm using some simple mechanical particle/biomass separator. In the expanded bed reactor, low upflow liquid velocities are employed to give a bed expansion of 10 - 20%. The fluidised bed process differs principally from the expanded bed reactor in the degree of bed expansion used, ranging from 30 - 100%.

Upflow Anaerobic Sludge Blanket (UASB) Reactor

The high cost of the digester packing media and concern over long-term problems characteristic of packed bed reactors such as plugging, hydraulic short-circuiting, biofilm sloughing and high pressure drops, have led to the development of 'unpacked' reactors which still incorporate immobilised cell feature. In the upflow anaerobic sludge blanket reactor, the biomass is retained as a blanket which is kept in suspension by controlling the upflow velocity. The washout of biomass released from the sludge blanket can be reduced by creating a quiescent zone within the digester and the reactor operates without any internal mechanical agitation. The wastewater flows through an expanded bed of active sludge, while the upper part of the reactor contains a three phase separation system, allowing biogas collection and internal sludge recycling. It has been shown that it is possible to develop a granular sludge with excellent sedimentation characteristics in such a reactor (de Zeeuw and Lettinga 1980, Lettinga et al. 1981, Hulshoff Pol et al. 1983). However more work needs to be carried out to study the mechanism by which the granular sludge is developed. While certain wastes result in a granular sludge quite readily (sugar-processing waste and wastes containing mainly volatile acids), other wastes develop this granular sludge very slowly or not at all.

Membrane Anaerobic Reactor

The membrane anaerobic reactor system uses a suspended growth reactor in conjunction with an external ultra/micro-filtration membrane unit for solid-liquid separation (Li and Corrado, 1985; Anderson, et al., 1985). The reactor contents are constantly being pumped to the membrane unit for solid-liquid separation. The permeate becomes the effluent, and the biomass is returned to the reactor. Recirculation of the reactor contents also provides the mixing in the reactor. The ultrafiltration membranes provide positive biomass retention and control and essentially particulate-free effluent.

Anaerobic Rotating Biological Contactor

Rotating biological contactors (RBC's) have primarily been used for aerobic treatment of domestic sewage from small communities. The performance capabilities of the disc and packed-cage forms of RBC operating under aerobic conditions are well understood. It has been noted for its trouble-free operation and flexibility in receiving variable loads. Extensive research (Anderson et al., 1984) are currently being carried out to study the full potential for this type of process in the anaerobic mode of operation.

IMPROVED BIOMASS ACTIVITY IN ANAEROBIC DIGESTERS

Recent microbiological and biochemical advances have led to a better understanding and control of the anaerobic treatment process as well as to a means of improving the activity of the biomass.

Perhaps the most significant development in the biochemistry of anaerobic digestion is the realization of the role of hydrogen gas in regulating methane formation. Traditionally the consortia of bacteria responsible for the bioconversion of organic matter to carbon dioxide and methane were loosely classified into two main groups, namely acid forming bacteria and methane bacteria. More recently it has been shown that there is a third intermediate group called the obligate hydrogen-producing acetogenic bacteria which exist in symbiotic relation with the methanogens (Bryant et al. 1967, McInerney et al 1979). The complex consortia of organisms involved at each stage of methane fermentation is shown in Table 3.

Table 3: The organisms involved in the three stages of methane fermentation

Hydrolytic organisms	Acetogen	Methanogens
Clostridium Eubacterium Peptococcus Propionibacterium	Syntrophobacter Syntrophomonas Desulfovibrio	Hydrogenotrophic Methanobacterium Methanobrevibacterium Acetoclastic Methanothrix Methanosarcina Methanospirillum

Complex organics are first hydrolyzed by the hydrolytic organisms to produce free sugars, alcohols, volatile acids, hydrogen and carbon dioxide. The obligate acetogenic bacteria can ferment alcohols and higher volatile acids to produce acetate and hydrogen which can then be utilised by the methanogenic bacteria. An obligate, syntrophic relationship exists between the hydrogen-producing acetogens and the hydrogen-utilising methanogens. To enable favourable thermodynamic conditions for the conversion of volatile acids and alcohols to acetate, the concentration of hydrogen in the digester must be kept low by an active population of hydrogen-utilising (methane) bacteria. The acetogens respond to an increased hydrogen concentration by altering their metabolism to form a broad spectrum of acids such as propionic, butyric, valeric and lactic acids instead of acetic acid. The methane bacteria can only produce methane from a number of simple substrates such as carbon dioxide, hydrogen and acetic acid. Hence the continued build up of higher volatile acids will depress the pH value of the growth medium and could result in a digester failure should no action be taken.

The reaction below is not only important as a method of generating methane but also in controlling the redox potential of the fermentation and as mentioned previously in removing hydrogen:

$$CO_2 + 4H_2 = CH_4 + 2H_2O$$

The other transformation which occurs is the direct conversion of acetic acid to methane and carbon dioxide. About 75 % of the methane produced is derived through this route:

$$CH_3 \ COO \ H \ = \ CH_4 + CO_2$$

These discoveries have resulted in dramatic advances in the design and control of anaerobic systems. It is now appreciated that, under high substrate loading conditions or after a sudden large increase in substrate load, volatile fatty acids and hydrogen can be formed more rapidly than they are removed. This type of process failure may be the mechanism underlying many digester breakdowns in the past.

These discoveries also provide opportunities for improved monitoring and control of the anaerobic digestion process. The concentration of hydrogen in the biogas together with the types of volatile acid can be monitored to give an early warning of impending instability.

Differences in the growth rates and optimal pH of the mixed microbial groups involved in anaerobic digestion have led to the suggestion that the acid and methane forming phases could be separated into two different reactors. The major disadvantage of the one-digester systems is that the two main digestion stages, which are quite different biochemical processes, are proceeding under the same operating conditions.

In a two-stage digester, the acidogenesis and methanogenesis stages take place in separate reactors. With this process, more attention can be directed towards determining and providing optimal environmental conditions for each group of organisms, leading to the production of the most suitable acid metabolites for the methanogens and consequently an increase of the rate of substrate turnover. The two-phase system will allow a reduction in total reactor volume and also ensure against organic and hydraulic overloading and fluctuations which can result in serious lowering of efficiency.

A considerable amount of literature has appeared in recent years about tne benefits of treating wastes in two-phase reactors (Pohland and Massey 1975, Cohen et al. 1980, Verstraete et al. 1981, Ghosh and Henry, 1982). However it must be noted that two-phase systems are not necessarily cheaper than single-phase systems because the overall loading rate is not necessarily higher with a two-phase system, while additional expensive equipments (pumps, valves) are required. In some instances, addition of alkali may be required for complete acid formation. Hence it would appear that the two-phase anaerobic systems will be useful under certain circumstances, depending on the wastewater characteristics and subsequent substrate changes within the process.

CONCLUSIONS

With the present state of process technology, anaerobic digestion represents an attractive alternative to aerobic methods for waste water treatment. It offers the potential for energy savings and an ability to operate at organic loadings far in excess of equivalent aerobic reactor types, which will ultimately result in more economic industrial waste water treatment.

The recent advances in anaerobic biotechnology have made it possible to improve performance of these reactors further or modify them to become cheaper to install and simpler to operate. New process developments and reactor configurations should ensure a much wider application of this form of waste treatment.

REFERENCES

1) Anderson,G.K., James,A., Saw, C.B. and Le, S. (1985). Proc. 40th. Industr. Wastes Conf., Purdue Univ., U.S.A.

2) Anderson,G.K., Pescod,M.B. and Norton,T.S. (1984). 2nd Int. Conf on Fixed Film Biological Processes, Washington, U.S.A.

3) Anderson,G.K. and Senaratne,A.U. (1985). Water Sci & Technol, 17(1),241.

4) Blade,M.G., Brown,J.M. and Kaye,E. (1974). J. Wat. Pollut. Control Fed., 73, (5), p532.

5) Bryant,M.P., Wolin,E.A., Wolin,M.J., Wolfe,R.S. (1967). Arch. Microbiol., 59, p20-32.

6) Cohen,A., Breure,A.M., van Andel,J.G. and van Deursen,A. (1980). Water Research, 14, p1439.

7) De Zeeuw,W. and Lettinga,G. (1980). Proc. 35th. Purdue Industr. Waste Conf., U.S.A., p39-47.

8) Ghosh,S. and Henry, M.P. (1982). Proc. 1st Int. Conf. on Fixed Film Biological Processes, Pittsburgh, U.S.A.

9) Hulshoff Pol,L.W., de Zeeuw,W.J., Velzeboer,C.T.M. and Lettinga,G. (1983). Water Science and Technology, Vol. 15, (8/9), p291.

10) Huss, L. (1982). In Anaerobic Digestion 1981, Hughes, D.E. et al (eds.), Elsevier Press, Amsterdam.

11) Lettinga,G., de Zeeuw,W., Ouborg,E. (1981). Water Res, 15, p171-182.

12) Li,A., Corrado,J. (1985). Proc 40th Purdue Industr Wastes Conf, U.S.A.

13) McInerney,M.J., Bryant,M.P., Pfenning,N. (1979). Arch. Microbiol., 122, p129-135.

14) Mosey, F.E. (1982). Wat. Pollut. Control, 81, (4), p540-552.

15) Pohland,F.G. and Massey,M.J. (1975). Proc. Water Technol, 7, 173.

16) Ragan,J.L. (1980). Dept. of Energy/EPA Seminar/Workshop, Jan. 9-10, Howey in the Hill, Fl.

17) Rantala,P and Vaananen (1984). Water Sci. & Technol, 17, (1), p255.

18) Rippon,G.M. (1977). British Patent No.1,491,502.

19) Verstraete,W.,de Baere,L. and Rozzi,A. (1981). Trib. CEBEDEAU, 453-454(3), p367-375.

20) Zehnder, A.J.B. (1978). In Water Pollut. Microbio., Vol.2, Ed. Mitchell,R., Wiley New York.

147

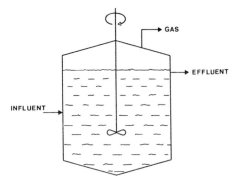

Fig. 1: Conventional Digester

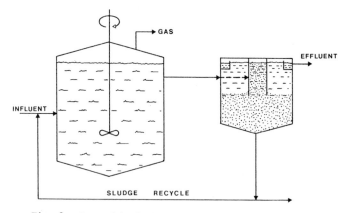

Fig. 2: Anaerobic Contact Digester

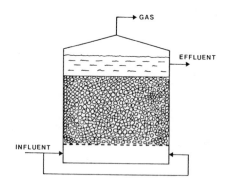

Fig. 3: Anaerobic Filter

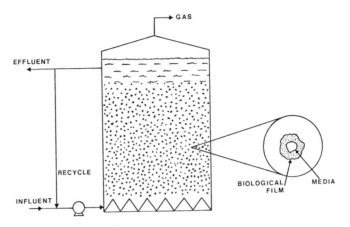

Fig. 4: Anaerobic Expanded/Fluidised Bed Reactor

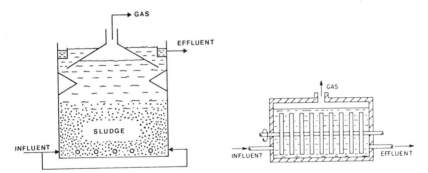

Fig. 5: Upflow Anaerobic Sludge
Blanket Reactor

Fig. 6: Anaerobic Rotating Biological
Contactor

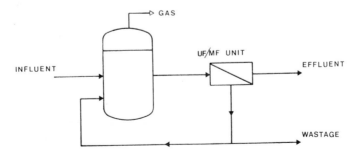

Fig. 7: Membrane Anaerobic Reactor

The Control and Optimisation of Anaerobic and Aerobic Waste
Treatment Systems

D.A. Stafford (Executive Chairman); R.A. Spensley (Managing Director)
CLEAR, Cardiff

Biological treatment is being increasingly applied to the
detoxification of organic wastes. A greater degree of waste
treatment control is called for, due to stricter requirements on the performances of biological teatment units.

We present here a concept of using biological parameters to
measure treatment activity and to link such measurements to
microprocessor monitoring and control.

The technology to do this is now available and we look
forward to incorporating these devices to full-scale treatment facilities.

INTRODUCTION

Environmental problems are becoming an increasing part of the industrial scene
which have forced many companies to provide their own treatment facilities.
Increasing energy costs have at the same time led to a need for more efficient
methods of treatment. With increasing pressure from the Water Authorities and
implementation of the Control of Pollution Act Part II, all industries producing organic wastes and in particular those in the areas of food processing have
been looking for suitable treatment methods. These problems therefore require
solutions, and treatment system development has attracted much research and
development support in recent years.

The control of biological treatment systems requires an understanding of the
biochemical reactions effected by the microbes encouraged to grow in such
treatment units. Also, a detailed knowledge of the characteristics of an
effluent, its volume flow and organic loading are important parameters to determine when linking effluent feeds to a biological treatment system. The basic
data needed to operate treatment plants may be obtained from the measurement of
process parameters and may be used to control waste processing to produce
maximum pollution reduction. Thus, a specific waste component (eg. carbohydrate) may be degraded sequentially by a consortium of microbes to produce,
eventually, carbon dioxide and water (aerobic) or methane and carbon dioxide
(anaerobic). The measurement of the substrate, metabolic intermediate or final
product provides an indication of the rates of reaction involved.

An ability to increase the effectiveness and efficiency of treatment processes
by careful maintenance and control of the microbial activity in waste treatment
systems has been shown to be possible, not only by measuring chemical changes
in the treatment medium, but by the measurement of biochemical activity within
cells performing the treatment. For example, the process is designed to
increase the purification of wastewater by contact with a large concentration of

micro-organisms per unit time.

CONTROL OF WASTE TREATMENT SYSTEMS

Efficient operation and control has three major requirements:

1) Recognition of the fundamental basis for control;

2) Knowledge of the system constraints and limitations and;

3) Utilisation of a control strategy consistent with requirements (1) and (2);

While there have been great advances in our ability to meet the first two requirements, there has been a large technical gap in achieving the third. This is due in part to the complexity of the system and difficulty in accurate modelling.

Thus, the systems control of treatment units was introduced to optimise the efficiency of the process, to reduce further treatment requirements and thus reduce the costs of treatment. This process of optimisation of control also provided, as a main aim, the improvement in effluent quality. Initially, it is worthwhile to consider how these improvements were achieved. In the early days of sewage treatment the process design was mainly by rule of thumb, and the experience gathered was designed into treatment concepts. The science followed later. As treatment moved from trickling filters to activated sludge plants there were more factors presented which operators could control. These included Return Activated Sludge (RAS) recycle rates, aeration efficiency, pH, temperature and solids concentrations.

The early use of dissolved oxygen probes to aid control of oxygen concentrations did not meet with success, mainly because of the limited service life of the probes and basic problems inherent in the use of sensors in direct contact with sewage (such as fouling both by microbial slimes and by gross solids). Problems also arose from the restriction placed on the range of variation in aeration intensity available by the need to maintain adequate mixing at all times, lag in the response of the system, and the general lack of accuracy of the monitoring/control system. Whilst the usual design dissolved oxygen level was 2mg/l., the measurement system accuracy was frequently as poor as ±0.5mg/l. and the actual plant dissolved oxygen control system could vary widely in the range 0-2.5mg/l. In some plants, the actual method of control of aeration intensity had adverse effects on the performance of the treatment system. In plants where the aeration intensity of surface aerators was controlled by 'rise and fall' weirs, the hydraulic surges resulting from operation of the dissolved oxygen control system could have severe deleterious effects on the performance of the secondary clarifiers.

Progress in the development of activated sludge plant technology resulted in high purity oxygen systems with totally enclosed reactor tanks which enabled automatic and precise control of the aeration plant. In these systems, reliable control of the rate of oxygen supply could be effected via measurement of reactor headspace pressure with none of the problems of sensor fouling. This system was further defined by inclusion of vent gas purity control systems which enabled even further power savings to be achieved.

Without the above oxygen-controlled systems with precise measurements, it is necessary to use diagnostic systems which do not have sensor fouling. Thus, chemical measurement for control such as total organic carbon content of the wastewater were used experimentally, but with limited success. It then became essential to measure biological activity which related waste treatment performances to bacterial cell numbers and activity.

Mathematical models are now available which can use our knowledge of bacterial growth and substrate utilisation and, for example, specific growth rates of sludge encountered in the process, can be determined. A measurement of sludge biomass activity can also be linked into this physico-chemical measure to determine treatment efficiency using the sludge solids present.

ACTIVATED SLUDGE PROCESS

The two parameters which can be used most readily for the control of, for example, the activated-sludge system are:

1. The rate of wastage of sludge;

2. The rate of recycle of sludge;

3. The rate of aeration;

For equilibrium to be maintained to a dynamic system, input must be matched by output. In the case of the activated-sludge system, therefore, growth of new biomass is balanced by the rate at which solids are wasted from the system, ie. specific growth rate = specific wastage rate = 1/sludge age.

Simulations with a mathematical model showed that variations in effluent quality were reduced if the volumetric flow rate of wasted sludge was kept constant, instead of continually adjusting the wastage rate in an attempt to keep the concentration of active solids constant (Curds, 1973).

Since it is important to understand the fundamental (biological) nature of the secondary waste treatment processes in order to control them, biochemical parameters have been proposed as measures of both biomass and bioactivity. The most widely used methods for estimating activated-sludge cell concentration are total suspended solids (TSS) and volatile suspended solids (VSS). However, a more reliable estimate is required which is related to the biological activity of the sludge. This reliability could itself be coupled with a sophisticated main-frame computer and produce a cost-effective means of control.

Using the measurement of a specific cell constituent such as adenosine triphosphate (ATP) to calculate such total microbial biomass, the following requirements may be satisfied:

i)   The measured compound must be present in all living cells and must be absent from all dead cells.

ii)   It must not be found associated with non-living, detrital material.

iii)   It should exist in fairly uniform concentrations in populations, but may be influenced by environmental stresses.

iv)   The analytical technique for the measurement of the biomass indicator must be capable of measuring milligram quantities and must be relatively quick and easy to use for large-scale programmes involving numerous samples.

POSSIBLE USES FOR ATP MEASUREMENTS IN THE ACTIVATED SLUDGE PROCESS

Use Of Mixed Liquor - Returned Activated Sludge (ML:RAS) ATP Levels to Estimate Sludge Wastage Rate

Since ATP measurements of active biomass content are more accurate than suspended-solids determinations, the use of ML:RAS ATP will permit more accurate control of the activated sludge plant. Thus, any alteration in ATP levels in response to changes in plant environmental conditions may be used to control the wastage of surplus activated sludge. This has been shown to be the case, (Johnson and Stafford, 1984).

Use of ATP Level as an "Early Warning" System

The use of ML:RAS ATP levels in controlling the wastage of activated sludge provides a simple and effective early warning of perturbations in the incoming sewage. Therefore, if a toxic discharge enters the aeration tank treatment lane the plant operator, by knowing ATP sludge levels, can reduce the wastage rate thereby retaining more biomass in the system to combat the discharge. If ATP remains at a reduced level, the flow of sewage containing the toxic discharge can be diverted either for preliminary treatment or to holding tanks. When the discharge ends, the ATP levels increase again and the wastage rate may be steadily increased to its original value, (Figure 1). The sludge wastage rate may also be adjusted to accommodate diurnal variations in sewage volume and composition, as well as to control the aeration rate.

Levels of ATP in sludge respond rapidly to changes in environmental conditions, and therefore the method provides a sensitive control of the treatment process. With elaborate instrumentation and process control, this system could be shown to have further practical significance for full-scale treatment plants. To fully utilise the technique, automatic monitoring and control with a microprocessor will be necessary. Other parameters can now be considered for measurement and used for microprocessor control of both aerobic and anaerobic treatment systems.

COMPUTER CONTROL OF ANAEROBIC DIGESTERS

A. System Development, Hardware Procurement & Installation

Thus far, microprocessor control of anaerobic digester systems has not been successfully applied using microcomputers. CLEAR Ltd. has developed designs of microcomputer control systems for anaerobic systems and it is now considered that microcomputer control is an important and new development for the operation of such units. CLEAR has now produced integrated hardware and software which are now being used to remotely monitor and control anaerobic digester units.

The recently developed and installed computer system to monitor waste treatment plants using the latest low cost microcomputer technology, has been accomplished in conjunction with Dr. R. Marshall of the University of Wales College of Medicine in Cardiff. The system has shown the versatility of the microcomputer control of such systems and how they may be used in future to fully monitor a wide variety of parameters for successful effluent treatment.

A. System Development, Hardware Procurement & Installation (Contin.)

The system based at a treatment plant site collects and stores performance
data over a 24 hour period and then transfers this data to CLEAR's main
offices in Cardiff. Alarm conditions are reported to CLEAR's offices
immediately using the Public Switched Telephone network with data transfer
occurring at off-peak times to reduce expenditure on phone calls.

The Homebase System in Cardiff allows collection, storage and viewing of
the data transferred from the plant. A request for the current plant status
and remote control of the feed pump can also be implemented from Cardiff.

Two main types of data are collected from the plant by the on-site system:

1) Analogue data (dc signals) from temperature sensors, a gas analyser and
    kilowatt hour meters.

2) Logical data (on/off) from the contactors controlling plant equipment.
    These logical inputs fall into two groups; those from contactors cont-
    rolling the on/off state of the equipment and those from contactors
    activated to disable equipment in response to a fault.

Digitisation of the analogue inputs and monitoring of the logical inputs is
carried out by a Multifunction Interface package (MFI). The package consists of three units, a controller with 8 analogue inputs and a relay output,
with in addition two slave devices, one with a further 8 analogue inputs and
a second relay output, and the other with 32 analogue input channels.

The controller unit can be programmed in a subset of BASIC to collect data
from its own inputs and those of its slave units. The MFI units have
limited storage capacity and so all data collected must be transferred to a
host computer for storage, presentation and display at CLEAR.

The microcomputer was chosen as the host because of its flexible interfacing
reliability and excellent software development tools (operating system,
basic interpreter and assembler). The data from the MFI units was transferred in serial form (RS232) to the computer. This serial data is
communicated via an extra serial RS232 port connected to the computer.

B. Software Development

In summarising the function of the finished software package, the software
can be divided into three main sections:

1) Control of the MFI Interface Units;
2) Control of the Remote Site Computer;
3) Control of the Homebase Computer;

C. Operation Experience of Installed System

Overall, the computer system has proved particularly robust and well able to operate under industrial conditions, provided sufficient cooling is available.

The computer system has enabled CLEAR at its central laboratories in Cardiff to closely monitor digestion plants, particularly during commissioning of electrical power generation. The notification of alarm conditions has greatly aided fault-finding, particularly in the case of those problems which have occurred at weekends or overnight.

On-going measurement of parameters such as gas flow, methane content, KW output and temperatures has also proved extremely valuable in the monitoring of the performance of the digester plants. For example, the efficiency of the waste heat digester heating system has been closely evaluated through the continual measurement of the temperature profile of the tank and the heating distributions system at a total of 7 independent points.

A data processing package is being developed which will automatically process collected data at the Homebase and produce high-resolution graphical output.

How then will these novel biochemical measurements be used to monitor anaerobic digester units? The parallel with ATP measurement for aerobic units is evident; we now review a similar scheme for anaerobic systems.

D. Anaerobic Digester Systems - Biochemical Control

This approach can be made more specifically with anaerobic digester systems whereby other parameters can be measured to demonstrate metabolic activity. ATP measurement is not suitable for measuring metabolic activity in anaerobic digester systems, but recently the estimation of methanogenic biomass and activity has been possible with the assay of Coenzyme F_{420} (Whitmore et al. 1985).

Coenzyme F_{420} is largely confined to the methane producing bacterial group and is a 5-deazaflavin analogue of Flavine Mono Nucleotide and functions as a low potential electron carrier, participating in both catabolic and anabolic redox reactions. This technique has been applied (Whitmore et al. 1985) to samples taken from different pilot scale anaerobic digesters in order to determine their specific methanogenic activity and in order to correlate digester performance with methanogenic activity, determined by Coenzyme F_{420} assay.

In Figure 2 it can be seen that there is a high correlation between the rate of methane production and F_{420} concentration in relation to the amount of volatile solids present for 2 reactors: plugflow ($r = 0.987$) and hydraulic ($r = 0.999$) digesters.

In Figure 3 the Coenzyme F_{420} concentration and methane production can also be shown to be related to digester volume. It is shown that the correlations are fairly good for the plugflow ($r = 0.874$) and very good for the hydraulic type digesters ($r = 0.978$), (Stafford and Etheridge, 1983). Thus, with effective mixing producing useful digester volume, higher efficiency in methane production can be achieved. This provides therefore, a higher correlation for the hydraulic reactor than the plugflow.

Of great value in this type of data collection and usage is to note that in both Figures 2 and 3, the gradients of the regression lines for the plugflow digester are greater than those observed for the hydraulic digester. The difference between the specific methane production rates determined may reflect differences in the composition of the methanogen communities in the two digesters. It has been demonstrated that significant differences exist between the Coenzyme F_{420} levels of different methanogen strains, (Van Beelen et al. 1983: Eirich et al. 1979). It may also be possible that, due to the lower hydraulic retention time at which the hydraulic digester was operated, compared with the other digesters, the net specific growth rate of the hydraulic digester methanogens was comparatively higher, thus increasing the levels of Coenzymes and resulting in a lower specific methane production rate. The work of Pause and Switzenbaum (1984) has also demonstrated decreasing Q_{CH4} F_{420} values with decreasing retention times in laboratory-scale CSTR digesters. Thus, if F_{420} could be measured on a more automated basis, with feedback loops to feeding and mixing systems, this could be of import in controlling some digestion systems, especially for the treatment of soluble wastes. The higher the loading the less specific the gas yield will be produced and the higher the stress on the system.

One potential problem in the use of the estimation of F_{420} has been its inability to detect some inhibitory effects since inhibition has been shown to coincide with high levels of Coenzyme F_{420} (Pause and Switzenbaum, 1984). Further investigation is necessary to fully quantify the significance of this assay to the operation and performance of anaerobic digesters, but the potential has been demonstrated and may even be made to be highly sophisticated. The performance characteristics exhibited by a digester therefore are influenced by a combination of the microbial population and engineering design.

With the advent of reliable and sophisticated microprocessor control our attention is now turned to an improvement in measuring the parameters which will provide a more sensitive approach to improving the efficiency of anaerobic digester performance. Such systems being developed for the future include the measurement of methane and hydrogen in solution within anaerobic digesters using mass spectometry and the measurement of biochemical parameters specific to those microbes generating biogas from waste with digesters.

CONCLUSIONS

Although the foregoing are still to be fully automated and proved to have practical value, future digester systems will require to be monitored and controlled automatically to optimize performance. This will be shown to be cost effective in terms of early warnings of digester malfunction due to inhibitions, overloading, pH, and temperature changes, and will allow maximum throughput of waste feed within design performance parameters.

The future application of F_{420}, ATP and methane in solution sensors, when developed commercially, can be easily applied to the computer control system with appropriate readouts and feedback data.

Such a system, using more conventional measuring systems, has been designed by CLEAR Ltd. and has now been put into operation at a number of digester installations. The Microcomputer Control facility enables not only 'on-site' monitoring, but remote monitoring and hardware control. The parameters used for measurement are not only the more conventional ones of temperature, pH, biogas flow rate and methane percent, but also of the energy generation systems and pumping mechanisms.

It is now possible that with the received data processed and displayed that the integration of predetermined parameters will allow a more sensitive control of digester systems. Thus, for example, computing the rate of change in gas flow rates and methane percent will allow a more accurate control of preset feed rates. These rates of change in gas production can also be related to changes in F_{420} concentration, pH and possibly temperature with preset override patterns. In this way, full feed control will be possible and linked with diversion of feed should the conditions as measured prove this to be necessary.

With the application of much more sensitive biosensing systems, such as the measurement of hydrogen and/or methane in solution or even F_{420}, a new type of digester control will be available to those providing units to optimise the treatment of organic wastes.

To summarise therefore, the benefits developed:-

1.   Old control systems were both inefficient and were slow to react and thus were unable to monitor crucial parameters.

2.   Computerised systems using microcomputers can now monitor sensitively the performance data from treatment plants. This allows the operator to make intelligent decisions.

3.   The systems may be further developed which will enable the microprocessor to make internal intelligent decisions derived from data trends.

4.   Systems based upon biochemical indicators are already available and, together with others being made available shortly, will be used to monitor and control the performance of biological treatment systems.

REFERENCES

1. CURDS, C.R.: (1973) A theoretical study of factors influencing the microbial population dynamics of the activated sludge process In: A Computer Simulation Study to Compare Two Methods of Plant Operation. Water Research 7:1439.

2. EIRICH, L.D., VOGELS, G.D. and WOLFE, R.S.: (1979). Distribution of Coenzyme F_{420} and properties of its hydrolytic fragments. J. Bacteriology Vol. 140: 20-27

3. JOHNSON, I.R., and STAFFORD, D.A.: (1984). Control of the activated sludge process using adenosine triphosphate measurements. In: Microbiological Methods for Environmental Biotechnology. Eds. J.M. Grainger & I.M. Lynch. Academic Press p.183.

4. PAUSE, S.M. and SWITZENBAUM, M.S.: (1984). Investigation of the use of fluorescence to monitor activity in anaerobic treatment systems. J. Biotechnology Letters Vol. 6: 77-80.

5. STAFFORD, D.A. and ETHERIDGE, S.P.: (1983). The anaerobic digestion of industrial wastes, farm waste and sewage sludges: An assessment of design types and performances. In: Effluent in the Treatment Process Industries. I. Chem. E. Symp. Series, No. 77: 141.

6. VAN BEELAN, P., DIJKSTRA, A.C. and VOGELS, G.D.: (1983). Quantitation of Coenzyme F_{420} in methanogenic sludge by the use of reversed-phase, high-performance liquid chromatography and a fluorescence detector.

7. WHITMORE, T.N., ETHERIDGE, S.P., STAFFORD, D.A., LEROFF, U.E.A. and HUGHES, D.A.: (1985). The evaluation of anaerobic digester performance by coenzyme F_{420} analysis. J. BIOMASS (In Press).

FIGURE 1

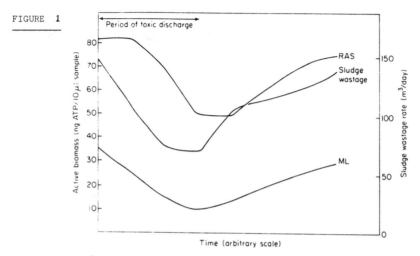

Representation of effect of toxic discharge to sewage input on mixed-liquor (ML_4) and returned activated-sludge (RAS) active biomass and their influence on control of sludge wastage rate.

FIGURE 2

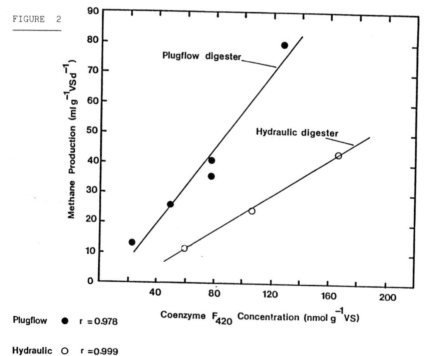

Plugflow ● r = 0.978

Hydraulic ○ r = 0.999

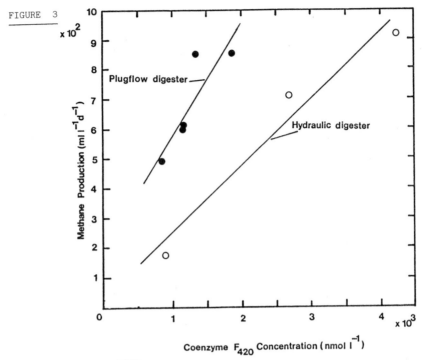

FIGURE 3

Plugflow   ●   r = 0.874

Hydraulic   ○   r = 0.978

AEROBIC THERMOPHILIC HYGIENIZATION - A SUPPLEMENT

TO ANAEROBIC MESOPHILIC WASTE SLUDGE DIGESTION.

G. Hamer* and H.P. Zwiefelhofer**

The concept of incorporating an aerobic thermophilic treatment step, as a means of effective
hygienization, for the treatment of waste sewage
sludge is discussed. The complexity of waste sludge
as a feedstock for treatment processes is examined
and a discussion of the process stoichiometry for
the aerobic biodegradation of microbial solids, i.e.,
waste secondary sludge, is provided. Technical-scale
processes for aerobic thermophilic sludge treatment
are discussed. Test results obtained during the
stable operation of a UTB Aerotherm system operating
with a conventional anaerobic mesophilic digestion
system are reported.

INTRODUCTION

Increasingly stringent environmental legislation in most West
European countries has resulted in increased capacity for
municipal sewage and industrial wastewater treatement by combinations of mechanical, biological and physico-chemical process
technology. The major by-product of both mechanical and aerobic
biological treatment processes is waste sludge, a putrefactive,
aqueous suspension of biodegradable, partially biodegradable and
essentially non-biodegradable solids and similarly degradable
dissolved and sorbed matter. Waste sludge presents a serious
disposal problem, particularly in regions remote from the sea,
where frequently the policy for ultimate disposal involves
spreading treated sludge on agricultural land so as to cause
minimum nuisance. Conventional waste sludge treatment technology
involves mesophilic, anaerobic digestion, but such technology is
no longer considered entirely satisfactory for the removal of
either pathogenic organisms or toxic chemicals from sludge.

*   Institute of Aquatic Sciences, Swiss Federal Institute of
    Technology Zürich, Ueberlandstrasse 133, CH-8600 Dübendorf,
    Switzerland.

** UTB Umwelttechnik Buchs AG, CH-9470 Buchs/SG, Switzerland.

Further, the physical characteristics that affect the dewatering of conventionally treated sludges are frequently such as to result in high dewatering process costs, a feature of increasing economic concern.

Thermophilic, anaerobic sludge digestion processes have been proposed as cost effective alternatives to conventional, meso-philic, anaerobic processes, but plants constructed for the latter technology, and comprizing pre-stressed concrete reactors, cannot easily be converted for thermophilic process operation. Most compounds that are biodegradable under aerobic conditions are also biodegradable under anaerobic conditions, usually at markedly different rates, some important pollutants commonly found in waste sewage sludges, including hydrocarbons and some synthetic organic compounds, particularly detergent residues (1), are recalcitrant to anaerobic biodegradation. In view of both this and of the question of recently installed mesophilic, an-aerobic digestment capacity in many treatment plants, the most realistic approach for more effective waste sludge treatment would seem to be the introduction of either pre- or post-treat-ment processes operating in conjunction with conventional in-stalled, anaerobic, mesophilic, waste sludge digestion processes, that enhance treatment effectiveness with respect to the criteria discussed.

In Switzerland an ordinance, issued in revised form by the Fede-ral Government in 1981(2), requires treated sludge that is to be spread on agricultural land to have a count of Enterobacteria-ceae, essentially pathogen indicator bacteria, of less than 100 per gramme of wet treated sludge and no virulent worm eggs. Originally, it was envisaged that such objectives could be most effectively achieved by one of several sludge pasteurization schemes, but, in practise, all schemes, with the exception of pre-pasteurization, failed as supplementary treatment steps, and attention became focused on the hygienization potential of auto-thermal, aerobic, thermophilic biotreatment for waste sludge. The self-heating and hygienization potentials of aerobic composting processes used for solid wastes was widely recognized, but the realization that suspended carbonaceous solids destruction and/or solubilization could be undertaken as effectively under aerobic as under anaerobic conditions was latent. In addition, the heat production capacity for aerobic biodegradation is markedly higher than for complete anaerobic biodegradation of the same carbona-ceous matter, because in the former case energy release is in the form of heat, whilst in the latter case, it is in the form of methane. For either mesophilic anaerobic digestion processes operating in cold climates or for thermophilic anaerobic digestion processes operating under virtually any climatic conditions, a significant part of the methane produced must be used for processes heating.

The question of energy efficiency dominates discussions of treat-ment process economics, and hence, process acceptability. Clear-ly, aerobic processes produce only low-grade heat, that must be deployed for either process heating or, if not required, wasted. On the other hand, anaerobic processes, in producing methane, mixed with carbon dioxide in the approximate ratio 2 : 1, provide a fuel gas of greater general utility, but even so, small parcels or gas, frequently produced at times of non-peak energy demand and of inappropriate quality for injection into gas distribution networks, command only relatively low prices in industralized countries, rather than the premium prices, so often used in economic evaluations of anaerobic digestion processes. In spite of this, methane production remains emotionally attractive, and therefore, has encouraged the concept of combinations of aerobic and anaerobic technologies(3), rather than processes that seek complete sludge treatment under aerobic conditions alone.

SLUDGE TREATMENT PROCESS FEEDSTOCKS

Waste sludge produced from primary mechanical and secondary biological sewage and wastewater treatment processes is a highly complex and variable process feedstock. Its main fractions are:

(i)   Non-biodegradable solids;

(ii)   Biodegradable solids of microbial origin;

(iii)   Biodegradable solids of non-microbial origin;

(iv)   Soluble biodegradable compounds;

(v)   Soluble non-biodegradable compounds;

(vi)   Immiscible biodegradable compounds;

(vii)   Immiscible non-biodegradable compounds;

(viii) Sorbed biodegradable compounds;

(ix)   Sorbed non-biodegradable compounds.

Clearly, both the mode and the kinetics of biodegradation of these several biodegradable fractions varies, and obviously, this must be taken into account when developing realistic process descriptions.

Non-biodegradable matter, irrespective of its physical state is not, by definition, biodegradable. However, such matter can be modified during digestion processes as a result of mechanical effects, physico-chemical effects such as the pH of the aqueous phase and, probably, most importantly, as a result of either complete and partial biodegradation of sorbed compounds, such that the surface properties of non-biodegradable solids are

significantly modified and the resultant behaviour of the
residual solids suspension, after treatment, is markedly
different and may facilitate dewatering.

Biodegradable, microbial solids include pathogenic microbes present in the original sewage or wastewater, and non-pathogenic
microbes, both similarly present and produced, in large quantities, during secondary biotreatment processes. In spite of the
fact that the destruction of pathogenic microbes, i.e., hygienization is a primary objective of sewage, wastewater and sludge
treatment processes, the elucidation of mechanisms involved in
microbial cell destruction have received only cursory study.
However, two mechanisms by which microbial cells lyse, autolysis,
a process involving the actions of endo-enzymes of the cell
undergoing lysis, and exo-enzyme lysis, brought about by enzymes
excreted by other microbes present in the process environment,
have been identified. Even so, the question whether death either
preceeds or is coincident with cell lysis remains a matter for
conjecture. Recent evidence(4), suggests that the latter is
probably the case in those environments where the cells do not
become "fixed" as they probably do when subjected to temperatures
greater than $100^{o}C$ in sterilization processes.

A wide and variable range of biodegradable solids of non-microbial origin are encountered in waste sludge. Amongst these,
cellulose, in its various froms, predominates. Relative to other
solid substrates, the microbial degradation of cellulose has been
widely studied, but in spite of the effort expended, hypotheses,
rather than clear elucidation of the mechanisms and kinetics of
the process still predominate.

The most plausible hypothesis for microbial growth on and
degradation of cellulose is the shrinking-site model(5,6,7),
which is based on the apparent mode of attack on cellulose by a
thermophilic Thermomonospora sp. The essential logic of the model
is that cellulose is first converted into cellobiose by the
synergistic action of an endo-gluconase/exo-cellobiosylhydrolase
enzyme complex, which is inhibited by cellobiose. The cellobiose
is then converted into glucose by a cellobiase, which is inhibited by glucose. The glucose is then utilized for growth by the
microbial cells in accordance with Monod kinetics and the enzymes
required for the previous steps are produced as growth associated
products, although glucose is considered to be a repressor of
both the endo-/exo-enzyme complex and the cellobiase. Further,
the model assumes, that attack on crystalline cellulose occurs at
projections, edges and dislocations (active sites), that the
cellulose particles are essentially spherical and that for the
enzymic degradation to proceed, it is necessary for the enzymes
to adsorb, in accordance with a Langmuir adsorption isotherm
relationship, at the active sites. The assumption of spherical
shape leads to a cellulose degradation rate that is related to
concentration to the 4/3 power. Close substrate-microbe contact
is also a feature that might be difficult to sustain in vigorously mixed bioreactors. Such a model indicates that the com-

plete degradation of cellulose is likely to be an inordinately long process such that in any continuous-flow process discharge there will always be some non-degraded cellulose when realistic residence times are employed. However, it should also be noted that cellulose is a natural, non-noxious compound and when treated sludge is spread on agricultural land, any cellulose present will decay slowly and without significant adverse effects.

The microbial degradation of soluble carbonaceous compounds, the concentration of which will be relatively low in waste sludges, can be realistically described by Monod type kinetics, modified if necessary, to take account of either substrate or product inhibition.

Water immiscible carbonaceous compounds were widely studied as feedstocks for commercial fermentation processes prior to 1973(8). Several hypotheses, primarily concerned with the rôle of microbially produced emulsifying agents, for microbial hydrocarbon degradation, have been postulated, but essentially such hypotheses apply to cultures of microbial mono-species. In multi-species process environments any emulsifying agents produced might be rapidly degraded by components of the wide spectrum of micro-flora present. Before proceeding, it is important to comment briefly on why biodegradable hydrocarbons are found in waste sludge, when one might assume that they should have been degraded during secondary biotreatment. In spite of the fact that discharge into sewers is not an acceptable means of oil disposal, the practise is, none the less, widespread in many countries. Any oil present in either sewage or wastewater can be present as dispersed droplets, films or sorbed onto particulate matter, depending on characteristics governing phase distribution. During sewage and/or wastewater treatment oil will be removed either by skimming or, if sorbed onto solids, by sedimentation. Both sedimented solids and skimmed material form primary sludge, which is a major fraction of the total waste sludge produced.

Just as with particulate substrates, hydrocarbons present to those microbes that are able to degrade them, the problem of multi-phase substrate transfer. Although microbes grow at hydrocarbon/water interfaces, they do not grow strictly submerged in hydrocarbons, and for immiscible hydrocarbon biodegradation, the main question concerning substrate uptake is whether the microbes obtain their substrate directly from the hydrocarbon/water interface or from trace concentrations of hydrocarbon dissolved in the aqueous phase, a question that still remains unresolved.

The final biodegradable fraction, i.e., sorbed biodegradable compounds, represents a physical situation that has yet to be examined either from the point of view of hypothesis development or experimentally, in spite of the importance of sorbed substrates in virtually all natural and technical process environments.

SLUDGE HYGIENIZATION

Sludge hygienization requires the death, destruction or permanent deactivation of both the pathogenic organisms and those organisms that are considered to be indicative of faecal contamination present in the sludge. Because the survival of a single viable microbe can, at least theoretically, result in reinfection, microbial death rate data are expressed in terms of microbial numbers rather than in terms of dry weight. Most data concerning microbial death are based on plate-count techniques and, at best, are indicators of viability rather than latent activity. The death (loss of viability) of vegetative microbes, at any given temperature, is usually described by a first order rate expression. The specific death rate constants in such expressions are species and strain dependent and are also functions of both temperature and prior treatment conditions. Few data exist concerning the death of mesophilic microbes, i.e., those microbes with temperature optima for their growth in the range 15-40°C, at temperatures within the optimum range for thermophilic growth, i.e., 50-70°C. However, thermal death data for Escherichia coli, the well known faecal contamination indicator bacterium, is an exception and Aiba et al.(9) have shown that, for E. coli, the effect of temperature on the specific death rate constant is described by the Arrhenius equation, i.e., a linear relationship exists between the logarithm of the rate constant and the reciprocal of the absolute temperature, such that the specific death rate constant increases some 150 fold between 54°C and 62°C. More recent data for E. coli(10) suggest that this might be an underestimate. Specific death rate data for mesophilic bacteria at temperatures within the thermophilic growth range should not be extrapolated below 50°C, because Hedén and Wyckoff(15) have shown that E. coli exhibits a transition from reversible to irreversible heat damage at 50°C.

BIO-OXIDATION PROCESS STOICHIOMETRY

The stoichiometry of bio-oxidation processes is of overriding importance, particularly when heat production for autothermal process heating is a key process operating criterion. When biodegradable matter (substrate) is aerobically degraded by microbes, in the presence of all other nutrients essential for the aerobic growth of the microbes, a fraction of the biodegradable matter is converted into carbon dioxide and the energy generated is used by the microbes performing the oxidation to fix a further fraction of the substrate carbon to form additional microbial biomass. Depending on both the nature of the original substrate and oxygen availability, biodegradable and/or non-biodegradable products can also be produced together with a corresponding production of energy for fixation of substrate carbon into microbial biomass. In addition to the energy requirements for growth, there is also a small energy requirement for maintenance.

Mixed culture systems are obviously more complex, in every
respect, than are mono-cultures of individual microbial species,
but for effective sludge treatment the former systems are clearly
both more versatile and more efficient. Both aerobic and facultative anaerobic microbes function effectively in aerobic process
environments and in such process environments excess oxygen
availability frequently results in complete oxidation, with
predominantly microbial biomass and carbon dioxide production,
whilst oxygen limited growth conditions frequently result in
significant levels of soluble product formation.

Microbial growth substrates can be classified as either energy-
excess or energy-deficit substrates(12). Hydrocarbons and
alcohols are in the former category, whilst carbohydrates and
organic acids are in the latter. A perfect substrate is one that
is energy-balanced and the most obvious example of this is
"cryptic" growth, where microbes are utilizing other microbes as
their carbon ensubstrate, a process that must be optimized for
effective sludge treatment.

The microbial biomass yield coefficient is defined as the weight
of dry biomass produced from unit weight of carbon energy substrate. Analogous definitions exist for both the production of
microbial biomass from other nutrients and for the production of
growth associated extracellular products. Yield coefficients
depend on process operating conditions, and therefore, are not
constants. Optimization of process operating conditions allows
either maximization or minimization of yield coefficients as
required, particularly in the cases of either potentially
inhibitory carbon energy substrates(13) or aerobic processes
involving facultative anaerobes as process microbes(14). Most
yield coefficient data quoted refer to the growth of microbial
monocultures on essentially pure carbonaceous compounds under
conditions designed to maximize the biomass yield coefficient. In
contrast, sludge treatment processes involve the growth of
complex mixed microbial cultures on ill-defined mixtures of
carbonaceous compounds, as discussed previously, under process
conditions designed to minimize the biomass yield coefficient.
For realistic process design, it is essential to be able to
predict biomass, carbon dioxide, soluble product and heat
production, on the one hand, and oxygen requirements, on the
other. The basis for this is the establishment of appropriate
equations that describe the overall biodegradation process.

Empirical formulae have been determined for microbial biomass
produced by various microbes under various process conditions.
For aerobic bacteria grown at high growth rates the typical formula on an ash and moisture free basis, is $CH_{1.8}O_{0.43}N_{0.23}$(15).
The ash content of this dry biomass is approximately 6.4 percent.
Obviously primary and secondary waste sludges will have different
empirical formulae and the composition of mixed waste sludge will
obviously depend both on the relative amounts and the individual
composition of the individual waste sludges. Activated sludge
(secondary sludge) is reported to have the empirical formula

$CH_{1.4}O_{0.4}N_{0.2}$ (16), on an ash and moisture free basis. By using these empirical formulae an equation describing the aerobic biodegradation of waste activated sludge can, assuming no nitrification, be proposed, i.e.,

$$C\ H_{1.4}O_{0.4}N_{0.2} + a\ (O_2) \longrightarrow b\ (C\ H_{1.8}O_{0.43}N_{0.23})$$
$$+ c\ (CO_2) + d\ (H_2O) + e(NH_3) + f(C_nH_{2n+1}COOH)$$

where the numerical values of the variables a,b,c,d,e and f depend on the yield coefficient for biomass production from sludge and on whether the carbon not incorporated into biomass is completely oxidized to carbon dioxide or only partially oxidized to form in addition low molecular weight carboxylic acids.

For the complete oxidation of carbon energy substrates to form microbial biomass and carbon dioxide, Linton and Stephenson(17) have established a correlation between the maximum attainable microbial biomass yield coefficient and the heat of cumbustion of the carbon energy substrate. Using this correlation, the maximum biomass yield coefficient for microbial growth on waste activated sludge is 0.67, and for digestion process operation where biomass yield coefficient minimization is sought, can be expected to be as low as 50 percent of the predicted maximum value. If no soluble product (carboxylic acid) formation occurs the value of f in the equation will be zero and for a series of feasible values of the microbial biomass yield coefficient, the values of a, b, c, d and e can be calculated.

PROPOSED PROCESS TECHNOLOGIES

A major objective of all biological fluid phase waste treatment processes is minimization of the microbial biomass yield coefficient. For aerobic processes this automatically results in maximization of heat production. For low concentration waste streams, heat production during aerobic biotreatment is relatively insignificant and the structure of typical wastewater treatment plants, i.e., shallow open aerated basins, optimizes heat losses to the surroundings and equilibration of the process temperature with that of the surroundings. For the aerobic biotreatment of concentrated fluid waste streams such constraints on the process operating temperature need not apply provided the treatment process is undertaken in either high or medium aspect ratio, insulated, enclosed bioreactors under operating conditions where the dispersed air (oxygen) flow to the bioreactor is minimized and the potential for autothermal process heating, and hence, both process rate and hygienization, enhanced.

Aerobic processes for waste sewage sludge treatment have been researched and developed in the USA, Canada, South Africa and several european countries. Aerobic waste sludge treatment was first proposed in the late 1950's(22). Essentially four distinct processing concepts exist;

(i)   Mesophilic   (15-35°C) aerobic digestion;

(ii) Autothermic   (40-50°C) aerobic digestion;

(iii) Thermophilic (50-70°C) aerobic digestion;

(iv) Thermophilic (50-70°C) aerobic hygienization/

mesophilic   (30-40°C) anaerobic digestion.

Mesophilic aerobic digestion processes for complete sludge treatment are essentially extensions of conventional activated sludge type treatment technology for high concentration waste streams and the operating temperatures employed in such processes are unlikely to result in any thermal hygienization effects with respect to either pathogenic organisms or pathogen indicator bacteria. From the point of view of process effectiveness they are unlikely to be markedly superior to optimized, high rate mesophilic anaerobic digestion processes other than for the destruction of hydrocarbons and certain hydrocarbon derivateives that are anaerobically recalcitrant, but aerobically biodegradable.

Autothermic aerobic digestion processes are proposed either as complete treatment systems or as a second stage where mesophilic aerobic digestion is used as the first stage in two-stage operation. However, such processes do not function in the true thermophilic process temperature range; process microbes effective in the range 40-50°C exhibit thermotolerant rather than thermophilic characteristics. As far as pathogenic organisms are concerned, process operating temperatures between 40 and 45°C cannot be expected to result in markedly enhanced destruction levels, whilst between 45 and 50° C, predominantly reversible damage of pathogens, with possibilities of subsequent recovery and resultant reinfection, can be predicted.

Thermophilic operation requires process microbes that are genuine thermophiles, i.e., microbes with growth optima in the range 50-70°C. The diversity of such microbes present in waste sewage sludge subjected to thermophilic aerobic treatment has been investigated by Grueninger et al.(19). However, as far as aerobic thermophilic sludge treatment processes are concerned, caldoactive microbes, i.e., microbes with temperature optima for growth above 70°C, should be avoided because of their fastidiousness. For sludge treatment thermophilic processes to be attractive, with respect to energy input, they must be operated in an autothermic mode and provided with heat exchange between the processed sludge and the feed sludge. Such processes have been discussed by Pöpel and Ohnmacht(20), Kambhu and Andrews(21), Smith et al.(22), Jewell et al. (23) and Wolinski and Bruce(24). All processes operate at temperatures above 55°C and below 70°C, with one exception(23) where the operating temperature range used was 45-65°C. Simultaneous hygienization and stabilization are the objectives of aerobic thermophilic sludge treatment processes. However, the residence time required for these two distinct processes in a continuous flow process plant will be markedly different. Effective hygienization can be predicted to be achieved within hours, whilst stabilization of biodegradable sludge solids requires process residence times of several days. This discrepancy was recognized by Zwiefelhofer(25) who described a full-scale operating process combining aerobic thermophilic hygienization with subsequent anaerobic mesophilic digestion (stabilization) and by Keller and Berninger(45), who described pilot plant-scale investigations employing essentially the same concept.

Combined thermophilic aerobic hygienization/mesophilic anaerobic stabilization processes offer very considerable potential for effective and economic waste sewage sludge treatment. In view of the fact that very considerable installed mesophilic anaerobic digestion process capacity, that produces non-hygienized sludge, exists, it is appropriate to think in terms of installing a relatively short residence time thermophilic aerobic hygieniz-ation/pre-treatment processing stage to operate in conjunction so that the combined process produces an effectively hygienized sludge for ultimate disposal. One such pre-treatment process that has been installed at several sewage works in Switzerland and Austria is the UTB Aerotherm system. Several such processes have been in successful, essentially stable operation for several years and process data for a system installed at the community sewage treatment plant at Unterterzen/SG, Switzerland are reported below.

UTB AEROTHERM SYSTEM

The UTB Aerotherm system is a genuine thermophilic aerobic autothermal pretreatment process. A schematic diagram of the process is given in Figure 1. The essentials of the process, as installed at Unterterzen/SG, are a two compartment raw sludge heating tank where heat is transferred from the hot aerobically hygienized sludge to the cold raw sludge, operated in an inter-mittent mode, such that each batch of raw sludge is retained for a fixed time interval of 0.5 h in the tank and then transferred as a batch to the aerobic bioreactor, where thermophilic treat-ment occurs. The residence time of the sludge in the bioreactor can be varied between 0.75 and 2.5 d. At short residence times additional heat is sometimes required. The hygienized, but still unstabilized sludge is intermittently removed from the bioreactor and passes to the raw sludge heating tank where it is held for 0.5 h so that temperature equilibration occurs between the two sludge streams, but direct contact between streams is avoided. The feed of cold raw sludge is obtained from a prethickener and

macerated or sieved prior to pre-heating. After post-hygieniz-
ation cooling the sludge passes to a mesophilic anaerobic
digestor of a conventional design and with a residence time of
between 12 and 20 d, where digestion occurs. The stabilized
sludge then passes to a sludge storage tank, often the original
second stage of the conventional anaerobic digestion process,
where sludge thickening occurs prior to collection for ultimate
disposal. The aerobic bioreactor is agitated and aerated by
pumping the sludge undergoing treatment through an external
venture type injector. The aeration capacity of the injector is
such that oxygen limited conditions occur in the bioreactor.
Because of possible foam formation, a mechanical foam breaker is
fitted on the gas outlet of the bioreactor. Under the selected
operating conditions, the insulated aerobic bioreactor can be
maintained at operating temperatures $> 60^{\circ}$C. As far as effective
hygienization is concerned, the semi-batch operating mode of the
sludge pre-heating/post-cooling tank eliminates the possibility
of pathogen containing sludge bypassing effective hygienization
as could occur if sludge preheating was operated in a short
residence time continuous flow system.

The Unterterzen/SG sewage works receives a wastewater equivalent
of 2500 inhabitants and produces ca. $5m^3 d^{-1}$ waste sludge
containing 4-5% dry solids. For sludge treatment, the works was
originally provided with a conventional mesophilic digestion
facility, which because of prevailing climatic conditions, frequently operated in either the lower mesophilic or even the upper
psychrophilic temperature ranges and produced a sludge for
disposal that was, according to the quality standards prescribed
by Swiss law, neither effectively stabilized nor hygienized. In
order to satisfy legal requirements, the sludge treatment facility was fitted by integrating into the existing facility an UTB
Aerotherm system for raw sludge conditioning and hygienization.
Parallel with this, a rationalized energy programme was introduced and the modified system was commissioned in autumn 1983 and
effective process operation has been maintained for over two
years. Effective operation is defined as:

(i)   The production of safe, legally satisfactory, hygienized
        sludge by the UTB-Aerotherm system with heat
        requirements being met by heat produced from exothermic
        biooxidation reactions;

(ii)   The heat requirements for the mesophilic anaerobic
        digestor are met by heat production by the UTB Aerotherm
        system;

(iii)   The resultant treated sludge from the overall process is
        aesthetically unobjectionable, i.e., practically
        odourless and stable;

(iv)   A treated sludge dry solids content of 12% is achieved
        by gravity thickening.

(v)   A treated sludge that is entirely acceptable to farmers.

To evaluate process performance, laboratory tests were undertaken on samples from the plant during a three week period in June and July, 1984, and the results are reported. In these tests, chemical, physical and bacteriological parameters were assessed for sludge samples from the prethickener, the aerobic bioreactor outlet, the anaerobic digestor outlet and from both the supernatent liquid and thickened solid zones in the sludge storage tank. Additionally, outlet gas samples were taken from both the aerobic bioreactor and the anaerobic digestor for gas analysis. The sludge/liquid samples were analysed with respect to their pH, total suspended solids (TSS), volatile suspended solids (VSS), dissolved organic carbon (DOC), the carbon : nitrogen ratio of the TSS (C : N), volatile carboxylic acids and Enterobacteriaceae count. The temperature of each sample was measured at the time of sampling. Sludge/liquid samples were taken through valves, with the exception of those from the prethickener and the storage tank where a scoop and a sediment sampler were used, respectively. During the test period 4-5 m^2 d^{-1} of raw sludge were subjected to treatment and the average residence time in the aerobic bioreactor was 55 h. The results obtained are given in Tables 1-7.

DISCUSSION

The discussion of the results for the individual process units will be handled separately. However, it should first be clearly understood that direct comparisons between the results for samples from different process units should be avoided because of variability in raw sludge characteristics and the relatively extended residence times employed, particularly in the anaerobic digestor and the treated sludge storage tank.

For samples from the prethickener, the TSS values were variable as would have been expected. The VSS was relatively constant at ca. 50-60% of TSS. The DOC was significant at ca. 1 g l^{-1} and the carboxylic acid content suggested that anaerobiosis was occurring in the prethickener. The ratios of the various carboxylic acids, particularly acetate : propionate, remained essentially constant.

In the aerobic bioreactor outlet sample, the TSS were variable, but VSS : TSS remained relatively constant. TSS and VSS hardly varied from the values for raw sludge, suggesting that any expected increase due to evaporation of water at ca. $70^{o}C$ was counteracted by solids hydrolysis, which was clearly indicated by a doubling of DOC. Interestingly, the spectrum of carboxylic acids present changed, with branched chain acids becoming more prominent. The Enterobacteriaceae count was zero throughout, clearly demonstrating effective hygienization. The C : N varied little from the C : N in the raw sludge Insufficient gas samples were analysied, but oxygen conversion seemed, for two samples, to be very high and for a completely mixed bioreactor would suggest oxygen limitation. The traces of methane in the outlet gas can be explained as being stripped from the feed in which prior anaerobiosis occurred. Worm eggs were not tested for during this investigation, but a retention time of 55 h at $>60^{\circ}$C should result in complete deactivation.

As would have been expected, a significant reduction in VSS and DOC occurred as a result of mesophilic anaerobic digestion and only low residual concentrations of volatile carboxylic acids were detected. Therefore, the operation of this process step was entirely satisfactory.

For the treated sludge storage tank, a serious problem concerning representative sampling, occurred. However, this was solved by using a sediment sampler. Once effective sampling was established, a mean TSS concentration of 160 g l^{-1} was found for the thickened treated sludge, clearly implying effective operation. Constant DOC and percentage VSS indicate virtually no biological activity in the storage tank. The almost complete elimination of volatile carboxylic acids resulted in an essentially odourless treated sludge. The Enterobacteriaceae count remained below the legally permissible level for all but one sample. The relatively wide variation in the counts results from the inhomogeneous nature and high solids content of the sludge. The probable source of Enterobacteriaceae contamination in the storage tank was from non-hygienized sludge present in the tank at the time of process start-up in the previous autumn. The low TSS content of the supernatent liquid further emphasized the good settling properties of the treated sludge.

Comparison between C : N and TSS concentrations showed that the anaerobic digestion step reduced the suspended organic carbon content of the sludge by only 30% and clearly indicated the significance of the residual, non-biodegradable, carbonaceous components in waste sewage sludges.

ACKNOWLEDGEMENTS

Sampling and analyses were carried out by Ms. R. Arnold, Ms A. de Paolis, Mr. Th. Fleischmann, Dr. H. Leidner and Dr. Kl. Mechsner of EAWAG under contract number 20-4698.

REFERENCES

1. Giger, W., Brunner, P.H., and Schaffner, C., 1984, Science, 225, 623.

2. Bundesamt f. Umweltschutz, 1981, Klärschlammverordnung, 20 pp., Bern.

3. Zwiefelhofer, H.P., 1985, Conservation and Recycling, 8, 285.

4. Mason, C.A., Bryers, J.D., and Hamer, G., 1985, Chem. Engng. Commun, (in press).

5. Humphrey, A.E., Moreira, A., Armiger, W., and Zabriskie, D., 1977, Biotechnol. Bioengng. Symp., 7, 45.

6. Humphrey, A.E., Armiger, W.B., Zabriskie, D.W., Lee, S.E., Moreira, A., and Joly, G., 1976, Proc. 6th Internatl. Continuous Culture Symp., 85.

7. Moreira, A.R., Phillips, J.A., and Humphrey, A.E., 1981, Biotechnol. Bioengng., 23, 1325.

8. Hamer, G., and Hamdan, I.Y., 1979, Chem. Soc. Revs., 8, 143.

9. Aiba, S., Humphrey, A.E., and Millis, N.F., 1965, Biochemical Engineering, 333 pp. Academic Press, Inc., New York.

10. Reichart, O., 1979, Acta Alimentaria, 8, 131.

11. Hedén, C.-G., and Wyckoff, R.W.G., 1949, J. Bacteriol. 58, 153.

12. Babel, W., and Müller, R.H., 1985, J. Gen. Microbiol., 131, 39.

13. Harrison, D.E.F., Hamer, G., and Topiwala, H.H., 1972, Proc. 4th Internatl. Symp. Kyoto, 491.

14. Harrison, D.E.F. and Loveless, J.E., 1971, J. Gen. Microbiol. 68, 45.

15. Hamer, G., and Harrison, D.E.F., 1980, in Hydrocarbons in Biotechnology, (eds. D.E.F. Harrison, I.J. Higgins, R. Watkinson), 59, Heyden & Sons Ltd. London.

16. Hoover, S.R., and Porges, N., 1952, Sewage and Industr. Wastes., 24, 306.

17. Linton, J.R., and Stephenson, R.J., 1978, FEMS Microbiol. Lett., 3, 95.

18. Husmann, W., and Malz, F., 1959, GWF-Wasser/Abwasser, 100, 189.

19. Grueninger, H., Sonnleitner, B., and Fiechter, A., 1984, Appl. Microbiol. Biotechnol., 19, 414.

20. Pöpel, F., and Ohnmacht, Ch., 1972, Water Res., 6, 807.

21. Kambuhu, K., and Andrews, J.F., 1969, J. Water Poll. Control. Fed., 41, R127.

22. Smith, J.E., Young, K.W., and Dean, R.B., 1975, Water Res., 9, 17.

23. Jewell, W.J., Kabrick, R.M., and Spada, J.A., 1982, EPA Project Summary, EPA-600/S2-82-023, 5pp.

24. Wolinski, W.K., and Bruce, A.M., 1984, Paper at EWPCA Symp., Munich.

25. Zwiefelhofer, H.P., 1983, Phoenix Internatl., 2, 1.

26. Keller, U., and Berninger, I., 1984, Gas-Wasser-Abwasser, 64, 215.

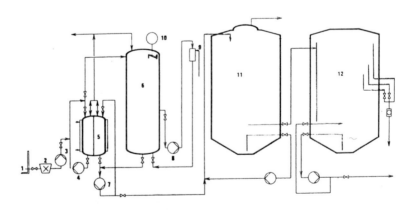

Figure 1. Layout of an UTB Aerobic-Thermophilic/Anaerobic-Mesophilic Sludge Treatment Plant (1 - Pre-thickening Tank, 2 - Macerator, 3 - Cold Sludge Pump, 4 - Warm Sludge Pump, 5 - Sludge Pre-heating Tank, 6 - Aerobic Reactor, 7 - Hot Sludge Pump, 8 - Reactor Circulation Pump, 9 - Aerator, 10 - Foam Breaker, 11 - Anaerobic Digestor, 12 - Sludge Storage Tank)

Date 1984	Temp °C	pH	TSS g l^{-1}	VSS g l^{-1}	VSS %	DOC mg l^{-1}	Carboxylic Acids mg l^{-1}						
							Ac	Pr	i-But	n-But	2-Mebut	i-Val	n-Val
14.6.	13	5.9	44.4	28.9	65.1	945	797.9	389.9	49.7	206.9	41.9	44.6	30.9
18.6.	14	7.1	51.1	27.4	53.6	900	890.0	400.8	48.6	184.5	40.0	45.8	32.5
19.6.	14	6.9	38.3	23.5	61.4	960	913.1	415.8	50.7	181.3	42.2	50.4	33.7
20.6.	14	6.9	36.5	22.2	60.8	1065	1080.6	498.2	60.3	215.1	50.3	59.9	37.9
22.6.	14	6.8	47.0	25.9	55.1	1035	915.6	437.5	59.8	165.9	48.9	64.2	30.6
25.6.	14	6.7	71.6	37.9	52.9	1005	1007.0	554.8	50.2	214.7	36.7	41.1	34.8
26.6.	13	6.5	48.9	25.6	57.4	1040	1106.2	615.3	62.4	234.6	48.4	67.7	38.9
27.6.	14	6.3	64.4	29.6	46.0	1245	1094.5	605.6	59.1	232.0	46.1	64.8	35.1
29.6.	13	6.7	68.1	33.2	48.7	750	749.8	408.8	36.3	134.4	24.9	34.5	18.0
2.7.	14	6.8	64.4	33.4	51.8	945	859.5	475.5	40.6	179.8	30.7	37.3	22.4
3.7.	13	6.9	64.2	35.6	55.5	1110	916.9	509.8	51.7	204.8	40.2	55.0	31.0
4.7.	13	7.0	47.5	21.9	46.1	960	838.6	472.7	44.0	209.2	29.1	36.4	25.8
6.7.	13	7.0	43.6	25.0	57.3	ND	323.7	198.2	43.8	294.4	40.4	18.1	25.9

Table 1. Results of Analyses of the Pre-thickener Samples and Operating Data (TSS - total suspended solids, VSS - volatile suspended solids, DOC - dissolved organic carbon, AC - acetic acid, Pr - propionic acid, i-but - iso-butyric acid, n-But - normal butyric acid, 2-Mebut - 2-methyl butyric acid, i-Val - iso-valeric acid, n-Val - normal valeric acid).

Date 1984	Temp °C	pH	TSS g l^{-1}	VSS g l^{-1}	VSS %	DOC mg l^{-1}	Carboxylic Acids mg l^{-1}						
							Ac	Pr	i-But	n-But	2-Mebut	i-Val	n-Val
14.6.	73	7.5	35.1	23.5	66.9	2220	590.6	55.2	180.7	8.0	250.1	309.9	28.9
18.6.	72	8.1	42.8	22.7	53.0	1830	921.1	48.9	128.2	10.2	164.3	227.0	14.4
19.6.	71	7.9	44.6	26.1	58.5	1980	89.4	23.9	113.5	1.9	187.3	325.2	19.6
20.6.	72	8.5	39.6	23.9	60.4	1920	599.7	61.2	111.1	18.5	179.0	301.7	10.4
22.6.	66	8.2	31.9	18.1	56.7	1920	710.4	52.1	166.0	41.9	178.5	282.5	23.6
25.6.	72	7.6	36.3	20.8	57.3	1960	1111.1	140.2	224.1	16.5	228.4	412.9	24.3
27.6.	72	7.3	50.7	26.4	52.0	1920	355.0	34.0	236.7	45.4	203.5	433.8	34.9
29.6.	70	7.0	60.3	28.6	47.4	2220	469.8	48.5	189.6	19.1	204.4	413.8	27.0
1.7.	70	7.1	56.0	26.1	46.6	2085	331.2	32.7	143.8	36.7	178.3	369.1	19.6
2.7.	74	8.1	52.5	26.1	49.7	2640	350.6	38.9	121.6	28.8	172.8	415.5	10.3
3.7.	72	8.1	53.5	26.5	49.5	2310	594.3	47.5	180.3	42.6	170.0	382.8	12.7
4.7.	60	7.7	53.0	24.2	45.6	2535	1712.8	274.9	213.7	65.4	149.4	323.9	22.5
6.7.	64	7.7	37.7	18.0	47.7	ND	715.4	112.5	309.6	ND	230.9	218.7	26.1

Table 2. Results of Analyses of the Aerotherm Samples and Operating Data (abbreviations as in Table 1).

178

Date 1984	Temp °C	pH	TSS g l^{-1}	VSS g l^{-1}	VSS %	CH$_4$ %	N$_2$ %	CO$_2$ %	DOC mg l^{-1}	Ac mg l^{-1}	Pr mg l^{-1}
14.6.	34.5	7.2	38.0	15.7	41.3	63.6	0.5	33.4	345	13.0	0.7
18.6.	36	8.1	37.5	14.1	37.6	63.6	0.1	33.4	315	7.0	ND
19.6.	36	8.0	40.8	17.2	42.1	64.1	0.07	33.6	300	5.9	ND
20.6	37	8.1	51.5	21.7	42.1	63.8	0.08	33.5	300	5.3	ND
22.6.	37	7.8	43.3	16.3	37.6	65.4	0.3	31.6	390	85.5	32.0
25.6.	36	7.1	44.8	17.8	39.7	65.6	0.1	31.6	345	7.2	ND
26.6.	35.5	6.9	48.7	18.7	38.4	66.4	0.09	30.7	325	84.6	39.1
27.6.	35.5	7.0	42.0	13.0	31.0	65.7	0.1	31.4	315	10.3	ND
29.6.	36	7.0	38.1	11.3	29.6	65.4	0.2	31.7	345	25.3	1.9
2.7.	35	7.6	45.4	12.1	26.6	64.3	0.2	31.9	330	18.7	2.7
3.7.	35.5	7.8	48.2	13.5	28.0	ND	ND	ND	345	31.9	8.9
4.7.	36	7.9	43.0	18.1	42.0	67.1	0.4	29.6	390	27.4	1.6
6.7.	35	7.5	53.7	17.5	32.5	64.1	0.2	32.5	ND	7.0	ND

Table 3. Results of Analyses of the Anaerobic Digestor and Operating Data (abbreviations as in Table 1).

Date 1984	Temp °C	pH	TSS g l^{-1}	VSS g l^{-1}	VSS %	DOC mg l^{-1}	Ac mg l^{-1}
14.6.	22	7.2	141.4	57.8	40.8	255	ND
18.6.	24	8.4	ND	ND	ND	300	ND
19.6.	24	8.2	ND	ND	ND	300	ND
20.6.	25	8.3	ND	ND	ND	285	ND
22.6.	23	8.4	ND	ND	ND	315	<10
25.6.	25	7.2	ND	ND	ND	300	<10
26.6.	25	7.0	165.1	72.2	43.7	315	<10
27.6.	23.5	6.8	145.0	57.7	39.8	300	<10
29.6.	23	7.2	144.8	56.2	38.8	315	<10
2.7.	25	7.6	174.2	69.4	39.8	345	<10
3.7.	24.5	7.6	177.8	70.4	39.5	300	<10
4.7.	20.5	7.6	169.5	59.5	35.1	345	<10
6.7.	20	7.3	156.3	61.7	39.4	ND	ND

Table 4. Results of Analyses of the Sludge Storage Tank Settled Solids and Operating Data (abbreviations as in Table 1).

Date 1984	Temp °C	pH	SS g l^{-1}	DOC mg l^{-1}	Ac mg l^{-1}
14.6.	23	7.6	2.53	345	ND
18.6.	24	8.3	2.20	300	ND
19.6.	25	8.3	2.14	270	ND
20.6.	25	8.3	2.25	405	ND
22.6.	24	8.4	2.48	345	<10
25.6.	25	7.2	1.97	325	<10
26.6.	23	7.1	2.04	345	<10
27.6.	25	7.0	2.23	330	<10
29.6.	23	7.2	2.02	330	<10
2.7.	25	7.6	1.76	340	<10
3.7.	24.5	7.6	1.82	315	<10
4.7.	24	8.0	2.29	375	<10
6.7.	24	7.6	2.18	ND	ND

Table 5. Results of Analyses of the Sludge Storage Tank Supernatent (abbreviations as in Table 1).

Sludge Date 1986	Pre-Thickener		Aerotherm		Anaerobic Digestor		Storage Tank	
	% C	% N	% C	% N	% C	% N	% C	% N
20.6.	30.86	3.26	28.83	2.46	18.79	2.09	22.79	3.15
22.6.	30.93	3.61	31.09	3.27	19.64	2.36	20.62	2.60
25.6.	23.97	2.89	30.25	2.40	20.20	2.40	22.47	2.90
26.6.	26.61	2.67	26.46	2.27	18.62	2.26	19.48	2.41
27.6.	23.26	1.91	25.69	2.18	17.89	1.88	19.56	2.43
29.6.	29.63	3.03	27.72	2.88	20.18	2.74	19.24	2.44
2.7.	26.87	3.13	22.36	2.55	19.33	2.49	19.28	2.52
3.7.	24.78	2.92	25.60	2.77	18.43	2.15	19.35	2.51
4.7.	25.44	2.96	24.27	2.06	17.77	2.26	19.40	2.27
6.7.	30.16	4.06	21.27	2.20	17.68	2.12	18.84	2.31

Table 6. Carbon and Nitrogen Analyses of Dry Solids from each Process Stage.

Date 1984	Number of Enterobacteraceae in sludge		
	Aerotherm		Storage Tank
	1 g$^{1)}$	10 g$^{2)}$	1 g$^{2)}$ (triplicates)
18.6.	0	0	60 / 0 / 0
20.6.	0	0	0 / 0 / 0
25.6.	0	0	180 / 160 / 120
27.6.	0	0	40 / 0 / 0
2.7.	0	0	20 / 0 / 0
4.7.	0	0	40 / 60 / 40

Table 7. Enterobacteraceae Counts in Samples from the Aerotherm and the Sludge Storage Tank.

1) Mossels enrichment medium

2) Violet Red Glucose Agar

THE USE OF MODERN LIQUID CHROMATOGRAPHY TECHNIQUES IN THE ANALYSIS OF
AQUEOUS LIQUORS FROM A COAL GASIFICATION PROCESS

L. Anthony*, A.F. Ivens*, R.P. Mounce*

Making gas from high pressure gasification of coal
results in the production of a concentrated aqueous
liquor. Extensive treatment is needed before it
can be discharged or recycled. Characterisation
and quantitative analysis of the liquor is required
so that the efficiency of treatment processes can
be evaluated. This paper describes the liquid
chromatographic methods which have been developed
to analyse quantitatively the phenols, nitrogen
compounds and the ionic species present in the
liquor.

INTRODUCTION

Early next century it is likely that there will be a need to supplement with
substitute natural gas, the supplies of natural gas. Currently extensive
research work is being carried out both worldwide and by British Gas at the
Westfield Development Centre, Scotland, to develop the technology to produce
substitute natural gas from the world's most abundant feedstock, coal.

In the British Gas, Lurgi Gasification Process, coal is gasified at high
temperature and pressure with steam and oxygen, and as a by-product, an
aqueous condensate is produced. Approximately one pound of liquor is
produced for every four pounds of coal gasified. The aqueous liquor cannot
be disposed of or reused in the process without further pretreatment.

The aqueous liquor is condensed from the gas stream together with tar and
oil during gas cooling. The latter components are separated by gravity
settlement and the clean liquor can then be discharged after suitable
treatment. The nature of the treatment processes has been the subject of
considerable research by British Gas and an essential part of that programme
has been to comprehensively characterise liquor, since the process route
used will be dependent upon liquor composition.

In the light of current analytical development techniques and the fact that
the samples were aqueous it seemed logical that liquid chromatography could
play a major role in the analytical schedule to characterise the aqueous
liquor.

This paper describes the role of liquid chromatography in the analysis of

*R&D Division, British Gas Corporation, London Research Station.

aqueous liquor from the slagging gasifier process. Both high performance liquid chromatography for the measurement of organic species and ion chromatography for inorganic constituents are used routinely for this purpose and the methods used are set out in detail.

CHARACTERISATION OF THE AQUEOUS LIQUOR

Background

The major components present fall into the following three groups:-

1) Phenol and associated phenols
2) Organic nitrogen compounds
3) Ionic species

All of these species are amenable to measurement by liquid chromatography, but the complexity of the mixture requires that the methods used be of high selectivity and, in many cases, of extended dynamic range.

Analytical Determination

Phenol and associated phenols

(a) Preliminary study

Since the aqueous liquor is condensed in the presence of tar and oil, organic compounds will tend to partition between the two phases. For this reason the aqueous liquor is preferentially enriched with the more polar phenols whilst more of the less polar species will stay in the tar and oil. Therefore, the phenols of greatest interest were phenol, quinol, resorcinol, catechol, cresols and xylenols. The analytical procedure was developed around these compounds and reversed phase high performance liquid chromatography (HPLC) was the technique successfully developed.

Early work showed that a full analysis could not be carried out using a single column. The presence of large concentrations of inorganic ions together with the complex and wide-ranging nature of the phenols gave rise to poor chromatography, and an unacceptably long analysis. The desire for a simple, cheap, routine method effectively precluded gradient elution and therefore, after a literature search, it was decided to try a combination of two columns, and this became the adopted technique.

(b) Analytical system

General layout

Figure 1 shows the layout of the system diagrammatically. Two Rheodyne 7010 valves were used. The first was for sample injection and was normally fitted with a 20µl sample loop; for the determination of low levels of phenols a 200µl or larger loop may be fitted. The second valve was used for column switching and allows the system to be operated with either the first column only or with both columns in series.

A Kontron 410 pump capable of delivering up to 10 ml min^{-1}, accurately controlled, at pressures up to 300 bar was used. The LKB UV absorbance detector was used with either an LKB twin pen chart recorder (100 mV FSD) or a Hewlett Packard 3390 integrator. All pipework connections were made with stainless steel microbore tubing and low dead-volume compression fittings.

182

Analytical columns

The first column was packed with Partisil 10 ODS (25cm x 0.5cm id). This gave inadequate separation of the more polar phenols but good separation of less polar species in a reasonable time.

The second column was packed with Zorbax ODS (25cm x 0.5cm id) that gave good separation of polar species but was unable to elute less polar species in an acceptable time.

Both columns were essentially the same material, i.e. 15% octadecylsilane on a silica support, but Partisil is 10 microns whilst Zorbax is 5 microns. To protect the columns a precolumn (Whatman Co. Pell ODS) was fitted.

The most suitable property for the detection of phenols is their UV absorbance. In common with many other compounds they display strong absorbance at 206 nm and also show a fairly specific but much weaker absorbance at 280 nm. Measurement at 206 nm thus offers greater sensitivity whilst measurement at 280 nm gives greatest freedom from non-phenolic organic species interference.

A fixed wavelength detector was selected (LKB Uvichord S). This unit is fitted with two alternative light sources; a mercury lamp for absorbance at 254 nm and an iodine lamp for absorbances at 206 and 280 nm. In each case the precise spectral band is isolated by an interference filter. The HPLC cell used has a 2.5mm path length and an 8 µl volume.

Mobile phases

A mobile phase in the range 2.5 to 5.0% methanol in water and using both analytical columns gave a good separation of phenols more polar than phenol itself. 30% methanol in water with only the Partisil column was ideal for a quick and effective separation of phenols less polar than phenol. 1 ml min^{-1} flow rate was suitable for all analyses.

Catechol and alkyl catechols have presented considerable difficulties in separation and detection. Initial attempts not only failed to separate the catechols but failed to even detect them at levels up to 1000 mg l^{-1}. Much higher concentrations of catechol did show some response but the peak shapes were poor with tailing. The presence of phosphoric acid in the mobile phase at a concentration of 0.01% v/v overcame the problem and there have been no corrosive effects. The need to use phosphoric acid to determine catechols has an additional advantage in that an unknown sample can be analysed using a mobile phase with and without the acid. Any differences between the two chromatograms can be explained by the presence of catechol or an alkyl catechol.

Standard Solutions of Phenols

Owing to the different extinction coefficients exhibited by individual phenols it was not possible to use a single standard for calibration. Standard solutions were made up to reflect the components and their concentrations.

(c) Analysis of aqueous liquors

Total analysis for phenols

On the basis of the work previously described a satisfactory means of analysis for gasifier liquors is clearly available using Partisil and Zorbax columns and alternative mobile phases. The precise form of analysis, and thus the time needed to complete it, depends upon the degree of detail required but the two part analysis described below will resolve and quantify most of the phenols encountered in gasifier liquor.

Analysis for polar species (up to and including phenol and the substituted catechols and resorcinols)

Mobile phase	– 5% methanol in water + 0.01% phosphoric acid
Eluent flow rate	– 1.0 ml min^{-1}
Detector wavelength	– 206nm
Columns	– Partisil 10 ODS and Zorbax ODS
Sample preparation	– Filtered and undiluted
Sample volume	– 20 μl

Figure 2 shows a typical chromatogram obtained under these conditions.

Analysis for less polar species

This includes phenol, cresols, xylenols, naphthols and trimethyl phenols.

Mobile phase	– 30% methanol in water
Eluent flow rate	– 1.0 ml min^{-1}
Detector wavelength	206 nm
Column	– Partisil 10 ODS
Sample preparation	– Filtered and diluted 10:1 with water
Sample volume	– 20 μl

Figure 3 shows typical chromatograms of a sample and standard calibration mixture obtained under these conditions. The quick separation used, co-elutes the cresols and ethyl phenols as one peak but individual xylenols are partially resolved. Naphthols and trimethyl phenols are well separated as groups but not resolved into individual isomers. The total xylenols is the sum of the three individual peaks, calculated from the single standard. The large concentrations of inorganic compounds, carboxylic acids and other extremely polar compounds are eluted very early, long before any of the phenols.

Table 1 below shows a typical aqueous liquor analysis for phenols

Table 1 - Major Phenols in Aqueous Liquor

Compound	Concentration mgl^{-1}
Phenol	5000
Cresols + ethylphenols	4400
Xylenols	700
Naphthols	20
Trimethylphenols	50
Quinol	30
Resorcinol	90
2-Methyl resorcinol	60
4-Methyl resorcinol	100
5-Methyl resorcinol	140
Catechol	270
3-Methyl catechol	130
4-Methol catechol	100

Organic nitrogen compounds

(a) Preliminary study

It was expected that organic bases which mainly comprise amines and
heterocyclic nitrogen compounds would be present in the oils and tar
produced in the gasifier. As the pH of the aqueous liquor is about 8.5-9.0,
organic bases (unlike phenols) will be largely unionised and thus can be
expected to be concentrated mainly in the tar/oil fraction of the
condensate. Their levels can therefore be expected to be much lower than
those of phenols which will partition predominantly into the aqueous phase.
Since the concentration of phenols present in liquor decreased rapidly with
increasing molecular complexity we looked initially for simple bases such as
aniline $C_6H_5.NH_2$, methyl aniline $CH_3.C_6H_4.NH_2$, pyridine etc. As the levels
found were quite low, complex molecules were unlikely to be present in
detectable amounts, and the analysis was not extended beyond quinoline.

(b) Analytical system

As the analytical requirement was to seek the simpler and thus more polar
nitrogen compounds, the appropriate technique to use was again HPLC in the
reversed-phase mode.

The HPLC procedure found to be suitable is shown in Figure 1, except that
only the Zorbax column is used, and 40% v/v acetonitrile (liquid
chromatography grade) in distilled water as the mobile phase at a flow rate
of 1 ml min^{-1}. A 10µl sample loop was used and the fixed wavelength
detector was set at 254 nm using an interference filter. Table 2 below
gives the retention times for the nitrogen compounds. These were
established using aqueous solutions of pure compounds.

Table 2 - Retention Times of Organic Nitrogen Compounds

Compound	Time in minutes
Aniline	7.10
Methyl aniline	8.40
Dimethyl aniline	15.45
Pyridine	9.10
2-Methyl pyridine	9.58
3-Methyl pyridine	10.40
4-Methyl pyridine	10.40
Quinoline	11.50
Isoquinoline	11.50
Methyl quinoline	18.40
Ethyl pyridine	21.10

(c) Sample pretreatment

Because of the presence of high concentrations of interfering species it was not possible to directly inject the aqueous liquor for analysis. The sample had to be treated as follows:

Concentrated hydrochloric acid was added dropwise to 25ml of the liquor until the pH was 1. This was extracted three times with 5ml portions of 4-methyl pentan-2-one and the organic layer discarded each time. The aqueous layer was then extracted three times with 5ml aliquots of dichloromethane, and the organic layer discarded. The 4-methyl pentan 2-one removes all the acidic components and the dichloromethane extracts any residual 4-methyl pentan 2-one together with any neutral components not previously removed. The sample was then air blown to remove any traces of dichloromethane although in practice this was very difficult to achieve completely.

The extraction technique was calibrated using known amounts of organic nitrogen compounds. Table 3 below gives the recoveries found which were used to calculate the levels of bases subsequently determined in the aqueous liquor samples.

Table 3 - Recovery of Selected Nitrogen Compounds

Compound	% Recovered
Aniline	96.2
Methyl aniline	84.7
Dimethyl aniline	66.3
Pyridine	97.1
2-Methyl pyridine	95.9
Quinoline	94.2
Methyl quinoline	86.4

(d) Analysis of aqueous liquors

A chromatogram of a typical liquor analysis is shown in Figure 4 and the
results obtained are given below in Table 4 as determined and corrected
using the recoveries shown in Table 3.

Table 4 - Analysis of Aqueous Liquor for Nitrogen Compounds

Compound	Concentration mg l^{-1}	
	Determined	Corrected
Aniline	101	105
Methyl aniline	30	35
Dimethyl aniline	5	8
Pyridine	204	210
2-Methyl pyridine	17	18
3- and 4-Methyl pyridine	28	30
Ethyl pyridine	Not detected	5
Quinoline/isoquinoline	33	35
Methyl quinoline	4	5
Piperidine	Not detected	5

The chromatogram shown in Figure 4 does not show the characteristic sharp
peaks normally associated with HPLC. The nitrogen compounds, and in
particular pyridine and its alkyl substitutes, being basic in nature tend to
adhere fairly firmly to the column packing material. Some peak sharpening
can be achieved if ammonia is added to the mobile phase (pH 8) but as the
column packing is silica based it is not recommended for continual use.

Ionic analysis

(a) Background

Traditionally, most of the analyses for ionic species in effluents were by
the classical techniques of distillation, titration, gravimetry and
colorimetry. These methods of analysis were often multi-stage processes and
the pretreatment necessary on liquor samples greatly increases the time of
analysis. The results obtained were not always accurate mainly because of
interferences between components. The use of ion chromatography has
replaced most of these methods by one technique, giving significant
improvement in the speed of analysis and accuracy of results. Ion
chromatography (IC) is a technique based on separations, and so removes many
of the interferences previously found with the classical methods. For
example, titration of a chloride and bromide mixture will not distinguish
between the two halides, whereas the same determination using IC will show
the halides as two clearly resolved peaks.

Coal gasification liquors contain a very wide range of ionic species, and it
is not possible to do a complete IC analysis in one chromatographic run.
However, it can be split into 5 groups:- small anions, large anions,
electroactive species, carboxylic acids and cations. Each group needs the
right combination of IC column, eluent and detector and these are summarised
in Table 5. Only the ammonium ion of the cation group is determined by IC
at present. The Dionex system was used throughout.

(b) Small anions, e.g. Fluoride, Chloride and Sulphate

After considerable development work, the most suitable column was found to be the efficient AS3 type which gives better baseline resolution on all peaks and an analysis time of less than 10 minutes. A chromatogram is shown in Figure 5 of dephenolated liquor. This is the aqueous liquor which has been extracted with 4-methyl pentan-2-one to remove phenols and then steam stripped to remove the residual 4 methyl pentan-2-one and it is the first treatment stage in our effluent treatment pilot plant. The large dilution needed to determine the chloride level, reduces considerably the peaks of the other components. However, the use of a high resolution integrator and expansion on a VDU enables the small peaks to be more clearly defined.

(c) Large anions

The term large anions is used to describe anions with a radius larger than the sulphate ion. Thiosulphate and thiocyanate are the only ions of this type that we have identified in effluents and our discussion under this heading will be restricted to them. They are very strongly retained by the ion exchange resin columns, consequently special conditions have to be set up to allow reasonably quick analysis whilst obtaining good chromatographic separations. We found the most suitable columns to be two AG3 precolumns in series. The first one acts as a normal guard column. The other as a short separator column. The eluent used is 5mM Na_2CO_3 modified with 0.75mM p-cyanophenol. The resolution for the thiosulphate and thiocyanate peaks 'c' and 'd' shown in Figure 6 is good but the sulphate coalesces with the other early eluting ions and clearly it cannot be determined under these conditions. The time taken for an analysis is about 15 minutes; we are not aware of any interferences and the procedure can be easily automated.

(d) Electroactive species

Both cyanide and sulphide are present in the aqueous liquor and can be determined using electrochemical detection at an applied potential and those interfering ions whose redox potentials do not match the applied potential will not be detected. The column type was an AS3 Fast Run with a silver working electrode at an applied potential of +60mV with respect to the standard hydrogen electrode. The eluent used was a mixture of 1mM sodium carbonate, 10mM sodium dihydrogen borate and 15mM ethylene diamine which acts as a chelating agent. Figure 7 shows a typical chromatogram of dephenolated liquor.

The method is sensitive down to $\mu g \ l^{-1}$ levels but has a narrow linear range which is fairly common with amperometric detection. Only free cyanide or very weak cyanide complexes can be determined by this method. Strong complexes like ferricyanides have to be reduced with cuprous chloride before the chromatographic analysis.

(e) Carboxylic acids

Short chain carboxylic acids make an important contribution to the chemical oxygen demand of a waste water. They are also responsible for some of the foaming and unpleasant scum formation that can occur in effluents. For these reasons it is essential to be able to determine their concentrations in coal gasification liquors.

Table 5

SCHEME FOR EFFLUENT ANALYSIS BY ION CHROMATOGRAPHY

CLASSIFICATION	SMALL ANIONS	LARGE ANIONS	ELECTROACTIVE SPECIES	CARBOXYLIC ACIDS	CATIONS
Species	Cl, F, PO_4, SO_4, NO_2, NO_3, SO_3, Br	Thiocyanate, thiosulphate	Sulphide, cyanide phenols	Formate, acetate "carbon dioxide"	Sodium potassium ammonium
Columns	HPIC AS1 HPIC AS3 with resin or fibre suppressor	2 x HPIC AG3 with resin or AFS-1 fibre suppressor	HPIC-AS3 resin suppressor	HPICE AS3 resin suppressor HPICE AS1 AFS-2 fibre	HPIC CS1 Resin suppressor or CFS-1 fibre
Detection system	Conductiometric	Conductiometric	Electrochemical	Conductiometric	Conductiometric
Eluent	3mM $NaHCO_3$ 2.4mM Na_2CO_3	5mM Na_2CO_3 0.75mM p-cyano phenol	1mM Na_2CO_3 10mM NaH_2BO_3 15mM ethylene diamine	1mM HCl	5mM HCl

Until recently all our analyses for this type of component were by gas chromatography but this was not suitable for formic acid, the most abundant carboxylic acid present in these samples. Initial attempts to solve the problem involved the use of the standard IC technique and columns, but with a weak borate eluent. The method was not wholly satisfactory and there were difficulties obtaining adequate resolution between fluoride and acetate. We overcame the problems by using Ion Chromatography Exclusion (ICE). ICE is the Dionex version of ion exclusion partition chromatography. The main mode of separation is based on the Donnan exclusion principle and is an excellent method for removing strong acids like chloride and nitrate from mixtures with weak acids. The former are quickly eluted in the void volume and the weak acids like short chain carboxylics are separated roughly on the basis of increasing molecular weight. Tri- and di-acids generally elute before mono-acids of equal size. We used an HPICE AS3 column with hydrochloric acid (HCl) eluent and a silver form suppressor column to remove the background signal from the HCl.

Under the conditions shown, not only can the short chain carboxylic acids be determined but also fluoride. Figure 8 is a crude effluent analysis and one interesting feature is that carbonate can also be quantitatively determined by this method.

(f) Cation analysis

Our main interest in using IC for cationic analysis has been in the determination of ammonium, where substantial time savings can be made over the normal distillation and titration method. For most of our other metal ions we have standardised on the spectroscopic techniques of atomic emission and absorption. Figure 9 shows the determination of ammonium ion in the presence of sodium and potassium using a CS1 separator and a resin suppressor. Fibre suppressors are now also available for cation analysis. The CS1 column can also be used for divalent metals like calcium and magnesium.

(g) Analysis of aqueous liquor

Many of the above methods were used to obtain results for major and minor ionic components in a typical aqueous liquor - see Table 6. The concentrations shown highlight one of the difficulties in obtaining results from one single injection because of the large dynamic range and difference of sensitivity for each component peak.

Table 6

Component	Concentration mg l^{-1}
Free ammonia	15000
Fixed ammonia	3500
Carbon dioxide	18000
Hydrogen sulphide	2000
Chloride	7000
Thiocyanate	1250
Total cyanide	300

CONCLUSIONS

Liquid chromatography has proved to be a valuable aid in the analysis of coal gasification aqueous liquors. Its versatility has enabled us to perform most of the non-metal inorganic analysis, all of the phenols and organic nitrogen compounds. The level of detection has been more than adequate to enable us to determine all the significant compounds at a level down to about 1 mg l^{-1} and in some cases 1μg l^{-1}.

Because liquid chromatography is a separation technique, much of the interferences that occurred using classical methods of analysis have been avoided, and in many cases a much more reliable result has been obtained.

Provided care is taken with sample pretreatment, the life of the equipment and columns is good, and the speed of analysis is in many cases a major improvement on earlier methods.

ACKNOWLEDGMENTS

We are grateful to our colleagues at British Gas London Research Station for their contributions and to the Research and Development Division of British Gas Corporation for permission to publish.

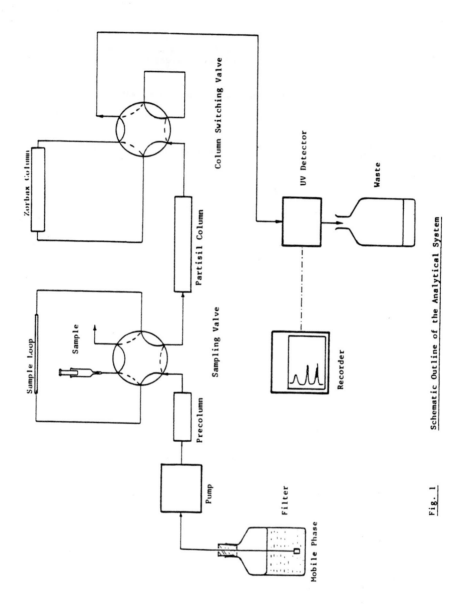

Fig. 1   Schematic Outline of the Analytical System

Fig. 2 Analysis of Liquor for Polar Compounds, except Phenol

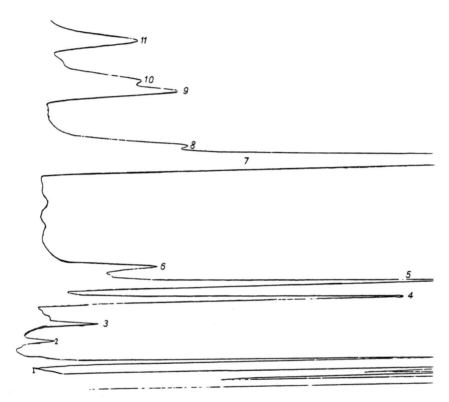

Inject 20 µl

Peak identification

I	Inorganics/carboxylicacids etc.	4	resorcinol	8	5 methylresorcinol
2	quinol	5	catechol	9	4 methylcatechol
		6	2 methylresorcino'	10	4 methylresorcinol
3	2 methylquinol	7	phenol	11	3 methylcatechol

Fig. 3 Analysis of Aqueous Liquor for Phenol, Cresols, Xylenols,
Naphthols and Trimethylphenols

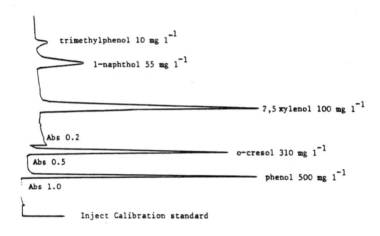

trimethylphenol 10 mg l^{-1}

1-naphthol 55 mg l^{-1}

7,5 xylenol 100 mg l^{-1}

Abs 0.2

o-cresol 310 mg l^{-1}

Abs 0.5

phenol 500 mg l^{-1}

Abs 1.0

Inject Calibration standard

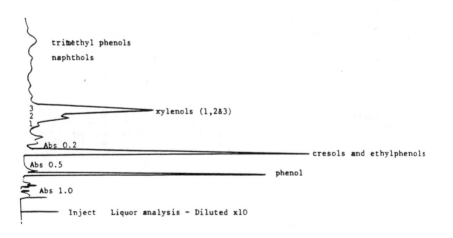

trimethyl phenols

naphthols

3
2
1

xylenols (1,2&3)

Abs 0.2

cresols and ethylphenols

Abs 0.5

phenol

Abs 1.0

Inject   Liquor analysis - Diluted x10

Fig. 4   Analysis of Aqueous Liquor for Organic Nitrogen Compounds

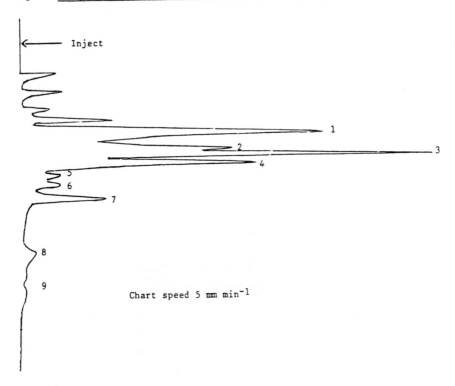

Chart speed 5 mm min^{-1}

Peak identification

1. Aniline
2. Dichloromethane (extraction solvent contamination)
3. Methyl aniline
4. Pyridine
5. 2 Methyl pyridine
6. 3 and 4 Methyl pyridines
7. Quinoline/iso quinoline
8. Dimethyl aniline
9. Methyl quinoline

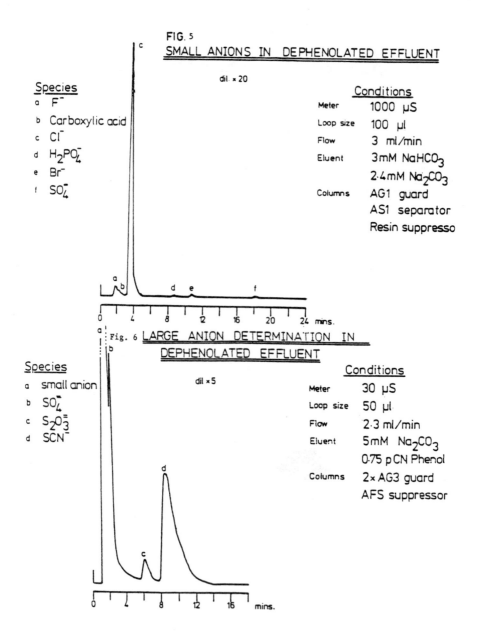

FIG. 5

SMALL ANIONS IN DEPHENOLATED EFFLUENT

dil. × 20

Species
a F⁻
b Carboxylic acid
c Cl⁻
d $H_2PO_4^-$
e Br⁻
f SO_4^-

Conditions

Meter	1000 μS
Loop size	100 μl
Flow	3 ml/min
Eluent	3mM $NaHCO_3$
	2·4mM Na_2CO_3
Columns	AG1 guard
	AS1 separator
	Resin suppresso

Fig. 6 LARGE ANION DETERMINATION IN DEPHENOLATED EFFLUENT

dil × 5

Species
a small anion
b SO_4^-
c $S_2O_3^=$
d SCN⁻

Conditions

Meter	30 μS
Loop size	50 μl
Flow	2·3 ml/min
Eluent	5mM Na_2CO_3
	0·75 pCN Phenol
Columns	2× AG3 guard
	AFS suppressor

196

Fig. 7 <u>ELECTROCHEMICAL DETECTION OF CYANIDE/SULPHIDE IN DEPHENOLATED EFFLUENT</u>

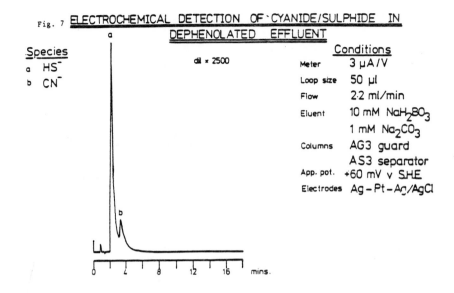

Species

a HS⁻
b CN⁻

dil × 2500

Conditions

Meter	3 µA/V
Loop size	50 µl
Flow	2·2 ml/min
Eluent	10 mM NaH_2BO_3
	1 mM Na_2CO_3
Columns	AG3 guard
	AS3 separator
App. pot.	+60 mV v SHE
Electrodes	Ag – Pt – Ag/AgCl

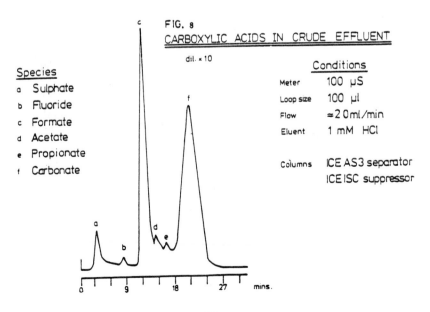

FIG. 8

<u>CARBOXYLIC ACIDS IN CRUDE EFFLUENT</u>

dil. × 10

Species

a Sulphate
b Fluoride
c Formate
d Acetate
e Propionate
f Carbonate

Conditions

Meter	100 µS
Loop size	100 µl
Flow	≈ 2·0 ml/min
Eluent	1 mM HCl
Columns	ICE AS3 separator
	ICE ISC suppressor

197

FIG. 9
SMALL CATIONS STANDARD

Species (ppm)

a   Na$^+$ 10
b   NH$_4^+$ 10
c   K$^+$ 10

Conditions

Meter	30 µS
Loop size	100 µl
Flow	1·3 ml/min
Eluent	5mM HCl
Columns	CG1 guard
	CS1 separator
	Resin suppressor

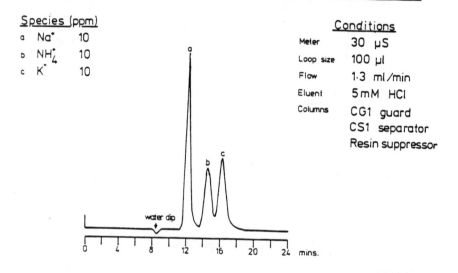

THE SORPTION OF DYES ONTO PEAT IN FIXED BEDS

Stephen J. Allen, Gordon McKay, Victor J.P. Poots

A design method for fixed bed adsorption columns has been presented and tested. The model is based on external mass transfer and pore diffusion. An optimisation technique using the empty bed contact time is illustrated. The models are tested using peat as adsorbent medium.

INTRODUCTION

Adsorption is a separation process involving two phases between which certain components can become differentially distributed. Adsorption operations are based on the ability of selected solids to concentrate specific substances from a solution onto their surfaces.

The treatment of waste waters by adsorption techniques is receiving growing attention since the standards for the quality of effluent disposal are becoming increasingly more rigid.

One of the earliest adsorbents to be used on a commercial scale was activated carbon. This hard material is extremely porous and has been used extensively for solvent recovery, water purifications and for many similar operations. The use of other adsorbents in treating textile effluents has been reported by McKay et al (1).

It is the purpose of the current paper to focus attention on the use of peat as an adsorbent in fixed bed columns, and to relate the kinetics of the mass transfer in a two resistance model.

EQUIPMENT

An outline diagram of the fixed bed contacting system is shown in Figure 1. The vertical fixed bed columns consisted of perspex columns (E and F). Several columns could be operated simultaneously, however only two are shown in the diagram. Sample points were available at specific bed heights in the column. Vessels A (60 dm^3), B (60 dm^3) and D (30 dm^3) were used in the storage and make up of the dye solution. The dye solution was fed, using upflow conditions, to the columns from a constant temperature, constant head

tank C and the flow rate to each column was flow controlled.
The dyestuffs used were Telon Blue (Acid Blue 25), Astrazone Blue (Basic Blue 69). Concentrations were measured on a Perkin Elmer 550 visible spectrophotometer.

FIXED BED ADSORPTION MODELS

(i) Mass Transfer Zone Model (MTZ)

In the MTZ the concentration of the solute in the adsorbent will change from the initial value Y_0 to the equilibrium value Y_e. The area below the wavefront reflects unused adsorbent capacity. The mathematical analysis has been reported by McKay (2) and is based on the assumption of an idealized breakthrough curve. The resultant design equation is:

$$Z_u = Z_0 - Z_e = Z_0 \left(1 - \frac{\theta_b}{\theta_s}\right) \tag{1}$$

(ii) Height of an Equivalent Transfer Unit (HETU) Method

This column design method is based on two concepts: the height of an equivalent transfer unit and the maximum permissible space rate at which full adsorption takes place. The HETU method is based on the variation in the bed void fraction, ε, with variation in mean equivalent particle diameter, dp, and packing density. A method for estimating the HETU for an adsorbent has been reported by Johnston (3), and the minimum adsorbent bed height for maximum product quality is suggested as 55 - 60 HETU i.e.

$$Z_{min} = (55 - 60) \text{ HETU} \tag{2}$$

(iii) Bed Depth Service Time (BDST) Model

In continuous flow adsorption columns it is essential to predict how much effluent the bed will treat, or how long the bed will last before regeneration is necessary. It is possible to correlate the service time, θ_b, with the adsorption variables. The BDST Method presented by Hutchins (4), is based on work by Bohart and Adams (5). The service time of a fixed bed of adsorbent, treating a solution of a single adsorbate, can be expressed as a function of operational variables as:

$$\theta_b = \frac{N_0}{C_0 u} \left[Z - \frac{u}{kN_0} \ln \left(\frac{C_0}{C_t} - 1 \right) \right] \tag{3}$$

This may be represented by equation (4) which is the Equation of a straight line. A plot of service time against bed depth can be used to test the model.

$$\theta_b = aZ + b \tag{4}$$

(iv) Kinetic Model Based on External Mass Transfer and Pore Diffusion

The adsorption of a material by an adsorbent is governed by the rate and mechanisms of mass transfer. Most models for adsorption are based on a film resistance (describing the transport rate from the

bulk to the particle surface) and a diffusion mechanism inside the adsorbent particle.
It has been established that four mechanisms for internal mass transfer can exist, Bruin and Luyben (6).

(i)   Homogeneous diffusion in the solid particles

(ii) Pore diffusion of adsorbate from liquid filled pores onto the pore walls

(iii) Surface diffusion of adsorbed molecules along the internal surface of the particle

(iv) A combination of pore diffusion and surface diffusion.

A literature review of all fixed bed models to 1974 has been reported by Weber and Chakravorti (7). Since then a number of fixed bed models have been proposed Svedberg (8), Neretnieks (9), Brauch and Schlunder (10), Liapis and Rippin (11), based on pore diffusion only and some models have been developed Balzi et al. (12), Fritz et al. (13) using pore and surface diffusion.

It is the aim of the present work to propose a rapid analytical method for designing fixed bed adsorption columns that will be amenable to design engineers. The work of Brauch and Schlunder (10) has formed the basis of the model; a wide range of fixed bed adsorption studies have been undertaken to test the versatility of this particular mass transfer model. The model is based on the unreacted core theory proposed by Levenspiel (14) and Yagi and Kunii (15), and applies for a non-linear isotherm system. Three assumptions have been made:

(a)   irreversible adsorption

(b)   the solute in the pore water is transferred only by molecular diffusion from the particle surface to the interior

(c)   adsorption equilibrium occurs between the pore-dye solution and adsorbent throughout the adsorption process.

The concentration profile is shown in Figure 2. Due to the external mass transfer resistance, the liquid phase concentration of adsorbate falls from a value C in the bulk liquid to a value C_e on the particle surface. The adsorbate in the pore water is transferred from the particle surface to the particle interior by molecular diffusion. The concentration of the adsorbate in the pore water therefore decreases from C_e to zero at a point r_f. The absorbate in the pores is adsorbed in a well defined concentration front, moving with a varying velocity from the particle surface inwards. It is possible to predict an equation for the adsorption rate based on certain conditions and assumptions.

(a)   The mass transfer from the external liquid phase is given by equation (5).

$$N(t) = 4\pi R^2 k_f (C - C_e) \tag{5}$$

(b) Diffusion in the pore water occurs according to Ficks first law

$$N(t) = \frac{4\pi D_p}{\frac{1}{r_f} - \frac{1}{R}} \cdot C_e \qquad (6)$$

(c) The velocity of the concentration front is obtained from the mass balance on a spherical element.

$$N(t) = -4\pi r_f^2 Y_e \; \rho_t \; \frac{dr_f}{dt} \qquad (7)$$

(d) The average concentration in the solid is given by

$$Y = Y_e \left[1 - (\frac{r_f}{R})\right]^3 \qquad (8)$$

By introducing the following dimensionless parameters,

$$\eta = \frac{Y}{Y_e} ; \quad \Psi = \frac{C}{C_o} ; \quad \tau = \left[\frac{C_o}{\rho_t Y_e}\right] \cdot \left[\frac{D_p t}{R^2}\right] \quad ;$$

$$Bi = \frac{k_f R}{D_p} ; \quad C_h = \frac{Y_e W}{C_o V}$$

the adsorption rate for a single particle can be expressed as a function of adsorbate concentration in the water phase, Ψ, in the adsorbent phase, η, the capacity factor, C_h, and of the Biot number, Bi, and is represented by equation (9).

$$\frac{d\eta}{d\tau} = \left[\frac{3\,(1- C_h \cdot \eta)(1-\eta)^{0.33}}{1- \left[1- Bi^{-1}\right] (1-\eta)^{0.33}}\right] \qquad (9)$$

The purpose of this model is to predict the concentration distribution in both fluid and solid phase in fixed beds and to compare the predicted with experimental results.

The adsorption rate equation (9) can be incorporated into the fixed bed kinetic equation (10). The kinetic equation (10) is combined with the differential mass balance in the column, equation (11) yielding equation (12) which predicts the local and time dependent concentration history in the solid phase.

$$\frac{d\eta}{d\tau} = \Sigma \qquad f(\eta) \qquad (10)$$

$$\frac{d\psi}{d\alpha} + \frac{d\eta}{d\tau} = 0 \tag{11}$$

$$\frac{d^2\eta}{d\tau d\alpha} \cdot \frac{f^1(\eta)}{f(\eta)} \cdot \frac{d\eta}{d\tau} \cdot \frac{d\eta}{d\alpha} \cdot \frac{d\eta}{d\tau} f(\eta) = 0 \tag{12}$$

A general solution of this equation was developed by Van Meel (16) and Brauch and Schlunder (10), for the boundary conditions

$$\eta(\alpha,0) = 0$$

$$\frac{d\eta(\alpha,0)}{d\alpha} = 0$$

thus

$$\frac{1}{\psi} \cdot \frac{d\eta}{d\tau} + \frac{1}{\eta} \cdot \frac{d\eta}{d\alpha} = 0 \tag{13}$$

To facilitate computation the integration region has been divided into two sections separated by a time, τ_1, which is the time for the first adsorbent layer to become saturated and for the wavefront to establish itself. The limits for the first integration period are:

$$\int_1^\psi \frac{d\psi}{\psi} = \int_{\eta(0,\tau)}^\eta \frac{d\eta}{\eta} \tag{14}$$

for boundary conditions $= (0,\tau)$ and $\alpha = 0$ and $0 < \tau < \tau_1$.

In the second boundary integration section the limits are:

$$\int_1^\psi \frac{d\psi}{\psi} = \int_1^\eta \frac{d\eta}{\psi} \tag{15}$$

for boundary conditions $\eta = 1$, $\alpha = \alpha_1$, and $\tau > \tau = 1$.

Equations (14) and (15) have been solved by McKay et al (17). Equation (14) predicts the liquid phase dye concentrations up to the time τ_1, and equation (15) predicts the dye concentration after the constant pattern breakthrough curve is fully developed.

The mathematical steps have been developed in a Fortran programme which enables several criteria to be predicted:

(a) dimensionless solid phase concentrations against time, (dimensionless time or volume of dye treated);

(b) dimensionless liquid phase concentration against time, (dimensionless time or volume of dye treated);

(c) dimensionless liquid phase concentration against dimensionless solid phase concentration.

Of the above criteria, item (b) is of particular interest. The theoretical dimensionless breakthrough curves can be compared with experimental curves. It is necessary to input certain design parameters into the programme. These include molecular diffusivity, effective diffusivity, adsorbent density, adsorbent mass, kinematic viscosity, initial adsorbate concentration, adsorbent particle diameter, adsorbate flow rate, equilibrium capacity, bed height and film mass transfer coefficient.

The molecular diffusion coefficient was obtained using the Wilke-Chang equation (18), and the film mass transfer coefficient obtained from correlations by Kataoka (19). The physical characteristics of the bed are determined and the equilibrium capacity is taken from either the isotherm or graphical integration of the experimental breakthrough curve. The effective diffusivity is obtained by trial and error, using the programme and the experimental data at one adsorbate flow rate. This value was then tested at all other flowrates.

The engineer is concerned with predicting how much effluent the bed will treat, or how long the bed will last before any regeneration is necessary, based on a predetermined breakthrough level. Consequently a knowledge of the breakthrough curves plotted against the volume of dye treated is useful information. Figures 3 to 5 show the data for the adsorption of Acid blue 25 and Basic Blue 69 onto peat.

The pore diffusion model, adopted for analysing the experimental data, has the disadvantage that a certain mass transfer model has been presupposed. Any effects of surface diffusion or combined pore and surface diffusion has not been considered. The prediction of molecular diffusivities for organic electrolytes is difficult due to the effects of impurities and micelle formation Kipling (20). Nevertheless it is possible to correlate experimental and theoretical breakthrough curves for important design variables.

OPTIMIZATION OF FIXED BED ADSORBER

The influence of dye velocity for the adsorption of Acid Blue 25 and Basic Blue 69 onto peat has been studied using a modified form of equation (3) and (4)

$$\theta_b = \frac{u_2}{u_1} (A*Z - b) \qquad (16)$$

where u_2 = test data velocity and u_1 = new velocity.

Four dye flowrates were studied with all other system variables constant. The flowrates for basic blue 69 solution were 2.58 x 10^{-3}, 3.33 x 10^{-3}, 5.0 x 10^{-3} and 7.0 x 10^{-3} dm^{3}s^{-1}. The Bed Depth Service Time results are shown by the solidus lines in Figure 6 and the points are experimental data. The intercept on the abscissa is the critical bed depth and this decreses with increasing dye velocity. This depth is the minimum depth for obtaining satisfactory effluent at time zero under the test operating conditions.

It is possible to optimise such data for adsorption using the following technique.

In fixed-bed effluent treatment systems using peat, the capital and operating costs are a function primarily of two variables.

(i) The peat exhaustion rate: this variable is usually expressed as kg of peat replaced (or reactivated) for volume of liquid treated.

(ii) Empty bed contact time (EBCT): this variable is the time that the liquid would take to fill the volume of peat bed and is a direct function of liquid flowrate and peat volume.

The total capital cost is primarily dependent on the volume of the peat beds. The operating costs are determined by the peat exhaustion rate since the largest variable is usually the cost of make-up peat.

The relation between these two variables can be established by tests and plotted as shown in Figure (8). For a given system to achieve a given performance, there is a single line relating these two variables which can be called the "operating line". The operating line information can be used to optimize the basic design to achieve the lowest cost or other objectives.

The points on the operating line for the desired maximum effluent concentration are obtained from column experimental data. Once the operating line is established, it is possible to select the combination of peat exhaustion rate and liquid retention time which gives the optimum or lowest cost design. Figure (7) shows a series of breakthrough curves for the adsorption of Basic Blue 69 onto peat at various bed heights. The data are plotted in Figure (8) which enables the optimum conditions to be predicted as shown, for the minimum exhuastion rate and minimum empty bed residence time for the system.

CONCLUSION

Methods of designing fixed bed adsorbers have been discussed and two methods were tested using experimental results for the adsorption of dyestuffs onto peat. The simplified BDST approach gives good results and may be used to predict adsorption breakthrough at different operating conditions. The kinetic model incorporates the fundamental transport steps and is applicable to the systems studied using a pore diffusivity for each system.

SYMBOLS USED

a	BDST constant
a*	modified BDST constant
b	BDST constant
Bi	Biot number
C	solute concentration in liquid at time t, mg dm^{-3}
C_e	equilibrium solute concentration in liquid, mg dm^{-3}
C_h	capacity factor
C_o	initial solute concentration in liquid, mg dm^{-3}
d	mean particle diameter,
D_p	pore diffusion coefficient, cm^2 s^{-1}
k	adsorption rate factor, mg m^{-1} dm^{-3}
k_f	external mass transfer coefficient, cms^{-1}
No	adsorption capacity factor, mg dm^{-3}
N(t)	mass transfer rate at time t, mg s^{-1}
r_f	radius of concentration front, cm

R	particle radius, cm
u	solution velocity, ms^{-1}
V	volume of solution, dm^3
W	mass adsorbent, g
Y	solute concentration on solid at time t, mg g^{-1}
Y_e	equilibrium solute concentration on solid, mg g^{-1}
Y_0	initial solute concentration on solid, mg g^{-1}
Z	adsorbent bed length, m
Z_e	length of equilibrium zone in adsorbent bed, m
Z_{min}	minimum adsorbent bed length, m
Z_0	length of adsorbent bed, m
Z_u	length of unused adsorbent bed, m

GREEK SYMBOLS

α	Dimensionless bed length
θ	time, s
ψ	C/C_0, dimensionless solute concentration in liquid
η	Y/Y_e, dimensionless solute concentration on solid
τ	dimensionless time
ρ	adsorbent particle density, gcm^{-3}

REFERENCES

1. McKay, G., Otterburn, M.S. and Sweeny, A.G. 1978. J.S.D.C., Sept., 357.
2. McKay, G. 1981. J. Chem. Tech. Biotechnol., 31, 717.
3. Johnston, W.A. 1972. Chem. Engng, 79, 87.
4. Hutchins, R.A. 1973. Chem. Engng, 80, 133.
5. Bohart, G.S. and Adams, E.Q. 1920. J. Amer. Chem. Soc., 42, 523.
6. Bruin, S., and Luyben, K.Ch.A.M. 1978. I. Chem. E. Symp. Ser. No. 54, 215.
7. Weber, T.W. and Chakravorti, R.K. 1974. A.I.Ch.E.J., 20, 228.
8. Svedberg, U.G. 1976. Chem. Eng. Sci., 31, 345.
9. Neretnieks, I. 1976. Chem. Eng. Sci., 31, 107.
10. Brauch, V. and Schlunder, E.U. 1975. Chem. Eng. Sci., 30, 539.
11. Liapis, A.I. and Rippin, D.W.T. 1978. Chem. Eng. Sci., 33, 593.
12. Balzi, M.W., Liapis, A.I. and Rippin, D.W.T. 1978. Trans. I. Chem. E., 56, 145.
13. Fritz, W., Merk, W. and Schlunder, E.U. 1981. Chem. Eng. Sci., 36, 721, 731, 741.
14. Levenspiel, O. 1962. Chemical Reaction Engineering, Wiley, New York.
15. Yagi, S. and Kunii, D. 1961. Chem. Engng Sci., 16, 372.
16. Van Meel, D.A. 1958. Chem. Engng Sci., 9, 63.
17. McKay, G. et al. Private Communication.
18. Wilke, C.R. and Chang, P. 1955. A.I.Ch.E.J., 1, 264.
19. Kataoka, T., Yoshida, A. and Ueyama, K. 1972. J. Chem. Eng. Japan, 5, 132.
20. Kipling, J.J., "Adsorption from Solutions of Non-Electrolytes", Academic Press, 1965, 267.

Figure 1   Apparatus for column adsorption studies

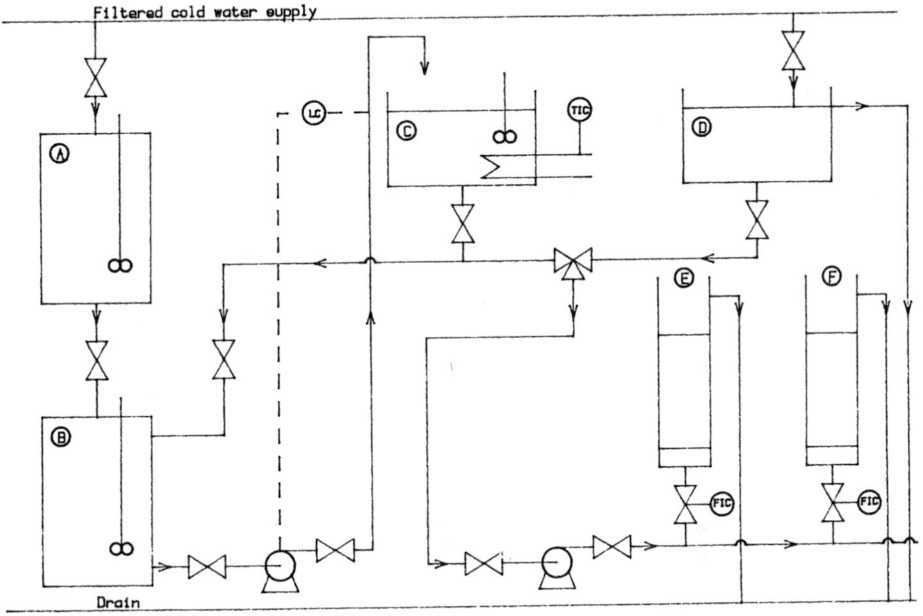

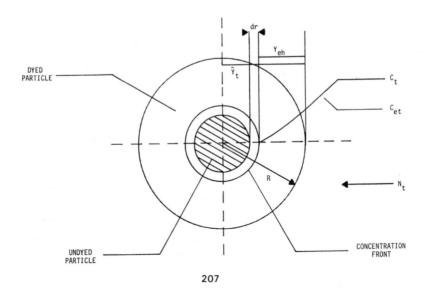

FIGURE 2.   CONCENTRATION PROFILE IN AN ADSORBENT PARTICLE

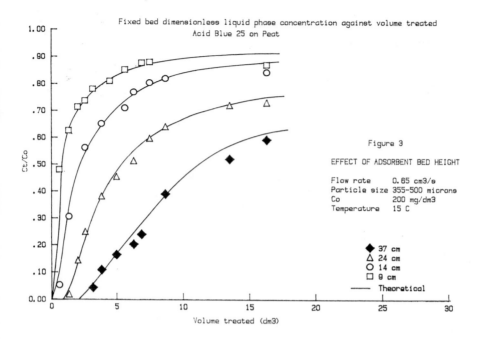

Fixed bed dimensionless liquid phase concentration against volume treated
Acid Blue 25 on Peat

Figure 3

EFFECT OF ADSORBENT BED HEIGHT

Flow rate   0.85 cm3/s
Particle size 355-500 microns
Co   200 mg/dm3
Temperature   15 C

◆ 37 cm
△ 24 cm
○ 14 cm
□ 9 cm
—— Theoretical

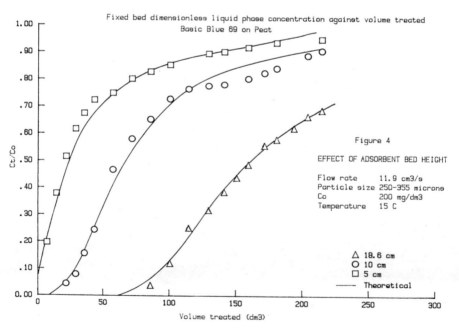

Fixed bed dimensionless liquid phase concentration against volume treated
Basic Blue 69 on Peat

Figure 4

EFFECT OF ADSORBENT BED HEIGHT

Flow rate   11.9 cm3/s
Particle size 250-355 microns
Co   200 mg/dm3
Temperature   15 C

△ 18.6 cm
○ 10 cm
□ 5 cm
—— Theoretical

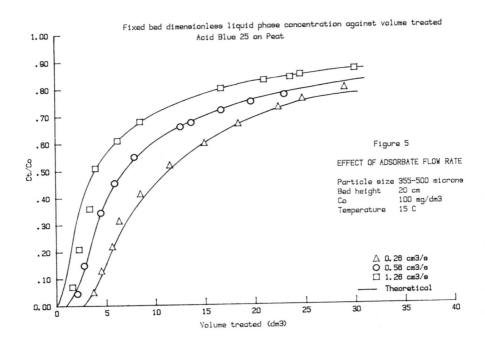

Fixed bed dimensionless liquid phase concentration against volume treated
Acid Blue 25 on Peat

Figure 5

EFFECT OF ADSORBATE FLOW RATE

Particle size 355-500 microns
Bed height   20 cm
Co   100 mg/dm3
Temperature   15 C

△ 0.26 cm3/s
○ 0.56 cm3/s
□ 1.26 cm3/s
—— Theoretical

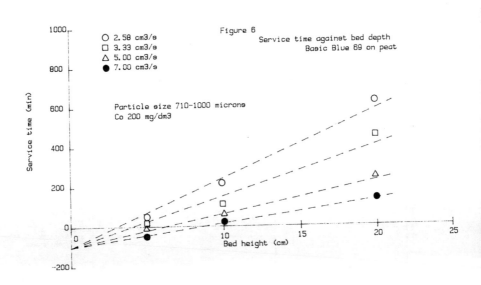

Figure 6
Service time against bed depth
Basic Blue 69 on peat

○ 2.58 cm3/s
□ 3.33 cm3/s
△ 5.00 cm3/s
● 7.00 cm3/s

Particle size 710-1000 microns
Co 200 mg/dm3

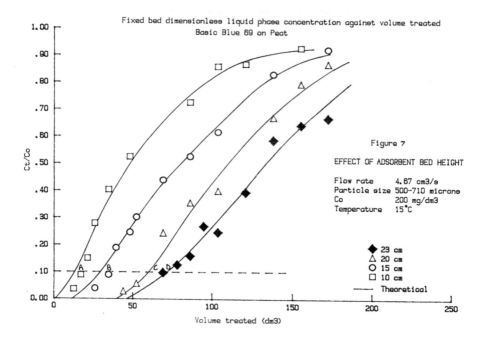

Fixed bed dimensionless liquid phase concentration against volume treated
Basic Blue 69 on Peat

Figure 7

EFFECT OF ADSORBENT BED HEIGHT

Flow rate   4.87 cm3/s
Particle size 500-710 microns
Co   200 mg/dm3
Temperature   15°C

♦ 23 cm
△ 20 cm
○ 15 cm
□ 10 cm
—— Theoretical

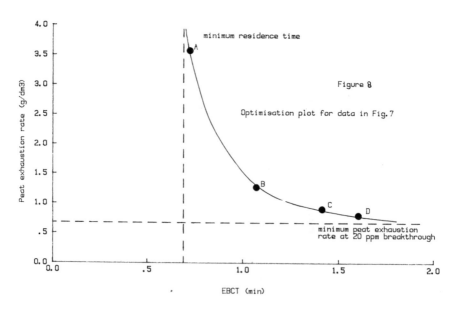

Figure 8

Optimisation plot for data in Fig. 7

minimum residence time

minimum peat exhaustion
rate at 20 ppm breakthrough

DECONTAMINATION OF LIQUID STREAMS CONTAINING CADMIUM BY BIOMASS ADSORPTION

J.A. Scott*, S.J. Palmer* and J. Ingham**

Previous studies have shown that a wide variety of micro-
organisms remain viable, even after accumulating relatively
high concentrations of heavy metal ions. The extracellular
excretion of a capsular coat is thought to be one means by
which certain organisms protect themselves against these
ions through surface adsorption. Application of this phenomenon is described as a means for decontaminating liquid
streams containing cadmium.

The organisms used are *Arthrobacter globiformis* and
Arthrobacter viscosus, the latter naturally excreting a
polysaccharide coating. At 10mg/l and 200 mg/l cadmium,
A.viscosus has uptake ratios (mgCd/g dry cell weight) 30%
and 320% respectively greater than the non-excreting
A.globiformis. In conjunction with investigating the merit
of this coating for cadmium adsorption, biological fluidised
beds are also under study to provide continual contact
between micro-organisms and contaminated liquid streams.

INTRODUCTION

Many aqueous industrial and domestic effluents are contaminated with heavy
metals in solution. If not removed prior to discharge, these metals (e.g.
Uranium, cadmium and mercury) can pose serious health hazards (1). Decontamination can be achieved by physico-chemical processes, such as precipitation
and ion exchange (2). However, the use of micro-organism biomass to adsorb
these ions extracellularly appears to offer a real alternative to such
techniques.

Discussed in this report is the use of viable biomass to adsorb cadmium, a
common constituent of metal finishing wastes. A highly toxic metal with no
apparent metabolic role (4), cadmium was selected on the grounds that it provides a rigorous test for the technique. Previous work has shown that
although cadmium is adsorbed, other ions such as mercury, copper and uranium
are preferentially taken up (5, 6, 7).

Intracellular intake, even at relatively low concentrations, can rapidly lead
to organism poisoning, for example by the ions replacing naturally occurring
metals in enzyme prosthetic groups (1). Although micro-organism species vary
in their tolerance (3), it is clearly preferable to restrict uptake to extracellular adsorption, thereby avoiding metabolic interference. Furthermore
metal recovery by desorption becomes feasible without causing cell damage
through disruption.

* Department of Chemical Engineering, Bath University, England
** Department of Chemical Engineering, Bradford University, England

The ability of biomass to adsorb cadmium has been found to be dependent upon environmental conditions, particularly pH (3, 8) and the culture age (9, 10). As it is intended to adsorb in a manner that facilitates easy controlled desorption, cell surface characteristics are also of essential importance.

Organisms that naturally excrete capsular coatings suggest one means of providing suitable surface characteristics for metal accumulation. Extracellular polysaccharide capsular excretions which afford a degree of physical protection for the cell (16) are one example. These coatings have also been shown to provide defense against toxicity associated with intracellular intake, or direct cell adsorption of metal ions. Isolated capsular excretions of metal tolerant strains of *Klebsiella aerogenes* when added to a less tolerant non-capsular strain, improved metal tolerance (17).

A strain of the common sewage treatment bacterium, *Zoogloea ramigera* which excretes a gelatinous coat has been found to adsorb more metal ions than a non-excreting strain (11). As this outer coating contains polysaccharides (12) it potentially provides ample negative sites for cationic attachment of the metal ion. It is this type of attachment that would enable straightforward metal recovery through desorption by altering the solution pH.

Previous work specifically on organisms that produce significant quantities of extracellular material is limited and based mainly on *Z.ramigera*. Therefore as part of a long-term programme on biomass accumulation of metals, initial confirmation was required as to whether natural excretions, in particular polysaccharides, do offer improved adsorption characteristics.

To provide this information two species of a ubiquitous soil bacterium, *Arthrobacter viscosus* (a polysaccharide producer) and *Arthrobacter globiformus* (a non-polysaccharide producer) have been cultured and treated with varying levels of cadmium. Apart from having these two distinct forms, the bacterium was selected as it is easy to culture and has not been previously exposed, and therefore acclimatised, to cadmium. The latter criterion is of particular importance to ensure that adsorption is attributed to natural cell surface characteristics and not affected by any preconditioning.

Although our initial trials were conducted batchwise in shake flasks, as most effluents are high volume, low concentration, scale-up would require a continuous treatment process. Biomass has been immobilised in polyacrylamide gel for use in packed columns (10), but by their nature such devices can be prone to blocking and poor liquid distribution. A biological fluidised bed (BFB) provides a seemingly ideal answer. With organisms grown on fluidised support particles (e.g. sand), excellent surface to liquid contact is maintained and controllable 'harvesting' is achieved by flushing through part of the bed.

What is uncertain is whether uptake ratios reported for organisms cultured in the ideal conditions of shake flasks can be duplicated in a BFB. Also as a treatment process will necessarily be run under septic conditions, it is probable that natural progression and competition may displace the original seed organism. Preliminary comparison trials using a BFB with an *Arthrobacter* sp. are reported.

MATERIALS AND METHODS

Culture of *Arthrobacter* species

Organisms were obtained from the National Collection of Industrial Bacteria (NCIB). They were *Arthrobacter viscosus* NCIB 9728, a polysaccharide producer

(14), and *Arthrobacter globiformis* NCIB 8605, a common soil bacterium and non-polysaccharide producer (15). The culture nutrient broth used is given in Table 1.

Table 1. *Arthrobacter* spp. culture nutrient broth

	g/l
Glucose	10.0
Peptone	5.0
Caesin hydrolysate	3.0
Yeast extract	3.0
Magnesium sulphate heptahydrate	1.0

Shake flasks (200 rpm) containing 1 l. of nutrient broth were inoculated with 5.0 ml of stored culture and incubated at 25°C. After 48 hours biomass production was $0.4\pm\pm 5\%$ mg dry cell wt./ml, *A.viscosus* and $0.6\pm 5\%$ mg dry cell wt./ml *A.globiformis*.

Measurement of cadmium uptake in shake flasks

Cells were harvested from the culture flasks by centrifugation for five minutes at 5000 g. The sedimented cells were washed twice with distilled water, re-centrifuged and then placed in shake flasks containing 100 ml of distilled water. Various cadmium concentrations were then made up by addition of analytical grade cadmium chloride. All glassware was pretreated with dimethyl-dichlorosilane to prevent surface adsorption of cadmium.

To measure cadmium levels remaining in solution after different exposure times (at 25oC), samples were withdrawn and any biomass separated by centrifugation at 5000 g for five minutes. Cadmium concentration in the supernatant was determined by differential pulse polarography with sodium acetate at 6 g/l as an electrolyte.

Dry cell weights were calculated from air drying at 100°C measured volumes of washed cell suspensions.

A pH of 7 ± 0.1 was maintained in all experiments without need for buffer addition. This level has been found to be best suited to biomass adsorption of cadmium (9).

Measurement of cadmium uptake in a BFB

A 1.06 m long, 0.055 m ID plexiglass tube was used as the BFB. The entire system was operated as a closed loop with a liquid volume of 20 l. The bed consisted of 800 g of 1.00-1.18 mm diameter sand, expanded to 200% by a liquid flow rate of 9.0 l/min. Air was injected at 10 l/min to maintain a dissolved oxygen level above 4 mg/l.

Control runs were conducted to determine the bed uptake in the absence of biomass. Cadmium chloride (2.0 g) was added to 20 l distilled water to make up a 100 mg/l concentration. After less than five minutes circulation uptake equilibrium was attained and bed adsorption was measured at 120 mg ± 3%, i.e. 6% of available cadmium.

Bed innoculation with *A.viscosus* was at the shake flask ratios of organisms to medium broth. The organisms were cultured in the bed for 48 hours in the nutrient broth (over which time the temperature was 26 ± 1^oC and pH 7 ± 0.5) before adding cadmium. The cadmium concentration in solution after exposure was determined as described previously.

RESULTS

Cadmium uptake by nutrient broth

Results on *Arthrobacter* spp. accumulation of cadmium discussed in this report are achieved with washed cells in nutrient-free conditions. This approach has been adopted primarily as industrial effluents are generally nutrient-deficient. In addition, apart from the wastage (and organic pollution) incurred by introducing a broth solution into waste streams, the complex organic molecules presented will probably compete for the metal ions. As it is intended that the biomass be immobilised, then any metals not adsorbed by it will be 'flushed' through the system and not recovered.

Experiments were conducted to ascertain the level to which cadmium is taken up by the broth used to culture the organisms. Agitated flasks containing 20 ml sterile broth and 80 ml distilled water were exposed to 50 mg/l and 100 mg/l cadmium and the depletion of cadmium in solution recorded over one hour.

Figure 1 shows the results of these trials. Equilibrium for both concentrations was reached within five minutes. Of available cadmium, uptake by 20 ml of broth represents 21% at 50 mg/l and 15% at 100 mg/l.

An additional study compared the cadmium uptake efficiency of 48 hour cultures of *A.viscosus* in broth (37 mg biomass in 20 ml broth/80 ml distilled water) and in distilled water only (37 mg in 100 ml). In the presence of nutrient, at 100 mg/l cadmium, uptake efficiency was decreased by 14%.

Cadmium uptake by *Arthrobacter* Species

Cadmium uptake by the *Arthrobacter* spp. was initially studied in 250 ml shake flasks. Duplicates of washed biomass from 48 hour cultures ($36.8 \pm 5\%$ mg *A.viscosus* and $55.2 \pm 5\%$ mg *A.globiformis*) were placed in 100 ml of distilled water, agitated and treated to cadmium concentrations of 10 - 200 mg/l. Solution pH was 7.0 and the temperature maintained at 25^oC. The depletion of cadmium in solution was recorded over one hour and the results presented in Figures 2 and 3.

For both species uptake equilibrium was reached within 10 minutes of exposure with over 85% of the accumulation level achieved before five minutes. In agreement with previous work for other types of biomass (9, 10, 13), increasing cadmium concentration does produce a corresponding increase in the uptake ratio (mgCd/g dry cell weight). However, above 50 mg/l cadmium, *A.globiformis* uptake increases only slightly suggesting near saturation. Whereas for *A.viscosus* the steady rise is similar to those recorded for *Bacillus cereus* and *Aspergillus niger* over the range 5-80 mg/l (13).

As anticipated, cadmium uptake by *A.viscosus* is significantly greater than by *A. globiformis*. From Figure 4 it can be seen that the excretion of a poly-saccharide gel matrix (analysed as galactose, glucose and D-mannuronic acid 14)) provides a progressively enhanced cadmium accumulation advantage with increased initial levels. After five minutes exposure *A.globiformis* removed 47% of available cadmium at 10 mg/l reducing to 6% at 200 mg/l. Despite 33%

less biomass per exposure test, *A.viscosus* performed significantly better with removal efficiencies of 65% and 17% respectively.

The nature of cadmium attachment is suspected to be primarily cationic and therefore sensitive to pH. Preliminary work to desorb the ions back into solution by decreasing the pH with nitric acid achieved 60-70% removal with 0.1 N HCl. Equilibrium was reached within 5 minutes of initial exposure to the acid and the biomass washed and returned to medium broth continued to grow.

Cadmium uptake in a BFB

The aim of our work is to devise practical means for using suitable micro-organisms in the continuous heavy metal decontamination of effluent streams. A BFB suggests one approach, especially as the biomass can be contained through immobilisation on support particles. However, as with any treatment system, it is important to ensure biomass re-use in the BFB by regeneration through metal desorption. Otherwise excessive production will add to disposal problems and raise costs through increased nutrient broth demand.

For re-use to be considered the micro-organisms need to be kept viable in order to maintain good adhesion to the support particles. Consequently the organisms will require feeding, but to avoid introducing nutrient into the effluent a simple two stage process has been used in this investigation. The bed is first innoculated with *A.viscosus* and broth circulated to encourage growth and sand colonisation. After a set period the broth is filtered and diverted to a holding tank, the sand and attached biomass washed and then cadmium charged water used to re-fluidise the bed.

By not running the BFB under aseptic conditions, contamination from airborne organisms was to be expected. As the intention of this initial work was to compare the performance of *A.viscosus* in BFBs and flask cultures, it was necessary to determine when the onset of significant contamination occurs. Several runs over 10 days were therefore initiated and in each case after 48-60 hours from innoculation, the presence of a foreign organism could be observed (a pink gram + ve coccus). In these runs, with broth continuously circulated, onset of growth contamination could also be detected by comparing the cadmium uptake ratios of sand and attached biomass.

In order to conduct adsorption trials without disturbing culture growth, approximately 20 g of sand and biomass was periodically removed, washed and exposed to 25 mg/l and 50 mg/l cadmium. By comparing uptake ratios 48 hours from innoculation with those after extended periods, between 48 and 60 hours a marked drop in the ratio can be readily detected (Figure 5). The ratios after 60 hours for 25 mg/l and 50 mg/l cadmium were 61% and 69% respectively of the 48 hour values.

In a further series of experiments, broth circulation was stopped after 48 hours and the bed flushed through with distilled water. Fresh distilled water (20 l) was then circulated and cadmium charged to concentrations of 25-100 mg/l. Uptake equilibrium was reached within five minutes and although uptake ratios were reduced to 29-38% of the 48 hour shake flask cultures (Figure 6), the percentage removal values were similar.

Uptake ratios do however compare favourably with the reported 1.9-3.6 mgCd/g dry cell wt. for a BFB (18). In the quoted reference, the BFB was innoculated with a mixed microbial population taken from a river contaminated with heavy metals. The organisms were allowed to establish over 10 days in growth medium before exposure to a 73 mg/l mixture of metals (cadmium, zinc, copper, lead and iron). The use of a metal 'cocktail' suggests a reason for comparatively poor cadmium uptake due to binding site competition. Nevertheless significantly lower *A.viscosus* dry cell weight to sand ratios of 0.32-0.44% (Figure 6), compared to 1.2-2.2% indicate superior adsorption capability, even after only 48 hours establishment.

CONCLUSIONS

Micro-organism biomass can provide a useful and rapid means of extracting cadmium from a contaminated liquid effluent.

Arthrobacter spp. which have not previously been exposed to the metal exhibit uptake ratios comparable, and in many instances better than, previously reported findings with other species. In particular *A.viscosus* through its tendency to excrete a capsular polysaccharide coating provides enhanced cadmium uptake. At 200 mg/l cadmium, *A.viscosus* adsorbs 93 mgCd/g dry cell weight compared to 22 mgCd/g dry cell weight by *A.globiformis*, a non-excreting organism. As the metal can be desorbed and recovered from *A.viscosus* by altering the pH, cationic attraction is a probable means of attachment.

The use of a biological fluidised bed is a potential means of contacting immobilised *A.viscosus* with a liquid effluent. However, development is necessary to discourage the growth of organisms which can reduce the bed's uptake efficiency by up to 67%. This may be achieved by providing a nutrient broth that restricts the organisms to those with optimal metal uptake. For example, a selective nutrient broth for *Arthrobacter* spp. is under trial which is claimed to inhibit other gram +ve bacteria (15), the major contaminant in the reported results.

REFERENCES

1.   VALLEE, B.L. and ULMER, D.D., Ann.Rev.Biochem. 1972, 41, 91.

2.   BESZEDITS, S. and WEI, N.S., B. and L. Information Service, Toronto, Canade, 1980.

3.   BABICH, H. and STOTZKY, G. App.Env.Microbiol., 1977, 33, 681.

4.   CHANG, L.W., REUHL, K.R. and WADE, P.R., "Cadmium in the Environment Part II, Health Effects". Ed. NRIAGU, J.O., John Wiley, New York.

5.   NAKAJIMA, A., HORIKOSHI, T. and SAKAGUCHI, T. Eur.J.Appl.Microbiol. Biotechnol., 1981, 12, 76.

6.   NEUFELD, R.D. and HERMANN, E.R., J.Wat.Polln.Cont.Fed. 1975, 47, 310.

7.   CHENG, M.H., PATTERSON, J.W. and MINEAR, R.A., J.Wat.Polln.Cont.Fed. 1975, 47, 362.

8.   SAKAGUCHI, T., TSUJI, T.,NAKAJIMA, A. and HORIKOSHI, T., Eur.J.Appl. Microbiol. 1979, 8, 207.

9.   NORBERG, A.B. and PERSSON, H. 1984 Biotechnol.Bioeng., 26, 239.

10. MACASKIE, L.E. and DEAN, A.C.R., J.Gen.Microbios. 1984, 130, 53.

11. FRIEDMAN, B.A. and DUGAN, P.R., Dev.Ind.Microbiol. 1967, 9, 381.

12. IKEDA, F., SHUTO, H., SAITO, T., FUKUI, T. and TOMITA, K. Eur.J. Biochem. 1982, 123, 437.

13. DOYLE, J.J., MARSHAL, R.T. and PFANDER, W.H., Appl.Microbiol. 1975, 29, 562.

14. GASDORF, H.J., BENEDICT, R.G., CADMUS, M.C., ANDERSON, R.F. and JACKSON, R.W., J.Bacteriol. 1965, 90, 147.

15. KEDDIE, R.M. and JONES, D. "The Prokaryotes" Vol. 2, 1983, Chapt. 142, 1842.

16. WILKINSON, J.F. Bacteriol.Rev., 1958, 22, 46.

17. CORPE, W.A., Dev.Ind.Microbiol. 1975, 16, 249.

18. REMACLE, J. and HOUBA, C., Env.Technol.Letts., 1983, 4, 53.

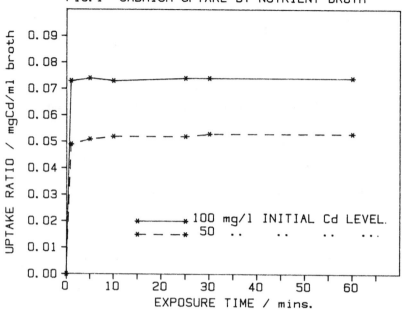

FIG. 1 CADMIUM UPTAKE BY NUTRIENT BROTH

100 mg/l INITIAL Cd LEVEL.
50 .. ..

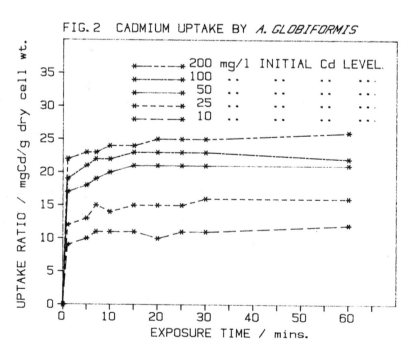

FIG. 2 CADMIUM UPTAKE BY *A. GLOBIFORMIS*

200 mg/l INITIAL Cd LEVEL.
100 .. ..
50 .. ..
25 .. ..
10 .. ..

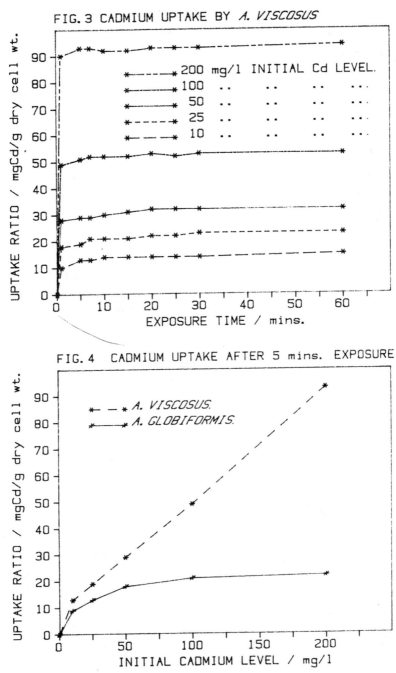

FIG. 3 CADMIUM UPTAKE BY *A. VISCOSUS*

FIG. 4 CADMIUM UPTAKE AFTER 5 mins. EXPOSURE

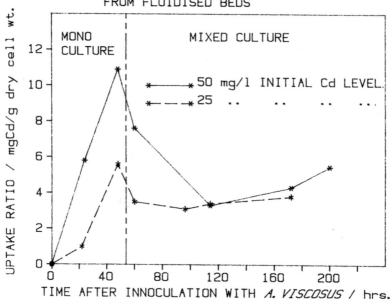

FIG. 5   CADMIUM UPTAKE BY ATTACHED BIOMASS
         FROM FLUIDISED BEDS

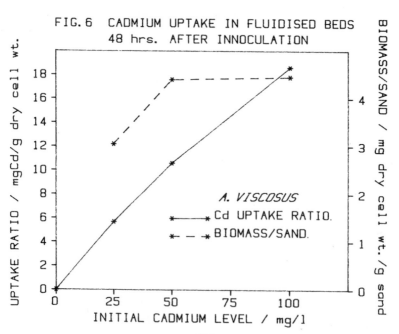

FIG. 6   CADMIUM UPTAKE IN FLUIDISED BEDS
         48 hrs. AFTER INNOCULATION

RECOVERY OF METAL FROM EFFLUENT BY ELECTRODEPOSITION

D.R.Gabe+ and P.A.Makanjuola

In a previous symposium (no. 77, paper 21) the need to treat metal-containing effluent in a positive manner was emphasised so that the product is immediately re-usable and not just dumped or recycled to a smelter. A range of electrowinning processes, especially tailored to effluent treatment, are now available and some criteria for selecting an appropriate process are discussed.

The processes also offer opportunities for optimization and enhancement both for efficiency and production rate and these aspects are described. One such method of enhancement - use of rough electrode surfaces - is discussed in detail.

ESSENCE OF A PROCESS

At a previous symposium in this series (1) the need to assume a positive approach to effluent treatment was emphasised. In the case of metal-containing solutions this implies the ability to recover metal in a directly re-usable form, and not as a precipitated salt or sludge which may necessitate steps for purification, possibly smelting and certainly reduction to the metallic state, or redissolution. For the metal finishing trade, or for in-house metal finishing operations, it is obvious that the technology of metal finishing ought to be exploited but while the advantages are clear the possible disadvantages should not be disregarded. Such disadvantages include the possible interference or accumulation of process additives and impurities and the difficulty of recovering metal efficiently from waste solutions which inevitably tend to contain low residual ion concentrations.

A number of commercial processes are now available for metal recovery by electrowinning (ie cathodic deposition) and they enable metal to be produced as a powder, as solid electrode capable of being melted or re-used as a soluble anode in an electroplating process, or as regenerated concentrated process solutions. The field has recently been reviewed (2,3) and the range of effective processes is summarized in Table 1.

+ Dept. of Materials Engineering and Design, Loughborough University of Technology.

TABLE 1 - Enhanced Mass Transfer by Cell Design

---

1. Two-dimensional electrodes.

    (a) Static electrode, superimposed flow:
         Parallel plate, filter press cells

    (b) Rotating electrodes:
         Rotating cylinder, disc, stacked discs.
         Pump cell, rolling tubes.

2. Three-dimensional electrodes.

    (a) Particulate electrodes:
         Fluidized bed, packed bed.

    (b) Solid electrode, three dimensional shape:
         Porous metal, mesh electrode,
         Trickle tower, carbon fibres etc.

Selection of an appropriate process depends upon the specific technical requirements, production throughput and cost-effectiveness, but it may also have to be compact, convenient, and simple to operate. Some of these criteria were discussed previously (1) and included cathode current efficiency at low metal concentration, some aspects of energy and materials costs, value of the recovered metal (and water), and control needed to operate the process. It is now proposed to discuss some other factors important in increasing process optimization and efficiency.

PROCESS OPTIMIZATION

Electrochemical processes for metal recovery are usually operated at or near their limit where quantity rather than quality of deposit is a prime consideration; ie they are mass transfer controlled. In cases where this is not so, process optimization depends upon a subjective characteristic - deposit quality - and the mode of optimization is radically affected. This being so, the simplest optimization is based upon a cost-effective and "horses for courses" basis where true process optimization is either irrelevant or inappropriate; it is often the attitude when an overriding factor prevails such as in the recovery of gold or when water utilization is vital.

When mass transfer control exists then the means of optimization can be simply expressed by a mass transfer coefficient or by the limiting current equation for the electrodeposition reaction:

$$I_L = \frac{ACDnF}{\delta(1-t)}$$

where
- A electrode surface area
- C concentration of metal ions
- D diffusion coefficient of metal ions
- n electron transfer number for the reduction reaction
- F Faraday constant
- δ diffusion layer thickness
- t transport number for the ion.

To maximize I_L, the limiting current, A.C.D.t must be large and δ small. In practice C is dependent upon the effluent feedstock and in any case decreases during metal recovery, D can be increased by increasing the temperature (usually energetically unfavourable) and t can be decreased by raising the level of supporting electrolyte. Consequently, A and δ are the two main design parameters for the process susceptible to real optimization.

The diffusion layer thickness, δ, arises as a consequence of the solution diffusional process of depositon and depends substantially upon the degree and type of agitation applied in the cell or reactor to the electrode/electrolyte interface; simply expressed, the greater the agitation the smaller is δ. Design therefore is concerned with establishing the most agitative and turbulent conditions at as low an agitation rate as possible by selecting the best reactor geometry. The onset of turbulence must be an integral part of this design selection and is expressed as a critical Reynolds number which is in effect a basic parameter of the reactor system; thus

for rotating cylinders   Re (crit) =   200
for pipe or annular flow   2,000
for rotating discs   100,000

where Re = Ud/ν, U being the relative velocity of movement, d the critical dimension of the system and ν the fluid's viscosity.

Having achieved turbulence for maximum effect, the effectiveness of the prevailing agitation can be expressed simply as the value of δ, the following values being average or typical:

natural convection   0.1-0.2mm
planar/annular surfaces   0.01-0.2
rotating cylinders   0.005-0.05
gas-generating electrodes   0.002-0.04
surface abrasion/scraping   0.01-0.1
ultrasonic agitation   0.005-0.01

Increasing the surface area of the electrolyte/electrode interface is achieved in two ways: firstly, by using bigger electrodes and secondly by using the catalysis principle of extended area surface ie rough or porous surfaces. Using bigger electrodes immediately implies bigger reactors and bigger capital costs, so ingenuity is necessary to increase the surface area within a given volume. Thus planar electrodes spirally sandwiched as in the "Swiss-Roll" or "Jelly-Roll" cells have been used. Three dimensional electrodes may include packed particles or fluidized beds, or porous/permeable electrodes. Roughened surfaces are usually described as enhanced electrodes because like turbulence promoters in a flow stream they leave the apparent surface area unchanged but act as enhancers by promoting microturbulence at an increased true surface area electrode. This approach will be discussed separately.

If reactor geometry and size, as a cost factor, is introduced a new criterion for optimization is required and this is usually expressed as a space-time yield (4). Kreysa (5-7) in particular has developed this concept to include energy consumption or throughput expressed as a fluid velocity term. Values for comparison can be found in the literature (4-8).

Other factors may become important in specific instances one of which should be noted. If a thermodynamic factor for reaction selectivity is significant the ability to control electrode potential may be a vital additional consideration. Three ways may be cited.

(a) As metal concentration falls in a depleted electrolyte during cathodic deposition of metal in a batch process, the evolution of hydrogen becomes more likely thereby leading to reduced cathodic current efficiency. Potentiostatic control can minimize this second reaction. However, it should be noted that this is not usually regarded as a serious loss of energy in the overall energy balance.

(b) If two or more metals are present in the waste liquor, selective separation is possible by careful choice of depostion potentials whereby the most noble metal deposits preferentially (9). This can be achieved by using a potentiostat with an equi-potential electrode surface, an important characteristic of some of the newer generation of reactor geometries notably the rotating cylinder. Other geometries do not have such selectivity as a feasible option and therefore operate best for single metal liquors.

(c) Potentiostatic control may also be desirable if, despite the presence of only one metal in the liquor, other side reactions can take place. Thus in the electrolytic recovery of silver from photographic wastes if the potential is allowed to rise too much cathodic decomposition of the thiosulphate anion may take place with the consequent co-deposition of sulphur or silver sulphide which makes the process unacceptable (10).

$$E > -0.7V \,(SCS) \qquad Ag^+ + \varepsilon \qquad Ag$$
$$E < -0.75V \qquad Ag^+ + \varepsilon \qquad Ag$$
$$\text{and} \qquad S_2O_3^{2-} + 2\varepsilon \qquad SO_3^{2-} + S^{2-}$$

Although this discussion has primarily been concerned with process design, reactor engineering design and design by materials selection are also important and a fuller consideration can be found elsewhere (11).

ENHANCEMENT THROUGH SURFACE ROUGHNESS

It is well-established that increased roughness at the electrode/electrolyte interface has two effects:

(a) it provides increased area for interfacial reaction;

(b) it increases the friction factor and consequently the interfacial micro-turbulence.

These are separate yet inter-related effects making them rather difficult to distinguish quantitatively or analytically. Thus the friction factor has been known substantially since the days of Reynolds yet for electrochemical mass transfer is only now being analysed, determined and measured numerically. Its effect is easy to recognize because when a metal is deposited under mass-transfer-controlled conditions the deposit becomes rough and powdery or dendritic and allows enhanced rates of metal recovery. Using a simple power law of the type

$$I = const \; U^n$$

where I is the deposition current, U is the relative velocity at the interface and n is a power indice, it has been shown that the value of n increases as the surface roughens. Typically, for a rotating cylinder electrode n = 0.7 for a smooth surface and n $\geq$ 0.9 for a rough surface (8). Expressed graphically (see fig. 1), however, it may be seen that both the power indice and intercept increase (12).

In fundamental mass transport terms a relationship of the type

$$Sh = const\ Re^a\ Sc^b$$

must be employed because other experimental parameters such as viscosity, diffusivity etc have to be considered (Sherwood No., Sh = $K_L d/D$; Schmidt No., Sc = ν/D). In this expression Sh can take account of area enhancement and the constant can take account of changes in the friction factor. It is only possible to separate these two effects if detailed mass transfer data is available for a surface of defined and characterized roughness, a condition not generally feasible for a growing dendritic metal electrodeposit during the production of metal in electrowinning at effluent treatment processes.

The changing character of the electrode surface and its effect on recovery efficacy can be recognized in several ways and examples are given. Firstly, if the process is operated at constant current the overpotential falls with time (13) because if the limiting current is being applied initially when the surface area increases the current used is necessarily less than the limiting value and the associated concentration overpotential is consequently lower (fig. 2). Secondly, if the process is operated potentiostatically at a potential substantially into the limiting current density region, limiting *current density* conditions can be maintained and the *current* will rise proportionally with the increase in active surface area (fig. 3) (13). Thirdly, the consequent effect on metal recovery expressed as a solution depletion is clear (fig. 4). If a smooth electrode is used throughout concentration falls exponentially with time (ie log C falls linearly with t). However, as a rough surface is nucleated and becomes stable faster depletion occurs making the reactor apparently excessively efficient. This feature has been exploited successfully and has been discussed in detail elsewhere (8,9,12).

This behaviour has recently been studied in depth and the key to its understanding can be seen in fig. 1, ie the changes in slope and intercept must be separately analysed. Clearly if the true current density can be determined or the true friction factor measured experimentally the influence of the two factors can be separated. This has been achieved by using especially pre-roughened electrode surfaces whose roughness or area can be geometrically determined and expressed in a quantitative manner. It is then possible to calculate a true mass transfer coefficient (K_L) or dimensionless group (Sh), the correlation replotted and a degree of mass transfer enhancement calculated.

The rotating cylinder electrode in turbulent flow has been used for this study and a range of roughened cylinders produced by machining, knurling, grooving and the use of superimposed meshes (14, 15). The limiting current has been measured using a pulse method, applicable in the period 20-50s of electrodeposition after a pseudo-equilibrium behaviour has been established and before significant additional rough growth has taken place on the pre-roughened surface (15). This pulse method can also be used to determine roughness when suitably calibrated. A typical set of data is given in fig. 5 for a longitudinally grooved cylinder compared to a smooth cylinder of classical form whose behaviour conforms to the well-known correlation:

$$Sh = 0.079\ Re^{0.66}\ Sc^{0.33}$$

These roughened cylinders behave in two ways.

(a) At 8000 < Re < 20000, $K_L \alpha U^{1.169}$ and marked enhancement occurs.

(b) At 20000 < Re < 100000, $K_L \alpha U^{0.578}$ which is still enhanced but shows a marked drop in coefficient.

The lower range is clearly very effective at increasing mass transfer but the higher range is also characterized by an increase in friction factor from 0.079 to 0.567. The onset of the upper range depends upon the type and degree of roughness and is associated with turbulent eddies within the roughness elements themselves and their mixing with the main stream fluid.

Comparison of the differing types of roughness may be made in several ways. The simplest is by a graphical approach in which a defined mass transfer parameter such as Sh is used and for which equivalent data can be obtained and numerically assessed. This also reveals that some roughness geometries have a wide effect while others are similar in effect despite apparent variations in degree of roughness (peak height values). In fig. 6 several types of roughness are compared using a modified Sherwood No. (taking account of area) over a range of Reynolds nos.

The effectiveness of various types of roughness can be compared in terms of an enhancement factor given by (Sh_R/Sh_s) at a given Reynolds number, where R and S refer to rough and smooth surfaces. Values are tabulated in Table II and assume that the whole surface area is active and that no catalytic action takes place.

TABLE II - Enhancement Factors for Rough Cylinders

Type of roughness	Enhancement factor $(^{Sh}R/^{Sh}s)$ range	
Longitudinal grooves	1.48-3.0	*
Spiral grooves	2.1-2.9	*
Pyramidal knurls	1.4-3.4	*
Truncated pyramidal knurls	2.1-3.5	*
Truncated 'v' grooves	1.1-2.5	*
Circumferential grooves	1.4-2.0	+
Wire wound	1.0-2.1	‡
Abraded roughness	2.3-2.8	*
Woven screen mesh	0.8-3.2	o

* Peak value at Re = 8-15 x 10^3

+ No sharp peak. Optimum at Re = 15x10^3

‡ Peak value at Re ~ 25x10^3

o Peak value at Re ~ 70x10^3

N.B. Sh_R has been calculated using rough electrodes and the true and not projected surface area.

On this basis an optimum type of roughness or geometrical style and range of velocity can be defined to give the most effective electrochemical mass transfer, and certain types of roughness pattern disregarded. It also explains the known behaviour in rotating cylinder cell reactors and although this data has been obtained for a metal cathodic deposition process should apply equally to other reactions whether redox or anodic. If platinized platinum catalytic surfaces are employed fresh considerations may need to be made depending upon the type of catalytic behaviour observed and obviously whether mass transfer control is still relevant.

Use of surface roughness clearly can increase the space-time yield for a reactor and when combined with highly turbulent conditions effectively combines two techniques. Whether the additional rotational power required is justifiable is probably a cost-effectiveness consideration for any given process.

In a conventional electrolytic recovery process smooth electrodes are used initially and which build up dendritic roughness over a period of $\frac{1}{4}$-1 hour during which time enhancement developes naturally. Powder is then removed by scraping whereupon the cycle is repeated[8-12]. The advantage of using pre-roughened electrodes is that the process is not dependent upon time-varying roughness and that performance is more consistent and is always enhanced.

REFERENCES

1. Gabe,D.R.,1983,Inst.Chem.Eng.Symposium Ser.No.77,291.

2. Walsh,F.C. and Gabe,D.R., 1982, Electrochem.Soc.Symp.,83-12, 'Electroplating engineering and waste recycle' (ed.Snyder, Landau and Sard) 314.

3. Marshall,R.J. and Walsh,F.C.,1985,Surf.Tech.24,45.

4. Goodridge,F.,1974,Proc.24th Int.Cong.Pure Appl.Chem.,Butterworths, London,5,19.

5. Kreysa,G.,1981,Electrochim.Acta.,26, 1693.

6. Kreysa,G.,1981,Metallob.,35,211.

7. Kreysa,G.,1985,J.Appl.Electrochim.,15,175.

8. Gabe,D.R. and Walsh,F.C.,1983,ibid,13,3.

9. Walsh,F.C. and Gabe,D.R.,1981,Surf.Tech.,12,25.

10. Walsh,F.C. and Saunders,D.E.,1983,J.Photo.Sci.,31,35.

11. Gabe,D.R. and Walsh,F.C.,Ref.2.

12. Gabe,D.R. and Walsh,F.C.,1984,J.Appl.Electrochem.,14,555,565.

13. Robinson,D.J. and Gabe,D.R.,1970,1971,Trans.Inst.Met.Fin.,48,35;49,17.

14. Makanjuola,P.A. and Gabe,D.R.,1985,Surf.Tech.,24,29.

15. Gabe.D.R. and Makanjuola,P.A., to be published.

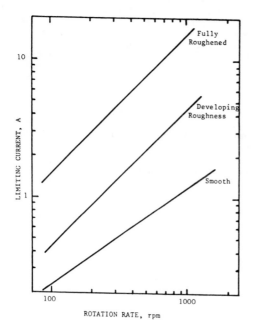

Fig.1.

Limiting current as a function of rotation speed for the RCE for cathodic deposition of copper from 0.014M CuSO$_4$ (data from ref.12).

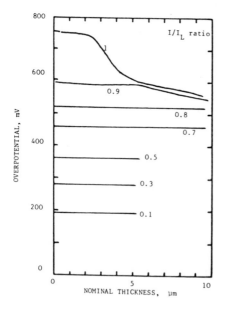

Fig.2.

Change of cathodic over-potential with time (or nominal deposit thickness) for various increments of limiting current (0.07M CuSO$_4$; 22°C; RCE at 900rpm) (see ref. 13).

228

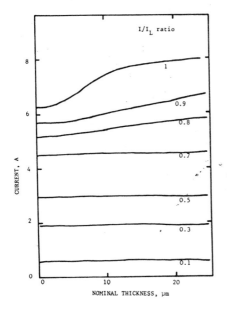

Fig.3.

Change of cathodic current with time (or nominal deposit thickness) at initial fractions of the limiting current under potentiostatic control ($0.7M$ $CuSO_4$; $22°C$; RCE at 300rpm) (see ref.13).

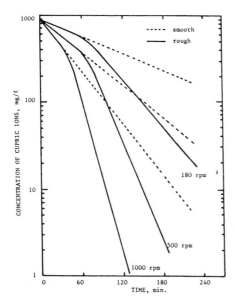

Fig.4.

Concentration decay with time for a RCE batch reactor and cathodic depostion of copper from acid sulphate solution (data from ref.9).

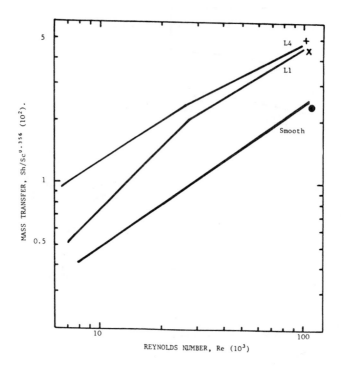

Fig.5.

Mass transfer correlation for smooth and 'v' grooved rotating cylinders (data from ref.14).

- ● smooth cylinder
- x 63 grooves, depth 0.0174cm, 3.0cm diameter cylinder.
- + 63 grooves, depth 0.054cm, 3.0cm diameter cylinder.

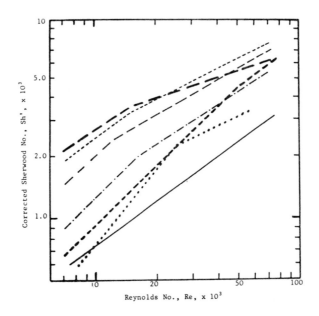

Fig.6.

Mass transfer correlation for several types of roughness using a
modified (corrected) Sherwood Number as a function of Reynolds Number.

Smooth cylinder	———————
Longitudinal 'v' grooves	— — — —
Circumferential 'v' grooves	— · — · — · —
Pyramidal knurling	- - - - - - - -
Wire wound cylinders	▬ ▬ ▬ ▬
Weave screen (fine)	· · · · · · · ·
Weave screen (coarser)	▬▬ ▬▬ ▬▬

THE DISPOSAL OF PRODUCTS AND WASTES FROM FLUE GAS
DESULPHURIZATION PROCESSES

W.S. Kyte* and J.R.P. Cooper**

One of the most rapidly expanding effluent treatment
processes is the use of flue gas desulphurization (FGD)
for removing sulphur dioxide from electric power plant
flue gases.

In this paper the various methods of flue gas
desulphurization are described and their potential
applicability to the United Kingdom is discussed.

Flue gas desulphurization processes remove sulphur
dioxide by converting the sulphur dioxide into other
sulphur compounds which must then be satisfactorily
disposed of in some manner. The various processes are
therefore discussed in relation to the disposal of their
products, by-products and wastes.

INTRODUCTION

One of the most rapidly expanding effluent treatment processes is the use of
flue gas desulphurization (FGD) for removing sulphur dioxide from boiler flue
gases. Over the past fifteen years about 100,000 MW of boilers worldwide
have been or are being fitted with flue gas desulphurization plant treating
over 3×10^8 m³/hr of flue gases.

Much of the debate about processes for the removal of sulphur dioxide
from the flue gas emissions of power plant has centred on economic and
technical questions. The imposition of sulphur dioxide emission limits on
power stations can substantially increase the cost of electricity production
and can involve the utility operator in technologies that lie in the realm of
the chemical industry. In order to be familiar with these technologies, their
cost and problems if such plant were to be installed in the United Kingdom,
the Central Electricity Generating Board (CEGB) has undertaken engineering and
cost studies of processes relevant to the UK situation. The results of these
studies have been presented elsewhere (1,2,3). Further studies are currently
being undertaken.
 One important fact that these studies have shown is that all flue
gas desulphurization processes can produce large quantities of solid and
liquid products. These products and any waste products must be disposed of in
a satisfactory manner so that secondary environmental pollution problems do

*Central Electricity Generating Board, Technology Planning & Research
Division, Central Electricity Research Laboratories, Leatherhead, Surrey.
**Central Electricity Generating Board, Generation Design & Construction
Division, Barnwood, Gloucester.

not occur. It is the intention of this paper to examine some of the issues that could arise in considering the disposal of the products and wastes of FGD processes. However, before discussing these a brief review of the FGD processes relevant to possible installation on large utility boilers in the United Kingdom will be given.

POST-COMBUSTION FLUE GAS DESULPHURIZATION (FGD) PROCESSES

There are well over one hundred different flue gas desulphurization processes available in various degrees of development, ranging from the laboratory bench through the small pilot plant scale to full scale commercial units. A detailed review of the more important FGD processes available has been published (4), and hence only a brief outline of those processes with some relevance to the UK will be given here.

Modern methods of FGD began with the construction of various British plants (Battersea, Fulham, Bankside, North Wilford) during the period 1930-1960 (5). No further FGD plants have been built in Britain since then due to the proven success of tall stacks in controlling ground level sulphur dioxide concentrations within acceptable limits at the points of maximum impact (6). On the other hand, the early British work on FGD has been extended in the USA, Japan and W. Germany and there are now many FGD plants installed in these countries. However, the differences between UK and overseas conditions make it difficult to extrapolate directly experience into the UK context; for example, British coals have an average chlorine content (0.25 wt%) which is considerably higher than that normally found elsewhere. On combustion this chloride is converted almost quantitatively to hydrogen chloride. Chlorides interfere with the process chemistry of most FGD processes and contaminate marketable products. Hence if such FGD processes were to be installed in the United Kingdom a chloride removal step would be required.

Once-Through Wet Processes

The first FGD units installed in the world, at Battersea and Bankside, were once-through processes which made use of the natural alkalinity of the River Thames. The river water was cycled through the FGD plant and then, after suitable processing, discharged back to the river. Since the FGD plants were small and the river was already relatively polluted the effect of the effluent on the river quality was minimal. The only other process in this category is one which uses sea-water as the scrubbing liquid, but for a modern large power station the natural alkalinity of sea water would not be sufficient and addition of extra limestone would be required. The dispersion of effluents from the sea-water process in estuaries and the sea and the effects of the effluents on marine life have not yet been fully assessed.

Throwaway Wet Processes

In these processes the alkaline absorbent liquor is recirculated in a closed loop. The sulphated reaction products are separated off and fresh absorbent is added. The only water usage is to cover losses by evaporation and that entrained with the product. A purge is usually required to control impurity levels.

Lime or limestone/sludge processes (Figure 1)

The vast majority of scrubbing systems installed in the United States use lime or limestone as the alkali to neutralize the sulphur dioxide. The resulting reaction product, a calcium sulphite/sulphate mixture is then disposed of in ponds or disused mines. This mixture is very difficult to de-water and forms a thixotropic solid commonly known as 'sludge'. Fixation methods, including mixing with fly ash, cement, lime, soil etc. are often used to stabilize the sludge but the disposal of the waste is still difficult (7).

This process has had little application in Europe or Japan and even in the US the trend is now towards the use of an oxidation step to produce a more amenable product, calcium sulphate (gypsum).

Because of the disposal difficulties and because the sludge processes have little or no overall economic advantages over similar processes producing gypsum, sludge processes are not considered to be applicable in the United Kingdom.

Gypsum Processes (Figure 2)

Since the disposal of sulphite/sulphate sludges is difficult there has been an incentive to produce a more amenable product. Gypsum ($CaSO_4 \cdot 2H_2O$) is such a product since if it is produced in a suitable form it may be possible to sell it for the manufacture of plasterboard, bag plaster or as a cement setting retardant. In principle, any lime/limestone processes can be made to produce gypsum by the addition of an oxidation step in which calcium sulphite is oxidized to gypsum by air injection. Some of these processes can produce gypsum of marketable quality.

A further advantage of these systems is that by recycling gypsum crystals back to the absorber to act as seeds for crystallization the propensity for scale formation in the absorber circuit is minimised.

Regenerative Wet Processes

In these processes the absorbent is chemically or thermally regenerated for reuse and a saleable product (liquified SO_2, sulphur or sulphuric acid) is produced. Ideally, there should be no disposal problems but all the processes produce some by-products which means that there is still a need for absorbent make-up and for by-product disposal.

Wellman-Lord process (Figure 3)

The Wellman-Lord process is based on the absorption of sulphur dioxide in a concentrated solution of sodium sulphite and the regeneration of the resultant bisulphite solution by steam stripping in an evaporator-crystalliser. The process produces a pure concentrated sulphur dioxide gas stream which can be readily converted to sulphur or sulphuric acid. Sodium sulphate must be disposed of as a by-product.

Magnesium oxide process (Figure 4)

In this process an aqueous slurry of magnesium hydroxide is used to absorb sulphur dioxide. The resulting magnesium sulphite is separated off and calcined to release sulphur dioxide and to regenerate the absorbent. The sulphur dioxide produced can be used to manufacture sulphuric acid. It is also possible to produce sulphur as the final product.

Alkali Injection Into the Combustion Chamber

Not all the sulphur present in the coal ends up as sulphur dioxide in the flue gases after combustion. A small proportion reacts with alkaline elements in the coal and is then fixed and removed with the ash, the actual amount depending on the alkalinity of the ash present in the coal. In the dry injection method alkali, usually slaked lime or limestone, is injected into the hot boiler gases where it reacts with the sulphur oxides and is then removed after reaction. Equipment for preparation of the alkali, its injection into and removal from the flue gas is required.

Under UK conditions, it is unlikely that the maximum removal efficiency will be greater than 40% with a limestone to sulphur stoichiometry of 2. This means that large amounts of limestone would need to be imported into a station and disposal would be required for large quantities of product and calcined reagent mixed with fly ash. A recent economic evaluation has shown that such a process would not be economic in the UK compared to wet processes (8).

Spray Drying Processes (Figure 5)

During the past few years, the use of spray driers for the absorption of sulphur dioxide has attracted increasing attention. The spray drier in effect replaces the absorber, sulphur dioxide absorption taking place in the aqueous phase of the droplets created by the drier's atomiser. The absorbent used can be either lime, sodium carbonate or bicarbonate. A mixture of product and unreacted absorbent is produced which is then collected in an electrostatic precipitator or bag filter, together with the fly ash produced by combustion. More efficient utilization of the absorbent can be obtained by recycling a proportion of this mixture back to the spray drier. Even so the utilization in lime spray dry systems is not generally as high as in wet lime/limestone systems.

Several advantages are claimed for spray absorption among which are the minimization of reheat, no scaling or plugging, the production of a totally dry product, and low investment. However, large quantities of lime or other alkali must be imported to site and large quantities of partially sulphated reagent are produced which are collected intimately mixed with the fly-ash. This mixture must then be disposed of in a satisfactory manner. This type of system is receiving particular attention in the USA as it is proving less complex and less expensive than wet scrubbers for high calcium-low sulphur coals. The high cost of lime and of disposing of the waste product may make the process less economic than wet processes in the UK for large power plant.

DISPOSAL OF FGD PRODUCTS

One of the most neglected areas of FGD technology is the treatment and disposal of the products, by-products and wastes generated. Some idea of the scale of the problem can be gained from Table 1 which shows the approximate annual imports and exports that might be expected from a 2000 MW power station when using design fuel.

Table 1: Approximate Annual FGD Imports/Exports of a 2000 MW Power Station

(design fuel - 2% S, 0.4% Cl)

Process		Wellman-Lord	Limestone/ Gypsum	Lime/ Spray-dry	Limestone Injection
SO_2 Removal Efficiency		90%	90%	70%	35%
IMPORTS					
Limestone	Solid	33,000	290,000	-	560,000
Lime	Solid	3,300	3,300	250,000	-
Caustic Soda	47% conc.	15,000	-	-	-
Natural Gas	Gas	2.7×10^7 Nm^3	-	-	-
Sulphuric Acid	96% conc.	-	13,000	-	-
EXPORTS					
Sulphur or	Solid	70,000	-	-	-
Sulphuric Acid	96% conc.	220,000	-	-	-
Gypsum	Solid	-	460,000	-	-
Mixed Product	Solid	-	-	450,000	500,000
BY-PRODUCTS					
CaCl$_2$ (impure)	Solid	60,000	60,000	-	-
Na$_2$SO$_4$ (impure)	Solid	12,500	-	-	-
WASTE-WATER					
Treated Water	-	2×10^6	2×10^6	-	-
Sludge (65% solids)	Solid	15,000	40,000	-	-

All quantities are in tonnes/annum.

For comparison the fly ash quantity produced in ~500,000 tonnes/annum.

It can be seen that the quantities of material from some of these processes are of the same order as the amount of fly ash produced. This means that if the CEGB were to undertake a significant programme of flue gas desulphurization it would have to dispose of amounts of products amounting to half or more of the present fly ash produced. Another perspective on the problem is illustrated in Table 2 which shows FGD products as a percentage of existing UK markets. It can be seen that there are only limited markets for all the FGD products and by-products.

Table 2: FGD Products as a Percentage of Existing UK Markets

	2000 MW (2% S, 0.4% Cl)	All UK Coal Fired
H_2SO_4	8%	>100%
S	8%	>100%
HCl	14%	>200%
Gypsum	15%	>200%

Two very important consequences arise from consideration of the imports and exports of these FGD processes. The first is that for any substantial FGD programme it is likely that more than one FGD process would have to be employed. The second consequence is that the location of a particular power station may dictate the process to be used due to the local marketability of the product.

Sulphur and Sulphuric Acid

These products can be produced by the regenerative FGD systems (e.g. Wellman-Lord). They are the most environmentally acceptable products in that both are marketable but in general, these processes are more expensive than the non-regenerative. However, in some situations the much reduced level of imports and exports from a regenerative system may outweigh the increased processing and energy costs.

The production of sulphur, though more expensive than the production of sulphuric acid, may be more attractive in that it has a ready market and is much more easily transported and stored. The production of sulphuric acid from FGD plants would displace sulphuric acid produced by the chemical industry. However, spare stand-by acid capacity would be required as FGD acid production would be governed by electricity demand and not by acid demand. This would affect the acid market and could result in a surplus of acid during periods of low acid demand.

In some cases it may be possible to export compressed or liquified sulphur dioxide to an existing user (e.g. sulphuric acid plants).

Lime Spray-Dry Products

In this process the FGD product is collected intimately mixed with the fly ash in an electrostatic precipitator or bag-house. The FGD product approximately doubles the amount of material (fly ash and product) for disposal and moreover may impart some undesirable properties to the fly ash due to the presence of the sulphated reaction products and of unused slaked lime. There will also be a significant proportion of soluble calcium chloride in the mixture. A typical product composition which might be produced under UK conditions is shown in Table 3.

Table 3:   Calculated Spray-dry Product Composition (UK Coal)

Component	%(wt)
Flyash and inerts	63
$CaSO_3 \cdot \frac{1}{2}H_2O$	21
$CaSO_4 \cdot 2H_2O$	7
$CaCl_2 \cdot 6H_2O$	5
$Ca(OH)_2$	4

The presence of these materials in the fly ash may mean that extra costs would be incurred for the disposal of the total solid product (i.e. the extra disposal costs for the fly ash must be charged to the FGD costs). The nature of the mixed product may mean that sales of ash from the station may be adversely affected unless extra particulate collection devices are installed upstream of the spray drier.

Dry Limestone Injection Products

The product from this process is again collected intimately mixed with the fly ash. The product will be similar to the product from fluidized bed combustion where limestone is added to the combustor for sulphur dioxide control. However, the concentration of free lime in the product will be significantly higher since in the dry limestone injection process the utilization of the limestone is much lower than is the case in fluidized beds. This free lime content of the ash will make ash handling much more difficult. A typical product composition which might be produced under UK conditions is shown in Table 4.

Table 4:   Calculated Direct Limestone Injection

Product Composition (UK Coal)

Component	%(wt) (dry basis)
Fly ash	50
$CaSO_4$	16
CaO	28
$CaCl_2$	6

Gypsum

The majority of FGD plants both in Japan and W. Germany produce gypsum. With a suitable design of plant it is possible to produce gypsum of such a quality that it can replace natural gypsum for the production of plaster-board or for use as a retardant in the manufacture of cement. As only a small percentage of gypsum is added to cements this market would be able to utilize only a very limited amount of FGD gypsum. In the UK the gypsum industry could probably absorb in the region of 6-12,000 MW worth of FGD gypsum. The specification for FGD gypsum to replace natural gypsum is stringent, particularly as regards moisture and chloride content, but with proper plant design and operation wallboard quality gypsum can be produced. An interesting fortuitous coincidence is that the typical UK wallboard plant is well matched to the gypsum output from a typical 2000 MW power station.

Since there is a limited market for gypsum, other disposal routes will be required. Gypsum is a naturally occurring mineral which might be able to be used as a landfill. Also a method of creating artificial hills known as stacking has been developed in the phosphoric acid industry where large quantities of low purity gypsum are produced as a by-product. Whatever the disposal method it would seem advisable to produce wallboard quality gypsum in all gypsum producing FGD processes so that continuity of product for sale could be maintained. This would probably incur very little economic penalty over producing one grade of gypsum for sale and one for dumping. Some typical gypsum guideline specifications are shown in Table 5 (10).

Table 5: Guidelines Issued by Users for Gypsum Purity (adapted from Ref. 10)

	National Gypsum Co.	Georgia-Pacific Co.	US Gypsum Co.	Westroc	German/ Japanese	UK
Gypsum content, minimum %	94	90	-	95	95	95
Calcium sulfite, maximum %	0.5	-	-	-	0.25	0.25
Sodium ion, maximum ppm	500	200	75	80	600	500
Chloride, maximum ppm	800	200	75	80	100	100
Magnesium, maximum ppm	500	-	50	50	1000	1000
Free water, maximum %	15	10	12	10	10	8
pH	6-8	3-9	6.5-8	6-9	5-9	5-8
Particle size, microns	-	-	20-40	-	-	16-63

CHLORIDE WASTE DISPOSAL

In all FGD systems in which the process water is recycled there will be a build-up of soluble species (in particular chlorides) in the absorber circuit. The rate of increase of these soluble impurities will be governed by the rate of input from the flue gas and alkali reagents and the rate of output with the FGD product. Where the input of these species is low (e.g. with low chlorine coals) then sufficient may be taken out of the system with the moisture retained in the product to maintain the impurities at a satisfactory level.

However with high chlorine levels in the flue gas or where a dry or pure product is required then the impurity levels must be controlled by the use of a purge stream.

In FGD systems where a marketable product is to be produced the impurities are generally removed in a prescrubber before the sulphur dioxide absorber. A continuous purge is removed from this prescrubber in order to control the impurity levels. This purge is highly acidic and contains suspended solids, heavy metals, chlorides and fluorides. The waste-water must thus be treated to make it suitable for discharge.

The high chloride content of UK coals means that special methods have to be evolved for the removal of chlorides before the FGD process. In Japan the chlorides are removed in a prescrubber in dilute solution and after waste-water treatment the solution is discharged with the cooling water into the sea. In W. Germany the chlorides are removed in a prescrubber or by washing the gypsum at the end of the process and the chlorides are discharged with the cooling water. However concern is being expressed about the amounts of chloride matter being discharged from FGD plants in W. Germany (9). In the UK these methods are impracticable for general application, as the volume of the purge from the prescrubber or the amount of wash-water would be unacceptably large for inland stations. For this reason a method of removing the chlorides in the prescrubber as a concentrated solution of calcium chloride has been developed (10). This concentrated solution after treatment to remove heavy metals would then have to be disposed of as there is no market for calcium chloride in the UK, since large amounts of waste calcium chloride are already produced by the chemical industry.

WASTE-WATER TREATMENT

In FGD plants where there is a purge to control the impurity levels a waste-water treatment plant will be required to make the disposal of this purge stream environmentally acceptable. The purge stream is highly acidic with a large burden of suspended solids.

A typical waste-water treatment plant is shown in Fig. 6. In the first step sulphites, sulphates and fluorides are precipitated as their calcium salts by the addition of lime. In the second step the pH is raised to 9-10 by the addition of caustic soda in order to precipitate heavy metals. The precipitation may be assisted by the addition of ferric chloride or a polyelectrolyte coagulant.

The resulting sludge is then removed in a thickener and may be further dried by filtration in a filter press. Substances which can create a chemical oxygen demand are then treated by ion exchange using weak anion exchange resins. The effluent is then adjusted in pH before discharge.

Typical heavy metal concentrations in the effluent from an operating FGD plant before and after the water treatment plant (12) are shown in Table 6. It can be seen that a very significant reduction in heavy metals is achieved in the water treatment plant. From a 2000 MW coal fired power station about 30 tons/day, of waste sludge may be produced from the heavy metal removal process (12). This can present some disposal problems. In some cases it may be possible to mix this sludge with some product gypsum and dispose of this gypsum to the cement industry which does not require such a pure gypsum as the wallboard industry. In other cases it may be possible to dispose of the sludge with the fly ash. However in some cases the sludge may have to be sent to a special disposal site.

Table 6:   Heavy Metals in FGD Effluent

(Sholven F Power Station - Reference 11)

(μg/l)

Metal	From FGD Plant	From Waste-Water Treatment Plant
As	170	15
Be	85	<0.2
Bi	<10	<3
Cd	40	<0.9
Co	60	<2
Cr	510	98
Cu	660	21
Hg	140	13
Ni	280	17
Pb	520	<10
Sb	<20	<10
Se	1120	26
Te	<30	10
Tl	<2	<1
V	250	17
Zn	4300	<50

About 1% of the nitrogen oxides in the flue gas are absorbed giving rise to nitrogen compounds in the waste water. This may necessitate the addition of a biological nitrogen removal step.

CONCLUSION

A brief survey of some of the products and wastes from FGD processes and the problems which would require solution if their disposal became necessary in the UK has been given.

Acknowledgement

This paper is published by permission of the Central Electricity Generating Board.

REFERENCES

1. Bettelheim, J., Cooper, J.R.P., Kyte, W.S., Rowlands, D.T.H., 1982, I. Chem. E. Symp. Ser. No. 72

2. Kyte, W.S., Bettelheim, J., Cooper, J.R.P., 1982, I. Chem. E. Symp. Ser. No. 78

3. Kyte, W.S., Bettelheim, J., Cooper, J.R.P., 1983, I. Chem. E. Symp. Ser. No. 77

4. Kyte, W.S., 1982, Trans. I. Chem. E., 59, 219

5. Kyte, W.S., Bettelheim, J., Littler, 1981, A., Chem. Engr., 369, 275

6. Barratt, G.W., 1979, Clean Air., 4, 119

7. FGD By-Product Disposal Manual, 1983, 3rd Ed., EPRI CS-2801

8. Burdett, N.A., Cooper, J.R.P., Dearnley, S., Kyte, W.S., Tunnicliffe, M.F., 1985, J. Inst. E., 63, 435, 64

9. Johnson, C.A., 1985, CoalTech '85, 11-13 December 1985, London

10. Kyte, W.S., Bettelheim, J., Nicholson, N., Scarlett, J., 1984 Environ. Prog., 3, 3, 183

11. Ellison, W., Luckerich, L.M., 1984, Power, 128, 6, 79

12. Gutberlet, H., 1984, Research Report ENV-492-D(B), Commission of the European Communities

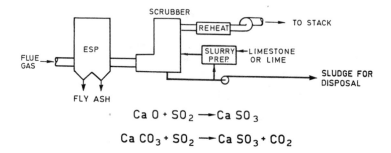

$$Ca\,O + SO_2 \longrightarrow Ca\,SO_3$$

$$Ca\,CO_3 + SO_2 \longrightarrow Ca\,SO_3 + CO_2$$

FIG. 1 LIMESTONE & LIME SLUDGE PROCESSES

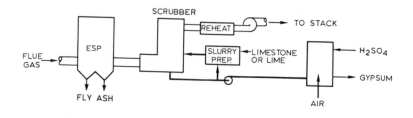

$$Ca\,O + SO_2 \longrightarrow Ca\,SO_3$$

$$Ca\,CO_3 + SO_2 \longrightarrow Ca\,SO_3 + CO_2$$

$$Ca\,SO_3 + \tfrac{1}{2}O_2 \longrightarrow Ca\,SO_4$$

FIG. 2 LIMESTONE & LIME GYPSUM PROCESSES

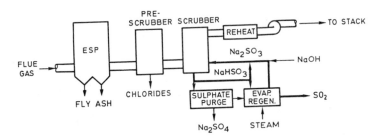

$$Na_2SO_3 + SO_2 + H_2O \rightleftharpoons 2\ Na\ HSO_3$$

FIG. 3 WELLMAN-LORD PROCESS

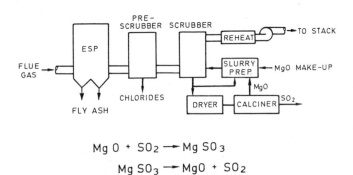

$$Mg\ O + SO_2 \longrightarrow Mg\ SO_3$$
$$Mg\ SO_3 \longrightarrow MgO + SO_2$$

FIG. 4 MAGNESIUM OXIDE PROCESS

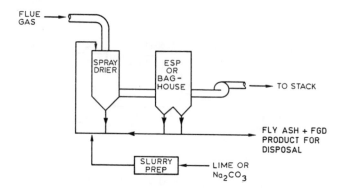

FIG. 5   SPRAY-DRY PROCESS

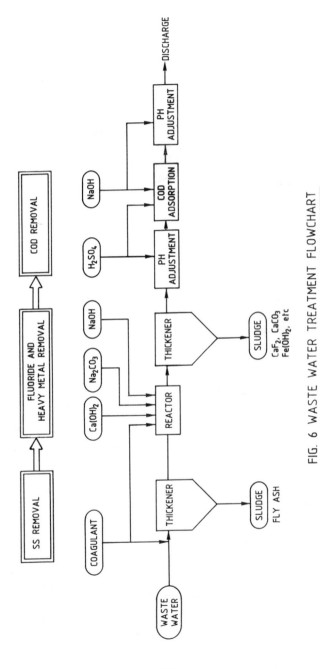

FIG. 6 WASTE WATER TREATMENT FLOWCHART

PERFORMANCE OF A GRAVITY SPRAY TOWER FOR PARTICLE SCRUBBING

D.M. Muir* and A.O. Kuye**

In this paper, a mathematical model is used to study the effect of scrubber design on the relationship between particle collection efficiency and power consumption for a gravity spray tower working over its normal operating range. The design variables studied include the height and cross-sectional area of the tower, the liquid-to-gas ratio and the size and number of spray nozzles used. Theory shows that there exists a given height of tower and range of superficial gas velocities for which the best tower performance is attained for all particle sizes; under these circumstances, maximum collection efficiencies are obtained at operating conditions that produce minimum droplet sizes.

INTRODUCTION

With the growing concern about the harmful effects of acidic gases emitted to the atmosphere, the gravity spray tower is likely to find wider application on gas cleaning plants in the near future. Whilst fairly reliable methods exist for predicting the performance of such a device when used for gas absorption or gas cooling, very little research work has been reported on its performance as a particle scrubber. Clearly, such information would be of considerable value to the dust and fume control engineer.

The work which is widely reported in the literature has considered only the target efficiency of particle capture by individual droplets in a spray tower rather than the overall collection efficiency of the device. It has been shown (1) that droplets in the size range of 500 to 1000 μm give maximum target efficiencies for the collection of any size of particle. However, a droplet size that yields the highest target efficiency may not necessarily give the maximum overall collection efficiency for the tower, particularly when power consumption is taken into account. For a given liquid-to-gas ratio, the droplet diameter will have a very strong influence not only on the number of droplets available for particle capture but also on the droplet residence time in the tower and on the volume of dust-laden gas swept by the droplet. To see how these factors (and others) affect tower performance, a mathematical model is used to derive overall collection efficiency vs. power consumption relationships for a gravity spray tower operating over a wide range of conditions.

* Dept. of Chemical & Process Engineering, University of Strathclyde, Glasgow, G1 1XJ.
** Dept. of Chemical Engineering, University of Port Harcourt, Port Harcourt, Nigeria.

The model assumes that the tower operates at ambient conditions, that there is no evaporation or condensation of scrubbing liquid and that the mechanism of particle collection is by inertial impaction alone. Clearly, the model does not apply to a tower in which the gas is being cooled; this would involve heat and mass transfer, a varying droplet size and perhaps also, subsidiary particle collection mechanisms such as thermophoresis and diffusiophoresis.

Meaningful experimental work on a gravity spray tower is difficult to carry out on a pilot scale; because of the wide angle of divergence of the spray from the nozzle(s) and the relatively small cross-sectional area of the pilot column, a high fraction of the droplets is inevitably sprayed directly on to the scrubber walls. It is very difficult, therefore, to investigate experimentally the effect of certain parameters (such as the tower height or the number of nozzles) on tower performance. For this reason, the work presented in this paper is theoretical. Despite the practical difficulties, some preliminary experimental work has already been carried out (2). With regard to the effect on tower performance of varying the liquid-to-gas ratio and nozzle pressure, there is good qualitative agreement between model prediction and experiment. However, the experimental results on the effect of the other system variables are inconclusive, primarily for the reason outlined above.

MATHEMATICAL MODEL OF A SPRAY TOWER

Physical Configuration of the Model

The model consists essentially of a chamber of rectangular or circular cross-section in which liquid droplets fall through a rising stream of dust-laden gas. The scrubbing liquid leaves the base of the tower. The droplets are formed by liquid atomised in a spray nozzle(s), located at a height H above the gas entry - see Figure 1. In a spray tower, the liquid pumping power is very important. The power is used not only to achieve the required liquid pressure in the nozzle but also to overcome the frictional and head losses in the piping system. Hence, the actual configuration of the piping system used is likely to affect the spray tower performance. For this reason, the piping system, shown in Figure 1, is included as an essential part of the model.

Mathematical Equations

In this paper, only the main equations are presented. A detailed derivation of these along with the underlying physical assumptions upon which the model is based is given by Kuye (2).

The overall particle collection efficiency (η) is obtained by equating the rate of particle capture by the droplets in the control volume Adx (see Figure 1) with the rate of particle loss from the gas stream and then integrating over the tower height H. This yields the following equation:

$$\eta = 1 - \exp\left\{ - \frac{1.5 \, m \, \rho_g \, v_t \, \eta_t \, H}{\rho_\ell \, D_d \, (v_t - v_g)} \right\} \quad \ldots (1)$$

In equation (1), v_t is the terminal settling velocity of the droplet which is calculated in the usual way. D_d is the droplet diameter which is dependent on the pressure drop across the nozzle and on the liquid flowrate (see below).

250

The target efficiency is found from the expression

$$\eta_t = \frac{K^2}{(K + 0.7)^2} \qquad \qquad \text{.... (2)}$$

where K is the inertial impaction parameter or Stokes Number. Equation (2) is a numerical approximation to the results of Walton and Woolcock (3).

The theoretical gas-phase power input, P_G, is given by

$$P_G = \rho_g A v_g \left[\frac{mg\, v_t H}{(v_t - v_g)} + 1.5\, v_o^2/2 \right] \qquad \qquad \text{.... (3)}$$

The first term in brackets represents the power input required to support the mass of droplets in the tower. The total pressure drop associated with the entrance and exit losses (including entrainment separation) is arbitrarily assumed to be equivalent to one and a half velocity heads (based on a nominal entry and exit duct gas velocity of 15.5 ms^{-1}). The pressure drops associated with the increase in head in the column and with wall frictional losses are found to be negligible.

The theoretical liquid-phase power input, P_L, is given by

$$P_L = m\rho_g A v_g \left[gH + f_F \cdot \frac{L'}{D} \cdot \frac{v_p^2}{2} + \frac{\Delta P_{ns}}{\rho_e} \right] \qquad \qquad \text{.... (4)}$$

For the piping layout given in Figure 1, the equivalent length of pipe, L' = H + 3 x 30D + 1 (allowing for 3 bends). For the different liquid flowrates, the pipe diameter (D) is chosen to maintain the liquid velocity in the pipe at 3.3 ms^{-1}. The Moody friction factor, f_F = 0.026 and is assumed to be constant.

For the type of spray nozzle used in this study, the pressure drop across the nozzle can be expressed as a function of the mass average droplet diameter ($\overline{D}_{Wd}$) and the volumetric liquid flowrate. Using the method of least squares, the data supplied by the manufacturer can be represented by the equation

$$\Delta P_{ns} = a\, \overline{D}_{Wd}^b\, Q_L^c \qquad \qquad \text{....(5)}$$

where a, b and c are constants whose values are as follows:

For $1.7 \times 10^5 < \Delta P_{ns} < 6.9 \times 10^5$ N/m^2, a = 9.32×10^{11}, b = -1.61 and c = 0.57

For $6.9 \times 10^5 \leqslant \Delta P_{ns} < 6.9 \times 10^6$ N/m^2, a = 14.90×10^{11}, b = -1.73 and c = 0.57

The theoretical power input to the system is given by the equation

$$P_T = P_G + P_L \qquad\qquad \dots (6)$$

where P_G and P_L are calculated using equations (3) and (4) respectively. It is assumed that in practice PG and PL would be divided by approximately the same fan and pump efficiencies respectively to obtain the actual total power input. In using equations (1) to (4) above, it is assumed that the droplets are monodisperse i.e. $D_d = \bar{D}_{Wd}$.

THEORETICAL STUDIES USING THE MODEL

A generalised computer program has been written to compute particle collection efficiencies and power requirements for the tower operating over a wide range of conditions. Details are given elsewhere (2). In this paper, calculations are based on a tower of cross-sectional area 0.1 m² (except in one case where the effect of changing the c/s area is explicitly investigated), handling a nominal gas flowrate of 1000 m³/hr; the model is typical therefore of the size of plant that can be operated conveniently in a pilot plant laboratory. The cross-sectional area of the model should be regarded as an elemental cross-section of a full-scale plant.

Calculations are made for particle sizes of 0.5, 1,2,3 and 5 μm. The physical properties of the gas and liquid are evaluated at standard conditions and the true particle density is taken to be 2600 kg m⁻³. The results are presented with P_T expressed in watts; for the gas flowrate used, this is equivalent to Whr/1000 m³ of gas.

To see the potential for using a spray tower for particle scrubbing, collection efficiencies are given in Table 1 for the different particle sizes.

Table 1 - Theoretical Collection Efficiencies at Different Power Consumptions (H = 2 m)

Particle Size (μm)	Collection Efficiencies (%)		
	P_T = 120W	180W	240W
0.5	0.2	0.9	2.9
1	2.5	10	26
2	11	50	85
3	40	93	>99
5	70	>99	>99

For the small particles ($D_p \leq 1\,\mu$m), the absolute efficiencies are very low. On the other hand, particles greater than or equal to $3\,\mu$m in size can be collected with moderately high efficiencies at higher values of P_T.

Effect of Tower Height and Cross-Sectional Area

Figure 2 shows the effect of tower height on the relationship between collection efficiency and power consumption for a particle size of $1\,\mu$m. Similar relationships are obtained with the other particle sizes. The tower operates with a constant liquid-to-gas ratio (L/G) of 1.6 l m^{-3}. P_T is increased by reducing the nozzle size and hence the average size of droplets produced. At any given power consumption, the collection efficiency increases with an increase in tower height, the actual increase in efficiency becoming progressively smaller as the tower height approaches 2 m. The effect of tower height also becomes less pronounced at higher P_T values.

To investigate whether a tower height of 2 m produces a maximum efficiency, further calculations were made for tower heights in excess of 2 m. The results are shown in Figure 3 for a particle size of 1 μm. Again, similar results are obtained with the other particle sizes. Clearly, for any given power consumption, a tower height close to 2 m gives maximum collection efficiencies. It should be noted that increasing H implies increasing the gas-phase power requirement. To achieve the same total power consumption for the different heights of tower, the liquid phase power must be reduced. This can only be achieved by a decrease in ΔP_{ns} and hence by an increase in droplet size. Once a tower height of 2 m is reached, increasing droplet size appears to result in a worse performance.

Figure 2 also shows the effect of increasing the cross-sectional area of the tower in order to reduce the superficial gas velocity, thereby allowing the use of smaller droplets in the tower; this clearly results in a worse performance. A gas velocity of between 2.8 and 3.7 ms^{-1} ($0.075 \leqslant A \leqslant 0.1$) then appears to be optimum, which is higher than that normally recommended for a spray tower (4,5). All further computations are carried out at H = 2 m and A = 0.1 m^2.

Effect of Liquid-to-Gas Ratio, Nozzle Size and Number of Nozzles

In a spray tower, the L/G ratio can be increased in a number of different ways:

(i)   using a constant nozzle size
(ii)   increasing the nozzle size
(iii)   increasing the number of nozzles of a given size
(iv)   a combination of (ii) and (iii)

The droplet size produced by a spray nozzle is dependent upon the L/G ratio and nozzle size. Generalised equations, such as equation (5), which are often found in the literature, usually exclude nozzle size. Specific information about individual types of nozzles can sometimes be obtained from the manufacturers. This type of information is used here to investigate the effect of increasing the L/G ratio and nozzle size on the theoretical spray tower performance. Four 'Betefog' spiral-type, full cone (90° spray angle) pressure nozzles of the same design but with different diameters are used. Details are given in Table 2. For each nozzle size, based on the data supplied by the manufacturer, a least-squares correlation has been obtained between the pressure drop across the nozzle (ΔP_{ns}) and the liquid flowrate (Q_L). The equation is of the form:

$$\Delta P_{ns} = a'Q_L^{b'} \qquad \qquad \ldots (7)$$

where a' and b' are constants whose values are given in Table 2

Table 2 - Values of Parameters a' and b' in Equation (7) for each Nozzle Size

Nozzle Designation	Dia. (m) ($\times 10^{-3}$)	a'	b'	Range of Q_L ($m^3 s^{-1}$) ($\times 10^{-3}$)
12 FCN	4.76	1.99×10^{12}	2.00	0.17 - 0.35
14 FCN	5.56	1.05×10^{12}	2.00	0.17 - 0.54
16 FCN	6.35	0.61×10^{12}	2.00	0.17 - 0.80
20 FCN	7.94	0.26×10^{12}	2.00	0.17 - 0.91

For a given value of Q_L, ΔP_{ns} is first calculated using equation (7) and then the corresponding mean droplet size obtained from equation (5). The mean droplet sizes that can be obtained with the different nozzles are shown in Figure 4.

Plots of collection efficiency vs power consumption, obtained by varying the L/G ratio using methods (i) and (ii) mentioned above, are shown in Figure 5 for a particle size of 1 μm. Again, similar results are obtained with the other particle sizes. For a given nozzle size, increasing the L/G ratio increases both the power consumption and the collection efficiency, the improvement in efficiency increasing at higher P_T values. The results also show that for a given power consumption, the smallest size of nozzle (12FCN) gives the highest collection efficiencies. For a given collection efficiency, the power consumption is minimised by using a low L/G ratio combined with a small nozzle size; this combination of operating conditions produces the smallest droplet sizes (see Figure 4). These droplets lie in the approximate size range of 780 to 1200 μm.

For a given power consumption, the L/G ratio can be increased by increasing the number of nozzles of a given size. The effect on spray tower performance of varying the L/G ratio and the number of nozzles of a given size (16 FCN size) is shown in Figure 6. Similar results are obtained with the other nozzle sizes and with the other particle sizes. Clearly, for each particle size and for a given power consumption, the collection efficiency is maximised by using one nozzle and a low L/G ratio. In this case, increasing the L/G ratio by increasing the number of nozzles results in a reduced flow through each nozzle for any given total power consumption. This in turn results in an increase in droplet size and a decrease in collection efficiency. Again, maximum collection efficiencies at a given power consumption are associated with operating conditions that produce the smallest droplets.

Search for the Best Combination of Nozzle Size and Number of Nozzles

In the above investigations, either the nozzle size or the number of nozzles is held constant as the L/G ratio is varied. Both sets of data indicate that using a low L/G ratio in combination with some other condition results in the best spray tower performance. A further choice is, however, available - i.e. to operate the tower with a small number (in this case, one for the cross-sectional area under consideration) of large nozzles or an increased number of small nozzles. The effect of using different numbers and different sizes of nozzles on tower performance is shown in Table 3 for a particle size of 0.5 μm. Similar results are obtained with the other particle sizes. For each combination of nozzle size and nozzle number, P_T is increased by increasing the L/G ratio. In Table 3, the nozzle configurations are presented in order of decreasing collection efficiency obtained. The results again indicate that at a given power consumption, the highest collection efficiency is obtained by using a low L/G ratio. In this case, it is in combination with 1x12FCN nozzle (the smallest size). There may, however, be a potential problem in using a low L/G ratio and a small number of nozzles. This combination may give incomplete coverage of the tower cross-section, resulting in much lower efficiencies and it may be necessary to increase the L/G ratio. In this case, using a higher L/G ratio of say, around 3 $1/m^3$, it is better to use a greater number of smaller nozzles rather than fewer larger ones. For example, Table 3 shows that using 4x12FCN nozzles gives better collection efficiencies than either the 3x14FCN, 2x16FCN or 1x20FCN nozzle arrangements. A comparison of the performance of the tower operating with the above four nozzle arrangements is given in Figure 7. Clearly, for a given collection efficiency and approximately the same L/G ratio, the power consumption is minimised by using the 4x12FCN nozzle arrangement. Again, the best tower performance is also associated with the operating conditions that give the smallest droplet sizes as shown in Figure 8.

Table 3 - L/G Ratios at Three Different P_T Values for the Various Nozzle Configurations Arranged in Order of Decreasing Collection Efficiency

Nozzle Configuration	P_T = 120 W	L/G Ratio $(1/m^3)$ 180 W	240W
1x12FCN	0.78	1.05	1.15
2x12FCN	1.14	1.68	1.97
1x14FCN	0.93	1.34	1.56
3x12FCN	1.40	2.15	2.59
4x12FCN	1.59	2.54	3.09
2x14FCN	1.35	2.06	2.48
1x16FCN	1.10	1.63	1.94
3x14FCN	1.62	2.59	3.18
4x14FCN	1.81	3.02	3.75
2x16FCN	1.54	2.44	2.99
3x16FCN	1.82	3.03	3.78
1x20FCN	1.39	2.15	2.62
4x16FCN	2.00	3.50	4.42
2x20FCN	1.86	3.13	3.91
3x20FCN	2.12	3.80	4.85
4x20FCN	2.27	4.30	5.61

CONCLUSIONS

Theory shows that there exists a given height of tower and range of superficial gas velocities for which the best tower performance is attained for all particle sizes. Under these conditions, for a given number of spray nozzles, the tower performance is maximised by using a low liquid-to-gas ratio and a small nozzle size. Increasing the liquid-to-gas ratio by increasing the number of nozzles (of the same size) results in a worse performance. Also, for a given liquid-to-gas ratio, a better spray tower performance is obtained by using several small-diameter nozzles rather than one large-diameter nozzle. These findings show that for a tower of the correct height and cross-sectional area, maximum performance is obtained under operating conditions that produce minimum droplet sizes. The maximum overall efficiencies recorded are associated with droplets in the size range of 780 to 1200 μm. Practical measurements on a full-scale tower are clearly required in order to test the above predictions.

SYMBOLS USED

Arabic Letters

A = cross-sectional area of tower (m^2)

C' = Cunningham 'slip' correction factor

D_d = diameter of droplet (m) or (μm)

$\overline{D}_{Wd}$ = mass average diameter of droplet (m) or (μm)

D_p = diameter of particle (m) or (μm)

D = diameter of pipe (m)

f_F = Moody friction factor

g = acceleration due to gravity (ms^{-2})

H = height of tower (m)

K = inertial impaction parameter or Stokes Number $\left(K = \dfrac{\rho_p D_p^2 \, v_t C'}{9 \, \mu_g \, D_d} \right)$

L' = equivalent length of pipe (m)

m = liquid-to-gas ratio on a mass basis

P_G = gas-phase power input (W)

P_L = liquid-phase power input (W)

P_T = total power input (W)

ΔP_{ns} = spray nozzle pressure drop (Nm^{-2})

Q_L = scrubbing liquid flowrate ($m^3 s^{-1}$)

v_g = superficial velocity of gas (ms^{-1})

v_t = terminal settling velocity of droplet (ms^{-1})

v_o = inlet and exit duct gas velocity (ms^{-1})

v_p = velocity of liquid in pipe (ms^{-1})

Greek Letters

η = overall collection efficiency

η_t = target efficiency

ρ_g = density of gas $(kg\ m^{-3})$

ρ_l = density of liquid $(kg\ m^{-3})$

ρ_p = density of particle $(kg\ m^{-3})$

μ_g = viscosity of gas $(Ns\ m^{-2})$

REFERENCES

1. Stairmand, C.J., 1950. Trans. I. Chem. E., <u>28</u>, 130.

2. Kuye, A.O., 1984. "Mathematical Modelling of Venturi and Spray Tower Scrubbers for Particle Collection". Ph.D. Thesis, University of Strathclyde.

3. Walton, W.H. and Woolcock, A., 1960. "The Suppression of Airborne Dust by Water Spray". Aerodynamic Capture of Particles (ed. E.G. Richardson), Pergamon Press, Oxford.

4. Theodore, L. and Buonicore, A.J., 1976. Industrial Air Pollution Control Equipment for Particulates, CRC Press Inc.

5. Perry, C.H., ed., 1973. Chemical Engineers' Handbook 5th edn., McGraw-Hill, N.Y.

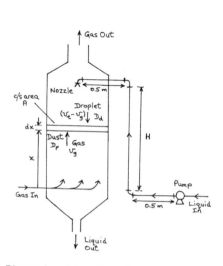

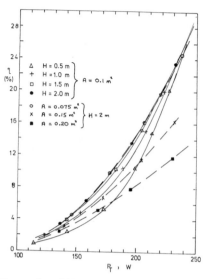

Figure 1 - Schematic diagram of gravity spray tower

Figure 2 - Effect of height and cross-sectional area on tower performance
($L/G = 1.6$ lm^{-3}, $D_p = 1$ μm)

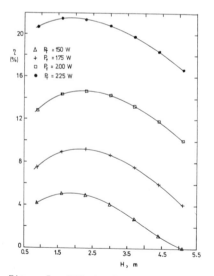

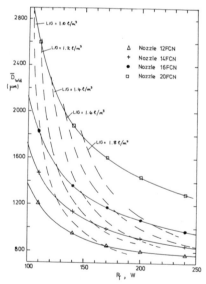

Figure 3 - Effect of height on tower performance ($L/G = 1.6$ lm^{-3}, $D_p = 1$ μm)

Figure 4 - Plots of $\overline{D}_{Wd}$ vs P_T for different nozzle sizes & L/G ratios

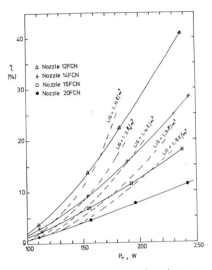

Figure 5 - Effect of nozzle size on tower performance (H=2m, D_p = 1 μm)

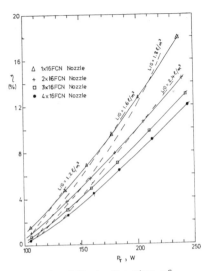

Figure 6 - Effect of number of nozzles on tower performance (H = 2m, D_p = 1 μm)

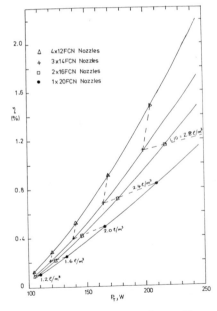

Figure 7 - Effect of nozzle configuration on tower performance (H= 2 m, D_p = 0.5 μm)

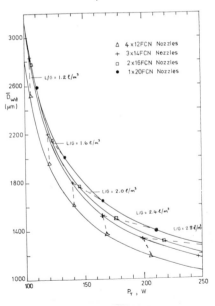

Figure 8 - Plots of $\overline{D}_{Wd}$ vs P_T for different nozzle configurations

NO_x FORMATION AND CONTROL IN STATIONARY COMBUSTION PLANT

A.G. Clarke and A. Williams*

Nitrogen oxides are formed either from nitrogen in the air
or from fuel nitrogen. The current understanding of the
chemical mechanisms involved is summarised and the main
factors affecting NO_x formation identified. The paper
then describes how the design of combustion systems taking
account of these factors can lead to NO_x reduction. The
basic configuration of a furnace, its shape and size, the
burner location and spacing, all influence NO_x levels but
these cannot normally be changed in existing plant. The
principle of two-stage combustion offers the most cost effective method of control. This can be applied to individual burner design or to overall furnaces using overfire
air. Exhaust gas recirculation presents considerably greater practical problems and additional cost. In situations
where the most stringent NO_x limitations are required, catalytic reduction using ammonia injection can be applied.

INTRODUCTION

Nitrogen oxide emissions were initially the object of attention in the United
States and in Japan because of their contribution to the problem of photochemical smog. Control technology both for vehicular emissions and for stationary combustion sources began to be developed in these countries and this
development has continued steadily. In Europe the different meteorological
conditions meant that photochemical smog was seen as a relatively minor problem and there was little incentive to embark on the control of NO_x emissions.
The first steps to control NO_x from vehicles was taken by the E.E.C. in 1977
with the Directive (1) which set limitations on NO_x emission in addition to
existing limitations on carbon monoxide and hydrocarbons. These limits have
subsequently been tightened (2) and a further lowering of the limits was
agreed in summer 1985. However, the recognition of the problems associated
with 'acid rain' has, in the last 3 years, brought the control of SO_2 and NO_x
emissions both from vehicles and from stationary sources to the forefront of
political debate in this country and in Europe as a whole.

In order to slow the die-back of their forests the German government has
committed itself wholeheartedly to the reduction of NO_x and SO_2 emissions both
from stationary sources and from vehicles. They have also been in the forefront of calls for a community-wide action within the E.E.C.. Following the

* Department of Fuel and Energy, Leeds University, Leeds LS2.9JT, U.K.

approval of the Convention on Long-Range Transboundary Air Pollution, the Commission have proposed a Directive on the limitation of emissions of pollutants into the air from large combustion plants which would: (a) require member states to reduce national emissions from such plants by 60% for SO_2 and by 40% for NO_x and dust (relative to 1980 levels), and (b) set specific emissions levels for SO_2, NO_x and dust. These requirements relate to combustion plant with thermal input greater than 50 MW. The specific requirements for NO_x as revised in February, 1985, (3) are indicated in Table 1.

The values in the first column are comparable to the current U.S. New Source Performance Standards for fossil fuel fired steam generators although the latter are given in terms of thermal input not flue gas volume (4). (Specifically 0.70, 0.3, and 0.2 lb $NO_2/10^6$ Btu for solid, liquid and gaseous fuels respectively).

To date the U.K. government has refused to agree to this Directive but it is likely that international pressure for them to do so will remain. In the meantime, operators of large combustion plant must seriously consider what steps could be taken to reduce NO_x emissions and manufacturers of combustion equipment are having to face the reality of stringent NO_x emission limits if they are likely to sell widely in Europe. In this paper the current state of technology for NO_x control in stationary combustion plant will be reviewed in the light of our understanding of NO_x formation mechanisms.

NO_x FORMATION

A considerable degree of control of NO_x emissions can be achieved by modification of the combustion conditions as determined by the design of the burners or furnaces. The reason for this relates to the chemistry of formation of NO_x during combustion which will be summarised briefly below.

Even in the absence of nitrogen as a trace element in the fuel, NO_x can be formed from the reaction of N_2 and O_2 in the air via the Zeldovich mechanism, a chain reaction involving N and O atoms:-

$$N_2 + O \rightarrow NO + N$$
$$N + O_2 \rightarrow NO + O$$
$$\overline{N_2 + O_2 \rightarrow 2 NO}$$

Because of the high activation energy of the overall reaction, the formation of so-called 'thermal NO_x' is very sensitive to temperature. Control of thermal NO_x can be achieved by:

(i) Lowering the peak temperatures
(ii) Minimising the residence time in the region of highest temperature
(iii) Minimising the excess air levels.

Another route by which air nitrogen can lead to NO_x formation is via the reaction with hydrocarbon fragments, e.g.:-

$$N_2 + CH \rightarrow HCN + N$$

The subsequent reactions from HCN to NO are similar to those in the case of fuel nitrogen described below. This route is termed 'prompt NO' because it is formed earlier in the flame than in the case of thermal NO. The relative importance of prompt NO in industrial flames is rather uncertain but it is

Table 1: Proposed Emission Limit Values for Oxides of Nitrogen in Waste Gases from Stationary Combustion Plant. (3)

Fuel	Plant size MW_{Th}	NO_x (expressed as NO_2, mg/m^3) From 1.1.85	After 31.12.1995
Solid	> 300	< 650)	< 200
	300-100	< 800)	
	< 100	< 800 but < 1300 for pulverised hard coal firing with extraction of fused ash.	< 400 as a rule but < 800 for pulverised hard coal firing with extraction of fused ash.
Liquid	All > 50	< 450	< 150
Gaseous	All > 50	< 350	< 100

Basis

(i) Waste gas volumes referred to 273K and 1 atmos; 3% O_2 for liquid and gaseous fuels, 6% O_2 for solid fuels, 200 mg NO_2/m$^3 \equiv$ 97.5 ppmv.

(ii) Continuous monitoring from which half-hour and daily averages are to be calculated. Compliance requires that over a calendar year

   - none of the daily mean values exceed the emission limit value
   - 97% of the half-hourly values do not exceed (6/5) x the limit value
   - none of the half-hourly values exceed 2 x the limit value.

thought to be small compared to thermal NO in most cases (5). It is generally neglected in discussions oriented towards control technology.

   Both coal and heavy fuel oils can contain 1 - 2% by weight of nitrogen. Lighter fuel oils contain smaller proportions. Volatilization and pyrolysis of nitrogen containing compounds leads to the rapid formation HCN, NH_3 and the radicals derived from them: CN, NH_2, NH. Oxidation reactions then lead to CO, NO and water vapour. However, there is also an interaction between NO and the NH_i species with the formation of gaseous nitrogen:-

$$NH_2 + NO \rightarrow N_2 + H_2O$$
$$N + NO \rightarrow N_2 + O$$

Consequently, not all the fuel nitrogen is necessarily converted to NO. Although the fuel-NO emissions increase steadily with fuel-N content the efficiency of conversion decreases at high nitrogen contents. Typically these conversion efficiencies are 50 - 100% for light oils with fuel-N below 0.5% wt but below 50% for heavier oils (6).

With coal combustion there is the added problem that a part of the fuel nitrogen is released with the volatile matter while the remainder is retained in the char. The volatile species burn in the same way as for oils while the char burns at a much slower rate by heterogeneous reaction with oxygen. The conversion efficiency of char-nitrogen is generally less than 20% which is lower than for volatile nitrogen. This may relate to the known capability of carbon to reduce NO:

$$NO + C \rightarrow CO + \tfrac{1}{2}N_2$$

Overall the conversion efficiency of fuel-N in coal is generally between 15 and 40% with the volatile nitrogen contributing about three-quarters of the fuel NO_x.

The primary factor affecting fuel nitrogen conversion is the oxygen concentration. Low levels of excess air or sub-stoichiometric combustion encourage N_2 formation instead of NO formation. This principle is employed in the technique of staged combustion. Staging the combustion has the objective of minimising NO formation in a fuel-rich first stage and completing combustion by the later addition of second stage air. Temperature is a relatively unimportant variable in contrast to the situation with thermal-NO_x.

PREDICTION OF NO_x LEVELS

It is relatively simple to compute the rate of thermal NO_x formation from chemical kinetic equations provided one can define appropriate temperature and O_2 versus time profiles, and provided one makes the assumption that O atoms and O_2 molecules are in equilibrium (7). This assumption is not generally true in a flame and therefore such calculations can only be approximate. Accurate calculations for ideal premixed flames can be carried out by solution of the coupled kinetic equations of all the molecular and radical species present in the combustion gases. This approach can also be extended to fuel NO_x by including all the relevant reactions involving N-containing species. Rapid initial conversion of fuel nitrogen molecules to HCN is assumed. In all, about 30 reactions must be included in addition to the normal reactions involved in hydrocarbon combustion (8). The computational task is therefore considerable.

Such detailed calculations are inappropriate for practical multiburner situations and it is more useful to adopt an empirical approach as described for example in ref. (9). The thermal NO_x is correlated with the heat release rate in lieu of the peak flame temperature. The specific parameter that is used, sometimes called the 'Burner Zone Heat Liberation Rate', is defined as the net heat input to the burner zone divided by the effective projected area of that zone. The thermal NO_x increases with increasing values of this parameter i.e. with increasing heat release rate or decreased surface area. The fuel NO_x for oils is estimated from the fuel nitrogen content using a standard curve which allows for decreasing conversion efficiency at high fuel-N contents. For coals, separate estimates of NO_x from the volatiles and NO_x from the char is made. The fuel NO_x values are assumed not to vary with the heat liberation rate. Fig. 1. If necessary, the thermal NO_x part of such calculations can be corrected for combustion modifications such as amount of air preheat, flue gas recirculation, etc. (9).

Several more detailed models of coal devolatilisation and combustion have been developed to account for laboratory data on fuel NO_x yields. Solomon et al (10) have modelled the rates of formation of coal pyrolysis products including HCN and NH_3. Hill et al (11) have developed a model of NO formation and reduction in turbulent coal flames.

CONTROL OF NO$_x$ EMISSIONS

The effect of operating conditions

Increasing the amount of excess air will generally result in increasing NO$_x$ emissions. The use of the minimum amount of excess air consistent with complete combustion will help to minimise NO$_x$ formation. Reducing the amount of air preheat will lower the peak temperatures and so reduce the thermal NO$_x$ contribution. This unfortunately also produces a direct penalty in terms of energy efficiency of the installation. Operation at part load conditions will result in proportionately less NO$_x$ because of the reduced heat release within the fixed volume of the burner zone (Fig. 1). None of these variables therefore provides a useful means of significant NO$_x$ reduction.

The effect of plant layout

It was appreciated at an early date that the location and spacing of burners within a multiburner system had a fundamental influence on the amount of NO$_x$ produced (6). Corner-fired boilers produce rather less NO$_x$ than front-wall or opposed-fired boilers. The rate of cooling of the flames by radiant heat transfer depends on the position of the burners relative to one another and to the walls. The close interaction of adjacent flames in the front-wall firing situation gives a longer residence time at the peak temperatures permitting more thermal NO$_x$ to be formed than in the corner-fired situation. Although fluidised bed combustion will not be covered in detail in this paper, it should be mentioned that the low bed-temperature ($< 1000^{\circ}$C) mean that little thermal NO$_x$ is formed and control of emissions is then focussed wholly onto fuel NO$_x$.

Flue gas recirculation

By recirculating flue gas (e.g. from the economiser exit at 300-350°C) and mixing it with the ingoing air the peak temperatures are reduced. The flue gas is effectively acting as an inert diluent. The main effect of this procedure is on thermal NO$_x$ formation. The recirculated gas may be injected into the duct leading to the wind box or to the burner itself. Recirculation directly into the furnace does not achieve significant NO$_x$ reductions. The optimum amount of recirculation is ca 20% beyond which there is little further gain in NO$_x$ reduction and an increased likelihood of flame instabilities together with increased CO and hydrocarbon emissions. Practical problems include the need to install the extra ducting and blowers operating at elevated temperatures and a redistribution of the heat transfer, i.e. reduced radiant heat transfer due to the lower temperature and increased convective heat transfer because of the larger flow rate of flue gas. Because of the high capital costs and practical difficulties this approach is not being seriously considered in this country.

Two-stage combustion

As previously mentioned two-stage combustion involves burning the fuel with substoichiometric air in the earlier part of the flame and then providing secondary air to complete the burn-out of CO, soot and hydrocarbons. Fuel NO$_x$ is reduced by encouraging fuel nitrogen conversion to N$_2$ in the fuel rich region of the flame. Thermal NO$_x$ is also reduced since the peak temperatures occur at a point where the oxygen concentrations are low. Staging the combustion can be achieved in a variety of ways. In multi-burner systems, providing there is the possibility of controlling the fuel/air ratio to individual burners, some burners can be operated fuel-rich and some fuel-lean. The over-all stoichiometry is normal but a part of the fuel is effectively burnt in a staged manner and NO_x emissions are reduced. This is described as 'off-stoich-iometric combustion'. Alternatively, all the burners can be operated fuel-rich and secondary air injected above them through additional 'overfire air ports'. This approach presumes that efficient mixing of the secondary air can be achieved and that the residence time is long enough for the combustion to be completed. These conditions are only likely to be achieved with the largest boilers.

Considerable attention has been given to the design of burners with the aim of achieving staged combustion. Since burner replacement is relatively straight-forward compared to the modification involved in other NO_x reduction techniques, this is the preferred approach when retrofitting existing install-ations. Within the U.K., trials have now commenced at Fiddlers Ferry Power Station with replacement low NO_x burners. This is a coal burning station with corner-firing (tangential) arrangement of the burners. As in a normal boiler the coal/primary air jets are directed tangentially to a small diameter circle at the centre of the furnace. However, a part of the secondary air is de-flected to a wider angle which serves to limit flame impingement but also leaves the central swirling flame zone fuel rich. Additional overfire air is injected at the top of the furnace. Initial results suggest that a 40%-50% re-duction in NO_x may be achieved.

For front-wall firing, swirl burners are used to achieve relatively short, intense flames. Several manufacturers now offer low NO_x burners which use an additional air register to promote the progressive mixing of secondary air into the flame. The principle is illustrated in Fig. 2. In the Foster-Wheeler design a further element of staging is introduced by segmenting the annular coal/primary air nozzle producing a split flame (12). Low-NO_x burners are ex-pected to be introduced into Eggborough Power Station within the next year. One disadvantage of low-NO_x burners is the increased length of the flame leading to the possibility of flame impingement.

Flue gas denitrification

The technology for flue gas denitrification has primarily been developed in Japan where numerous units have been installed in boilers ranging up to 700 MW in size. The majority of these installations have been an oil- or gas-fired plant but more recently the technology has also been applied to coal-fired units. The most widely used technology is 'selective catalytic reduction' (SCR) of NO_x by ammonia. The chemistry may be represented by the reactions

$$4NO + 4NH_3 + O_2 \rightarrow 4N_2 + 6H_2O$$

$$6NO_2 + 8NH_3 \rightarrow 7N_2 + 12H_2O$$

The products are harmless nitrogen gas and water vapour and because this is a catalytic gas phase reaction there are no liquid or solid wastes to be disposed of. Fig. 3 illustrates the basic layout of the system for a coal-fired plant. Ammonia diluted with air is injected into the flue gas downstream of the econ-omiser. The gases then pass through the reactor into the air heaters and the electrostatic precipitators before discharge to the stack. If flue gas desul-phurisation is also required the scrubber would be sited between the precipit-ators and the stack.

The catalyst operates at a temperature of $300-400^{\circ}C$. For use with 'dirty' flue gas it must be resistant to SO_x poisoning, not catalyse $SO_2 \rightarrow SO_3$ conversion and have an open structure to allow fly-ash to pass through without accumulation in the reactor. These requirements can now be met, providing a catalyst with a lifetime of several years. However, operating experience with coal-fired boilers is as yet fairly limited. Over 80% NO_x reduction can be achieved with NH_3/NO_x molar rations of 0.8-0.9. However, as this ratio increases, the amount of NH_3 slippage through the reactor increases. This can lead to problems of ammonium bisulphate deposition in the air heater arising from NH_3 reacting with flue gas SO_3. Residual levels of ammonia are therefore kept at or below about 5 ppm.

One practical problem associated with the use of such systems is the hazard arising from the transport and storage of the liquid ammonia. A 2000 MW power station would require ca 15 tonnes a day of ammonia. However, the overriding problem is undoubtedly the cost. Flue gas dentrification is comparable in cost per unit of boiler output to flue gas desulphurisation and therefore represents a very large capital outlay.

CONCLUSIONS

It is probable that combustion modifications would enable operators of large plants to meet the specifications for emissions shown in the left-hand column of Table 1. Achieving the national reduction of 40% in NO_x emissions may also be possible but there are no accurate cost estimates available. The proposed 1995 emissions limits represent what can be achieved with best available technology which involves flue gas denitrification. This has not been seriously considered in the U.K. and it is most unlikely that the E.E.C. directive in its present form will be agreed. On the other hand, the Federal Republic of Germany are pressing ahead with a demonstration denitrification plant on a 700 MW coal-fired power station and may decide to adopt this approach unilaterally in the absence of wider European agreement as they have done with flue gas desulphurisation. Meanwhile the research and discussion on the precise causes of the forest die-back and the involvement of nitrogen oxides in this problem continue.

REFERENCES

1. Official Journal of the European Communities, L 32, p.32, 1977.
2. Official Journal of the European Communities, L 197, p.1, 1983.
3. Official Journal of the European Communities, C 49, p.1, 1984 and C 76, p.6, 1985.
4. D. Pahl, Journal of the Air Pollution Control Ass., 33, 468, 1983.
5. A.N. Hayhurst and I.M. Vince, Prog. in Energy and Comb. Sci., 6, 35, 1980.
6. A.F. Sarofim and R.C. Flagan, Prog. in Energy and Comb. Sci., 2, 1, 1976.
7. C.T. Bowman, Prog. in Energy and Comb. Sci., 1, 33, 1985.
8. Y.H. Song, D.W. Blair, V.J. Siminski and W. Bartok, Eighteenth Symposium (International) on Combustion, The Combustion Institute, p.53, 1981.
9. R.H. Pai, R.E. Sommerland and R.P. Welden, A.I. Ch.E. Symposium Series No.148, Vol.71, p.103, 1975.
10. P.R. Solomon, D.G. Hamblen, R.M. Carangelo and J.L. Krause, Nineteenth Symposium (International) on Combustion, The Combustion Institute, p.1139, 1982.
11. S.C. Hill, L.D. Smoot and P.J. Smith, Twentieth Symposium (International) The Combustion Institute, p.1391, 1984.
12. J. Vatsky, Power Engineering, 86, p.44, 1982.

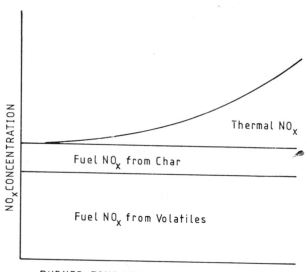

Fig.1 Simplified representation of the contributions to NO_x emissions arising from the combustion of coal.

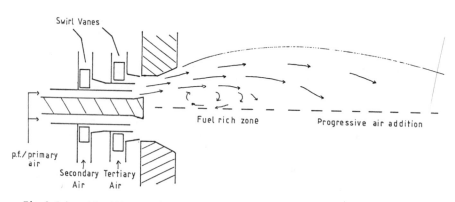

Fig.2 Schematic illustration of a low NO_x burner using dual air registers to produce staged combustion.

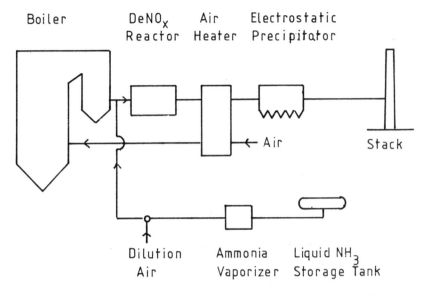

Fig.3 Plant lay-out for the application of catalytic denitrification to a large coal-fired boiler.

ODOUR CONTROL & ELIMINATION : OPTIONS FOR SEWAGE WORKS

M. J. PEARCE. M.Sc., B.Sc., ACGI, MIWPC and A. J. GOUGH, CCHEM, MRSC,
MIWPC,

Work carried out at a specific site over a period of 2
years, in order to solve a serious malodour problem is
described. The approach and technical methods of
assessment can be extended from the specific to the
general. A method for the quantification of relative
odour generation for various liquid phase streams has been
described. Short, medium and long term solutions
involving chemical, physical and biological processes have
been indicated. Operational and design considerations
conducive to odour reduction have also been identified.
Economic assessment of each treatment option has been
made.

INTRODUCTION

Strongford W.R.W., which is situated between Barlaston and Tittensor in
the Trent Valley, has been the subject of severe and increasing
criticism over recent years, due to the emanation of malodours from the
site.

The works treats up to 320,000 m^3/d of sewage arising from the bulk of
the Potteries Urban area.

Biological treatment of the 'liquid' streams is provided by plug flow
extended aeration activated sludge units whilst the 'sludge' streams can
follow one of two possible routes:- (a) Chemical conditioning,
mechanical dewatering by means of pressure filtration and disposal to a
tip site or (b) Anaerobic mesophilic digestion followed by dewatering
on drying beds and subsequent tipping on site.

Complaints about malodour from Strongford began to accumulate from 1976
onward, which coincided with the commissioning of the mechanical
dewatering plant. By 1979 the level of complaint resulted in an attempt
to ameliorate the problem by the installation of an odour masking
dispersal system. This, however met with little if any success. In
addition, by Spring 1980 polymer conditioning of sludge replaced the
original lime and copperas system, resulting in an almost immediate
increase in both number and strength of complaint which finally resulted
in the involvment of the Authority Chairman.

Extensive work was then carried out over the next 2 years to ascertain
the cause and find a suitable solution to the now acute malodour problem.

* SEVERN TRENT WATER AUTHORITY, Upper Trent Division,Burton-on-Trent.

MJPAAK

This paper details the general approach to the problem, the potential solutions and the relative costs in the short, medium and long term.

RECOGNITION, LOCATION AND QUANTIFICATION OF THE PROBLEM

In order to identify the source, quantify the nuisance and ascribe relative importance to individual processes on the site, three preliminary lines of investigation were initially pursued as follows:-

(a) A questionaire was issued to complainants over a fixed time period. Returns were subject to numerical analysis to elicit information on frequency and magnitude of nuisance and the effect of climatic conditions.

(b) A site survey was carried out, in which areas of exposure, degrees of turbulence and description of flow streams were detailed.

and

(c) Two methods of assessing the relative potential for odour generation from liquid streams were developed. The first and simplest method entailed a large panel of people simply smelling the sample contained in a jar and ascribing a score from 1 to 5. The raw results were numerically manipulated to produce a three point scale: low odour, border line and problem sample. The second, more rigorous method, involved generating a gaseous sample from the liquid sample and carrying out a Dynamic Dilution Factor (ref 1) analysis upon the gaseous sample.

The results of the questionaire and 'jar tests' are given in tables 1 and 2 respectively. In brief the former indicates that (a) there is no simple relationship between complaint and wind direction (b) there could be little doubt that Strongford W.R.W. was responsible for the bulk of the complaints (c) the most frequent description of the odour was one of rotting cabbage and (d) that the positive response rate should fall below 26% before any abatement measure could be considered to be having an effect.

The jar test results in conjunction with the site survey indicated the major sources of malodour to be due to the primary sludge flow streams and in particular the press filtrate.

A more detailed discussion of the above work can be found elsewhere, (ref 4).

SHORT TERM REMEDIAL MEASURES

The original site inspection revealed a number of simple steps could be taken to contain or reduce the emission of malodours.

a) All areas where sludge or sludge liquors were exposed to the air that could be easily covered were covered.

b) Dip pipes at tankered sludge discharge points were installed.

272

c) The return of press liquors to the head works was discontinued and the liquors were mixed with return activated sludge in the return pump well.

d) The operation of emptying the storm tanks was modified so that as much sludge as possible was removed before top water was removed. This entailed extensive modification of the Hudson scrapers.

The main sources of the malodour had been identified as the press plant and the associated storage and redundant conditioning tanks. The press drainage system was inadequate consequently large volumes of press liquors over flowed onto the drip trays and then to the floor. Large surface areas of very malodourous liquors were exposed to the air. A series of improvements were made to the drainage system that considerbly reduced the amount of exposure to the air of the press liquors with concomitant reduction in malodour. However, despite these efforts there was a residual malodour that could still be detected and was at an unacceptable level.

Although the main source of malodour had been identified as the press plant it was not obvious why it was so offensive. It was mooted that there was no real problem until the change to polymer conditioning in the spring of 1980 and therefore the polymer was causing the problem. Table 2 however shows that both the new and old co-settled sludge were judged offensive before the polymer was added. The diluted polymer solution was also very offensive but it was never exposed to the air. The polymer could not be directly blamed for the malodours although the change to polymer resulted in the sludge pH staying slightly acid thus enhancing the volatility of the sulphides.

Experiments were carried out to assess the effect of co-settlement of surplus activated sludge with crude sludge and the effect that increasing age had on the development of malodours.

These experiments concluded:

a) Co-settlement of activated sludge with crude sludge did not increase the level of malodour.

b) The malodour increased slightly as the sludge became older.

c) There was some evidence that malodours were associated with the production of volatile acids in the sedimentation tanks, but there was no practicable method of preventing the production of volatile acids.

An investigation into possible trade effluent sources of the malodour was made. In particular a search was made for firms using unsaturated organic solvents, organic sulphur compounds and selenium compounds. It was concluded that there were no significant discharges of these compounds.

Conclusions of Preliminary Stages

The work outlined above took place over a period of about three months,

MJ PAAK

although the modifications to the storm tank scrapers took considerably longer.
The first two phases of the investigation i.e. the identification of existing and potential malodour sources and the reduction or elimination of malodours by changes in process, plant design and management, resulted in the source of the malodour being identified and the containment or elimination of the potential secondary sources of malodour. However, the main sources of malodour i.e. the press plant and sludge storage tanks still remained and the remainder of the paper deals with steps taken to remove this cause for complaint.

MEDIUM TERM MEASURES

Of the five general methods for odour abatement, i.e. removal of cause, containment, dilution, neutralisation and masking, and destruction, the first four had either been implemented or discarded as impractical. Hence odour destruction in either the liquid or gaseous phases was the only remaining available option. Due to the urgency of the problem a speedy reduction of the odour emissions from the press plant and its associated storage tanks was required. Since liquid phase treatment, i.e. chemical dosing, required only minimal capital expenditure this offered the quickest solution in the medium term.

Since the source of the odour was the sludge in the holding tanks, the press liquors and press cake it was necessary to ensure that any measures taken to destroy the malodour were effective for at least two days because this is the average time taken for the sludge to pass through the press plant. The destruction of the malodour had to take place in the liquid phase and so the chemical selected had to be easy to mix with the sludge in the sludge transfer well.

Initially five potential treatment chemicals were screened using the 'Jar' test, these being: Lime, Sewage Conditioner A, Hydrogen Peroxide, Sodium Nitrate and Sodium Chlorite. The two most efective chemicals were Sodium Chlorite and Hydrogen Peroxide, hence further tests were performed with these and one additional chemical, Sodium Hypochlorite, the results of which are given in table 3.

On the basis of these results Sodium Hypochlorite was selected for a site trial. Due to inadequacies of the original dosing system together with poor persistence of treatment when using Sodium Hypochlorite the results were disappointing. Consequently an 'in line' dosing arrangement was installed and the chemical changed to Sodium Chlorite. This produced quite a dramatic improvement in odour levels but at a cost penalty of £69,000 per annum. Consequently while Sodium Chlorite dosing continued assessment of odour destruction in the gaseous phase was commenced.

LONG TERM MEASURES

Fortunately the areas requiring treatment were to all intents and purposes completely contained i.e. the press house and covered sludge storage tanks. Obviously these structures are not air tight and therefore to prevent egress of malodourous air requires a negative pressure to be applied to the interior. The rates of extraction

MJPAAK

required were calculated using the methods detailed in (ref 1) and are presented in table 4.

It is obvious from these figures that for gaseous treatment to be viable requires that all doors on the press house building be kept shut and that the cladding be completed on the sludge storage tanks. It was debatable how necessary it was to treat air from the sludge storage tanks, since the degree of turbulance and resulting odour generation for the vast majority of time was negligeable. Consequently all gaseous scrubbing investigations were made on the basis of treating 10m3/s. Even so this is still a high flow/low odour concentration situation which renders all but absorption techniques inappropriate on a cost basis.

For sensible trials to be performed one not only needs to know the required volumetric throughput but also the degree of treatment. For this purpose the parameter used was the dynamic dilution factor DF (ref 1). It was calculated that for the proposed throughput the output DF should not exceed 1000 if odour detection was to be avoided at the closest residence.

Hence the conditions of operation were stipulated as follows:-
    Throughput 10m^3/s
    Typical Input DF 50,000
    Max. Output DF 1000

Two absorption systems were chosen for pilot scale testing as follows:-

    (1) Simdean - Techfina Multicellular scrubber
    (2) Activated sludge treatment

Simdean Techfina Pilot Scale Trials

The schematic layout of the Simdean-Techfina Multicell Scrubber is shown in fig. 1. The equipment is a counter current wet gas scrubber. The shape of the scrubbing cell and the liquid flow pattern is shown in fig. 2. A number of runs under different conditions were made and are summarised in tables 5, 6, & 7.

Run 1 : Odour Removal Efficiency Under Unsteady State Conditions Using Water As The Scrubbing Medium

Operating Conditions Air Flow   189 m^3/hr
                      Liquid Flow   400 1/hr in both stages
                      Liquid gas ratio   1.83:1
                      Liquid volume   50 1 water in both stages

Water, with no added chemicals, was used in this run. Unfortunately the air in the press plant was not particularly malodourous during this run and so it was not a rigorous test of using water as the scrubbing liquid. However at the end of 24 hours there was a decrease in effectiveness indicating that the water was becoming saturated with the malodourous compounds. At zero hours which is equivalent to using fresh water for each pass the removal was only 95%.

275

MJPAAK

Run 2 : Odour Removal Efficiency Under Unsteady State Conditions Using Alkaline Sodium Hypochlorite Solution As The Scrubbing Medium

0.1% available chlorine sodium hypochlorite was used as the scrubbing liquid. The pH was adjusted during the run with sodium hydroxide but no further additions of sodium hypochlorite were made and none of the sump contents were bled during the run. From this run it was concluded that two stages were required and that the concentration of available chlorine should not fall below $0.05\%^{W}/_{V}$. The DF of the inlet air was again comparitively low but the overall removals, when the available chlorine concentration was high enough were greater than 98%.

Run 3 : Odour Removal Efficiency Under Pseudo Steady State Conditions Using Alkaline Sodium Hypochlorite As The Scrubbing Medium

0.1% available chlorine sodium hypochlorite was used as the scrubbing liquid. Daily additions of sodium hypochlorite were made to maintain the sump liquors at 0.1% available chlorine. Automatic pH control kept the pH between 10-11. The sump volumes were kept constant at 50 l. In addition to the normal DF monitoring, inlet and outlet air samples were taken for GCMS analysis at Finham Regional Laboratory. This run emphasised the need to keep the available chlorine levels at 0.1% because on day 4 there was no available Chlorine in the first stage with subsequent odour breakthrough. The overall removal of odour was satisfactory with acceptable DF's being obtained at the outlet of the unit even with inlet DF's of 200,000. The odour levels were deliberately enhanced for this run.

The GCMS chromatograms also showed that dimethyl disulphide, dimethyl trisulphide, benzo (B) thiophen, benzo thiazole and possibly methyl ethyl disulphide which were present in the inlet air were absent in the outlet air. Also, and not unexpectedly, there were a number of chlorinated species in the outlet air with 4 chlorophenol being dominant. None of the members of the DF panels however commented on being able to smell TCP.

From these three runs it was concluded that

i. Water scrubbing was not satisfactory.
ii. Ten cells disposed in series were needed.
iii. The availabe chlorine should be between 0.05 and 0.1% $^{W}/_{V}$ and the pH should be 10-11.
iv. Chemical usage 0.105g Na OH/m^3 air treated
0.005g Av Cl$_2$/m^{3}air treated

Table 8 shows the capital and running costs of a 10m$_3$/s unit, which would only be large enough to treat the air from the press plant.

Activated Sludge Odour Absorption Trials

The press plant liquors were being returned to the RAS pumpwell and it was noticed that, despite the fact that these liquors were the most malodourous on the works, no malodour could be detected at the flume used to proportion the RAS. There were also literature reports (2) (3)

MJPAAK

of biological filters and granular sludge being used to deodorise malodourous air. It was decided therefore to study the feasibility of ducting the air from the press plant to the inlet of the ASP plant blowers to see if the malodour would be removed by the mixed liquor.

The ASP plant was simulated by putting a single dome at the bottom of a 3m GRP column of 1.36 m^3 volume. This was equivalent to the depth and volume aerated by one dome in the ASP plant. Fig 3 shows the schematic layout of the equipment. Mixed liquor from the ASP4 was fed continuously to the base of the column with the effluent being discharged to a convenient well. Air from the press plant was pumped to the base of the column. The volume was measured using a rotameter.

The malodourous air was sampled at the press plant, at the column inlet and the column outlet and its DF was measured. Samples of the air were also taken for GCMS analysis at Finham.

Table 2 shows the results obtained from the column. There was considerable removal of the malodour by the pipe conveying the air from the press plant to the column. The column had to be sited 150m distance from the press plant and consequently the air had to be conveyed over this distance through a PVC pipe. The malodour was obviously being either absorbed by the pipe surface or being dissolved in the condensed moisture. The removal efficiencies are not particularly good but DF of the outlet air is less than or close to the required DF of 1000. The GCMS showed complete removal of organic sulphur compounds after the air had passed through the column. It is significant that final effluent was as effective as mixed liquor at removing malodours.

It was concluded that:-

i. the ASP plant would remove malodourous air provided the initial DF was 10000 or less.
ii. the removal mechanism was probably by dissolution in the aqueous phase rather than any biological activity.

On other plants this method could be successful but there were a number of factors that militated against its use at Strongford. The most important factor was the disparity in the required air extraction rate of 10 m^3/s from the press plant and the air usage of 5 m^3/s of the ASP plant. There were fears about the extracted air corroding the ASP blower casing and vanes. Consequently this option was not pursued further.

Summary of Gas Scrubbing Option

Gas scrubbing with alkaline sodium hypochlorite was successful. The annual running costs were about £21,000 per annum if the press plant alone was treated. This option would still leave the problem of the sludge cake that would be exposed during its transport to the tip.

Using the ASP plant for gas scrubbing was successful at low input DF's but there was a problem with a mismatch between the air input of the ASP plant and the required press plant and holding tanks output.

MJPAAK

Discussion Of Solutions

The cost and suitability of the medium and long term solutions have been
summarised in table 10. Had the situation remained static the obvious
choice of treatment option for the long term would have been wet
scrubbing with an Alkaline hypochlorite medium. However, unfortunately
another problem had come to the fore in the form of complaints regarding
the final disposal site. This represented a completely new situation
and one which would not be solved by gaseous scrubbing equipment.

In general the tipped cake was quickly covered with inert fill but
inevitably there were times when the cake was exposed. The tip at
Blurton is leased from Staffordshire County Council and at the time of
the complaints the lease was about to expire. The complaints created
some difficulties with the renewal of the lease, but in the event it was
renewed. It was estimated that the life time of the tip was about 5
years and so by the 1988/89 a new tip would have to be found.
Staffordshire County Council offered the possibility of two other tips
both 16 km distance from Strongford.

This would increase the transportation costs by £60,000 and there would
also be the costs of fencing and other establishment costs estimated at
£500,000 at the most favourable site.

It became obvious that the only remaining option which could offer a
complete solution was to radically alter the sludge flow sheet.

The proposed system at Strongford was to pump sludge from the
sedimentation tanks with either peristaltic or diaphragm pumps to a
closed buffer tank. This crude sludge could then be pumped to the
digester and the digested sludge could either be pressure filtered hot
or elutriated and thickened before pressure filtering. The digested
press cake could then be tipped at the existing drying bed site, 4 km
from Strongford.
With this scheme crude sludge would never be exposed to the air.

It was quickly established that the digestion plant and equipment on
site were inadequate both in capacity and design to digest the whole of
the sludge make at Strongford. Calculations also showed that, in order
to keep the costs of new digesters to a minimum the sludge feed would
need to be 7-8% DS. Also at this feed level, there would be no need for
post digestion thickening. Before proceeding along this extremely
costly path certain questions had to be answered:-

i) Would sludge from the new works digest?

ii) Would the digested sludge and the filtrate generate odours of a
sufficiently low DF to ensure that there were no complaints?

iii) Could the digested sludge be conditioned at a reasonable cost with
polymer?

iv) Would the pumped desludging of the sedimentation tanks enable a 7-8%
DS sludge to be produced consistently?

278

In order to answer these questions a programme of experimental work was started.

Sludge Digestability

Both laboratory and full scale trials were carried out on the digestability of the sludge from the new works. It was found that, provided heating and mixing were efficient, the mixed primary sludges from the old and new side of the works could be satisfactorily digested at a retention time of 12 days and a feed dry solids concentration of 8%.

Heavy metal levels were monitored, but found to fall well short of the concentration required for inhibition of digestion.

Malodour Assessment

Artificial gaseous samples were generated by bubbling odour free air through the following liquid samples: Digested sludge, digested sludge press filtrate, crude sludge and crude sludge press filtrate. Dilution factor analysis was performed on each gaseous sample in addition to gaseous samples taken from both the press house confines and storage tank head space under current operating conditions. Assuming that the press house atmosphere DF will be reduced in the same proportion as the artificially generated samples have shown a reduction it is possible to predict the likely future DF in the presshouse when treating digested sludge. These predictions are given in table 11, and although they cannot be regarded as precise it is reasonable to assume that they are of the correct order. Hence it is also reasonable to conclude that digestion would solve the malodour problem at Strongford.

Press Plant Trials

Laboratory scale trials on digested sludge from the laboratory scale digesters were done by a number of polymer manufacturers. Three suppliers were able to provide polymers that would condition the sludge at a cost of between £6 and £13 tonne D.S.

In order to obtain more precise information on:

a) Costs

b) Odour levels of filtrate and cake

c) Cake and filtrate quality

and

d) Cake stability

pilot scale tests were carried out. A pilot scale pressure filter was loaned free of charge by Manor Engineering Ltd, Stoke-on-Trent. Two Allied Colloids polymers were selected for the trial, Z51 a liquid polymer and Z87 a powder polymer. It should be noted that these

MJPAAK

polymers were chosen to test the parameters outlined above and would not necessarily be the ones used on the full scale press plant. The trials showed that the sludge could be conditioned for between £11-12.50 tonne/D.S. and some evidence of satisfactory performance at £8/tonne was obtained. The previous section concluded that the odour levels of the cake and filtrate were low enough not to cause offence. The cakes formed were generally in the range 30-35% D.S. which is similar to the cakes formed at present with crude sludge.

Hence it was concluded that polymer conditioning of digested sludge would produce a satisfactory product at a similar cost to that already experienced with crude sludge treatment.

Pumped Desludging

Trials with manual desludging showed that the initial sludge removed from the tank was 8-10% D.S. This was encouraging and so a 3" Double Disc Pump from MPL Pumps Ltd was installed. The results of the pumping trials are reported elsewhere (5) but they proved that a 7-8% D.S. sludge could be consistently obtained.

CONCLUSIONS

Probably the most important conclusion that can be drawn from the work done at Strongford is that a logical approach will provide effective and economic solutions to malodour problems. Too often because of the emotive nature of malodour complaints an unco-ordinated approach is adopted with ad hoc solutions being used.

The other more specific conclusions that have been drawn are as follows:-

1. The questionnaire distributed to the people who had complained provided information that:-

   a) confirmed the works as the main source of malodours,

   b) quantified the problems,

   and

   c) provided a baseline for comparision of the success of control measures.

   The questionnaire also improved public relations.

2. The malodour was increased by the retention of sludge in the sewers and sedimentation tanks.

3. The malodour was not increased by the co-settlement of activated sludge with crude sludge.

4. The malodour was not increased by the use of cationic polyacrylamide polymers as sludge conditioners. Lime, by altering the pH, did

MJPAAK

suppress the odour.

5. The major chemical components responsible for the characteristic malodour of Strongford sludge were Dimethyl disulphide and Dimethyl trisulphide. There were also a number of other malodourous organic sulphur compounds present.

6. Sodium Chlorite was found to be the best chemical for suppressing the malodours emanating from the liquid sludge. Sodium hypochlorite was also useful but its effect was not as long lasting as sodium chlorite. However neither of these two treatments reduced the malodour level sufficiently to avoid complaints.

7. The most effective gas scrubbing system for malodour removal was counter current gas/liquid absorption with alkaline hypochlorite.

8. The malodour was also removed by water or activated sludge in a "bio-absorption" system". This sytem however was not able to consistently produce an acceptable removal level of malodour.

9. The prevention of the exposure of malodourous sludge to air was found to be the most effective odour control system and the following scheme is to be adopted at Strongford. Crude sludge is to be pumped from the sedimentation tanks into closed buffer tanks and then into mesophillic anaerobic digesters. After digestion the sludge is to be conditioned with polymers and pressure filtered.

10. It was verified that this scheme is viable in all aspects and will result in an acceptable odour level at Strongford and at the disposal site.

11. A method for the comparative testing of malodours and for testing odour control chemicals was devised.

MJ PAAK

REFERENCES

(1) Valentin F. H. H. & North A. A., 1980.
Odour Control - A Concise Guide,
Warren Spring Laboratory.

(2) Rands M. B., Copper D. E., Woo C. P., Fletcher G. C.,
Rolf K. A., 1981, JWPCF, Vol. 53, No. 2.

(3) Garber W. F., 1980, Prog, Wat. Tech. Vol, 12, No. 5.

(4) Pearce M. J., Gough A. J., 1985 (Not yet published) JIWPC
Odour Control at Strongford W. R. W.

(5) Schnell A., Pearce M. J., Gough A. J., 1986.
(Not yet published) JIWPC. "Pumped Desludging".

ACKNOWLEDGEMENTS

The authors wish to thank the Divisional Manager of the Upper Trent
Division for permission to publish this paper.

The authors also wish to thank Mr. T. G. Tideswell, Mr. M. Riordan, Mrs.
S. Walker,the Area Controller at Strongford, Mr. G. Bayliss and his
staff.

Special thanks are due to Manor Engineering Stoke-on-Trent for the loan
of equipment.

MJPAAK

SIMDEAN – TECHFINA   TWO STAGE   FIG 1

MULTICELL   GAS   SCRUBBER

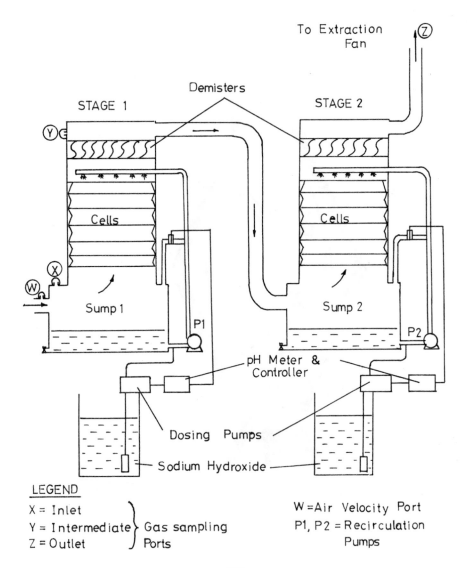

LEGEND

X = Inlet
Y = Intermediate ⎫ Gas sampling
Z = Outlet   ⎭ Ports

W = Air Velocity Port
P1, P2 = Recirculation
         Pumps

SCRUBBING CELL WITH AIR & LIQUID FLOW PATHS

FIG 2

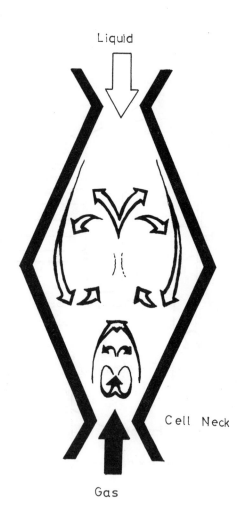

Liquid

Cell Neck

Gas

ACTIVATED SLUDGE ODOUR   FIG. 3

ABSORPTION COLUMN

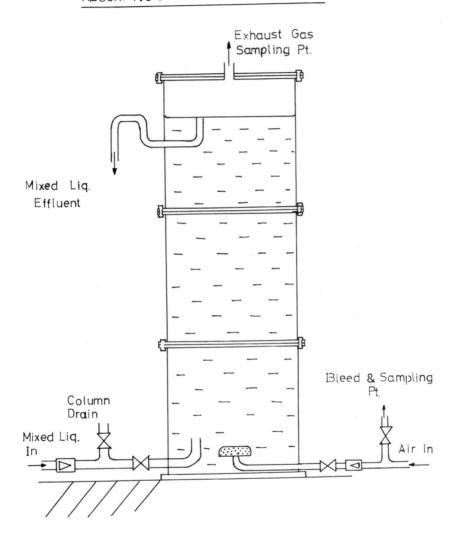

Exhaust Gas Sampling Pt.

Mixed Liq. Effluent

Bleed & Sampling Pt.

Column Drain

Mixed Liq. In

Air In

TABLE 1 - SUMMARY OF QUESTIONNAIRE
RESULTS FROM THE STRONGFORD AREA

OBSERVATIONS		MORNING	AFTERNOON	EVENING	TOTAL
Total observations	(a)	475	473	482	1430
Number of observations down wind of the works	(b)	85	68	84	237
Positive observations down wind of the works	(c)	26	20	22	68
Observations consistent with descriptions but inconsistent with wind direction	(d)	38	34	22	94
Observations consistent with wind direction but inconsistent with description	(e)	2	1	2	5
Observations inconsistent with wind direction or description	(f)	9	9	6	24

TABLE 2 - SURVEY OF MALODOUROUS FLOWSTREAMS ON STRONGFORD WORKS

	INTENSITY				ACCEPTABILITY			
	Total	Mean Primary Score	%> 3	2ndry Score	Total	Mean Primary Score	%> 3	2ndry Score
Trentham Pump Well Influent	10	1.3	0	1	25	3.1	12.5	½
Crude Sewage - New Side	20	2.5	0	1	27	3.4	50	½
- Old Side	12	1.5	0	1	23	2.9	0	1
Sed.Tank Effl. - New Side	18	2.3	12.5	1	26	3.3	37.5	½
- Old Side	18	2.3	0	1	30	3.8	75	0
A.S.P. Feed - New Side	17	2.1	0	1	26	3.3	25	½
- Old Side	14	1.8	0	1	26	3.3	25	½
A.S.P. Eff. - New Side	8	1.0	0	1	24	3	0	1
- Old Side	8	1.0	0	1	23	2.9	0	1
Final Effl. - New Side 3/4/5	12	1.5	0	1	26	3.3	12.5	½
- Old Side 1/2	15	1.9	12.5	1	27	3.3	25	½
Primary Co-settled Sludge - New Side	42	5.2	100	0	45	5.6	100	0
- Old Side	39	4.9	87.5	0	44	4.4	100	0
Returned Activated Sludge	20	2.5	12.5	1	28	3.5	50	½
Press Feed Sludge	40	5.0	100	0	46	5.8	100	0
Pressed Cake	36	4.5	87.5	0	42	5.3	100	0
Press Filtrate	49	6.1	100	0	52	6.5	100	0
Diluted Polymer Solution (1:10)	37	4.6	87.5	0	29	3.6	75	0

TABLE 3 - COST EFFECTIVENESS OF VARIOUS CHEMICALS

Chemical	Cost £/Tonne DS	Dose % on DS	Acceptability Day 1	Day 2	Day 3	Intensity Day 1	Day 2	Day 3
None	-	-	0	0	0	$\frac{1}{2}$	0	$\frac{1}{2}$
Sodium Chlorite	1	0.7	$\frac{1}{2}$	0	0	$1\frac{1}{2}$	$1\frac{1}{2}$	$1\frac{1}{2}$
	3	2.18	1	0	$\frac{1}{2}$	2	$\frac{1}{2}$	$1\frac{1}{2}$
Sodium Hypochlorite	1	1.2	1	$1\frac{1}{2}$	$\frac{1}{2}$	$2\frac{1}{2}$	2	1
	3	3.6	1	$2\frac{1}{2}$	1	$2\frac{1}{2}$	$2\frac{1}{2}$	$1\frac{1}{2}$
Hydrogen Peroxide	1	.28	0	$\frac{1}{2}$	0	1	1	1
	3	.83	$\frac{1}{2}$	1	$\frac{1}{2}$	2	2	1

TABLE 4 REQUIRED VENTILATION RATES

UNIT	CONDITIONS	VENTILATION RATE m^3/s
PRESS HOUSE	All Doors Shut	10
	All Doors Open	392
2 SLUDGE STORAGE TANKS	Existing Situation Cladding Incomplete	173
	Cladding Completed	10

TABLE 5 ODOUR REMOVAL EFFICIENCY USING WATER (UNSTEADY STATE)

TIME RUN (HRS)	DILUTION FACTOR (DF) IN	OUT	% REMOVAL
0	3162	158	95
3	3162	316	90
24	1987	630	68.3

TABLE 6 - ODOUR REMOVAL EFFICIENCY UNDER UNSTEADY STATE CONDITIONS USING ALKALINE SODIUM HYPHOCHLORITE SOLUTION AS THE SCRUBBING MEDIUM

DAY	1		1		2		3		4		5		6	
STAGE VARIABLE	1	2	1	2	1	2	1	2	1	2	1	2	1	2
CUMULATIVE RUN TIME HRS	1/4	1/4	3	3	22	22	45	45	69	69	92	92	116	116
AVAILABLE Cl USED (g)	-	-	7.5	26	6	6	3	-	3.5	3	6.5	5	-	-
DILUTION FACTOR (IN)	1987	63.2	-	-	1257	-	1257	50.2	1987	40	3162	125.7	2500	500
DILUTION FACTOR (OUT)	63.2	31.2	-	-	-	31.6	50.2	25.0	40	25	125.7	50.2	500	80
% D.F. REMOVAL	96.8	50	-	-			96	50	98	37.5	96	60	80	84
OVERALL	98.4				97.5		98		98.7		98.4		96.8	

TABLE 7 - ODOUR REMOVAL EFFICIENCY UNDER PSSEUDO STEADY CONDITIONS USING ALKALINE SODIUM HYPOCHLORITE SOLUTION AS THE SCRUBBING MEDIUM

DAY	1		2		3		4		5	
STAGE VARIABLE	1	2	1	2	1	2	1	2	1	2
DAILY RUN TIME HRS	17	17	24	24	?	?	24	24	24	24
AVAILABLE Cl USED (g)	10.2	8.7	18.2	4	14	5.5	12.2	2.6	34.2	12.6
VOL.NaOH2 W/V USED l	1.8	1.8	3	4.5	3	3.6	1.5	3.6	4.5	4.2
DILUTION FACTOR IN	158,000	2,000	126,000	6,300	25,000	630	20,000	3,200	200,000	6,300
DILUTION FACTOR OUT	2,000	200	6,300	400	630	158	3,200	1,300	6,300	502
% D.F.REMOVAL	98.7	90	95	93.7	97.5	74.9	84	59.4	96.9	92
OVERALL % REMOVAL	99.9		99.7		99.4		93.5		99.7	

289

TABLE 8 - CAPITAL & RUNNING COSTS OF 10m^3/s SIMDEAN UNIT

ITEM	COST
CAPITAL:- Scrubber	£28,000
Inlet Ducting	£13,200
TOTAL CAPITAL	£41,200
RUNNING	
COSTS p.a. Sodium Hydroxide	£ 4,650
Sodium Hypochlorite	£ 1,020
TOTAL CHEMICAL COST p.a.	£ 5,670
Extraction Fan)	
1 Recirc. Pump)	£15,000
TOTAL ELECTRICITY COSTS p.a.	£15,500
TOTAL RUNNING COST p.a.	£21,170

Price base September 1981

TABLE 9 - ODOUR STRENGTHS AND REMOVAL EFFICIENCIES OF THE BIO-ABSORPTION COLUMN

DATE	SAMPLE	DILUTION FACTOR	COMMENTS
11.3.82	Press House Atmosphere	50,000	FEED: Mixed Liquor Air Flow Rate:- 0.2-0.4 l/s
	Column inlet	12,570	
	Column outlet	1,265	% Reduction in DF:- 89%
15.3.82	Press House Atmosphere	25,140	FEED: Mixed Liquor Air Flow Rate:- 0.2-0.4 l/s
	Column inlet	3,100	
	Column outlet	250	% Reduction in DF:- 91.9%
7.3.82	Press House Atmosphere	6,300	FEED:- Mixed Liquor Air Flow Rate:- 0.2-0.4 l/s
	Column inlet	5,020	
	Column outlet	100	% Reduction in DF:- 92%
20.4.82	Press House Atmosphere	6,300	FEED:- Mixed Liquor Air Flow Rate:- 0.2-0.4 l/s
	Column inlet	2,500	
	Column outlet	199	% Reduction in DF:- 92%
20.4.82	Press House Atmosphere	6,300	FEED:- Final Effluent Air Flow Rate:- 0.2-0.4 l/s
	Column inlet	2,500	
	Column outlet	100	% Reduction in DF:- 96%

MJQAAA

TABLE 10 TREATMENT COST

TREATMENT METHOD	CAPITAL COST	REVENUE COST	LEVEL OF TREATMENT
Sodium Chlorite Dosing	N500	69,000	Border Line
Gaseous treatment in ASP	59,500	5,000	Satisfactory but volumetric shortfall
Gaseous treatment in Techfina unit	40,500	21,000	Satisfactory

TABLE 11 - CALCULATED AND MEASURED ODOUR STRENGTHS

LOCATION	TYPICAL EXISTING D.F.	REQUIRED D.F.	PROBABLE D.F. WHEN SLUDGE IS DIGESTED
Presshouse Atmosphere	50,000	1,000 - 2,500	500
Storage Tank Head Space	500	1,630	313

ENERGY RECOVERY FROM INCINERATION OF GASEOUS, LIQUID AND
SOLID WASTES CONTAINING CARBON COMPOUNDS

D.J.I.Davies* and P.Sainter*

The conditions necessary to incinerate waste materials to
produce stack gases of acceptably low content of
objectionable products are considered. Within these
conditions however the overall thermal efficiency of
incinerators with heat recovery arrangements can approach
that of normal combustion systems. What is desirable
however often differs from conventional heat recovery
practice. In terms of purchased fuel used incineration can
often produce worthwhile, and sometimes spectacular
savings. Examples are given.

INTRODUCTION

Thermal oxidation of wastes, whether liquid, gaseous, suspensions or solids
is a generally accepted method of converting unpleasant or noxious wastes
to non-polluting gaseous effluents and solids. Any known organic compound
can be oxidised to non-hazardous levels in the vent. If halogen, sulphur or
phosphorus compounds are present the resulting acids can be easily scrubbed
from the off gas. Noxious incombustible residues, notably heavy metals
appear either as solids in the combustion chamber or dust in the vent gas:
venturi scrubbers or bag houses are available which will clean the vent
gases to acceptable levels. The more typical application of incinerators
are to materials which have some fuel value. They can however be equally
used with aqueous solutions or suspensions or airborne dusts where most or
all the necessary heat must come from added fuel.

Thermal oxidation has the advantage that the fuel value of the waste and of
any fuel which has to be added to achieve appropriate conditions to oxidise
the noxious materials can largely be recovered. A thermal oxidiser with a
heat recovery system can give thermal efficiencies close to those of
conventional fuel burning plant of a similar heat output, so that the use
of supplementary fuel to augment the heat value of the waste is reasonably
economical. Used in this way incinerators can save the capital cost of
alternative fuel burning installations giving systems which are
economically attractive.

* Hirt Combustion Engineers, Northwich, Cheshire.

Heat from an incinerator appears as hot flue gases. Thermally a most attractive use is to replace gas burners directly with this hot gas stream and where the material requiring incineration arises from gas heated processes this is normally possible (eg on gas heated drying and paint ovens). Alternatively the hot gases can be used to produce steam, hot water or hot oil for other heat users on the site. The economical extent of heat recovery follows the normal rules, balancing the extra capital and maintenance costs of heat recovery plant against the useable heat recovered down to an economical limit of off gas temperature: except that what is being burnt may impose some limits (eg if chlorinated materials are burnt it will usually be found that heat transfer surfaces below the HCl dew point can not be justified as HCl resistant equipment is expensive). Incineration off gases from a properly designed and operated incinerator are remarkably free of objectionable constituents or odour. The off gas from the incineration of a typical paint or curing oven exhaust is low enough in carbon monoxide, hydrocarbons and odour to use directly in space heating. In this case the fuel value of the solvent and other fume in the oven exhaust, usually with some added fuel gas, replaces the fuel value of the gas which would be used in a flueless gas heater.

As in any combustion problem, heat recovery is a great deal easier if the burning conditions can be controlled and steady. Incineration adds the requirement that the hot gas retention conditions (temperature, time and oxygen concentration) need to be held between limits which ensure the destruction of the noxious materials. Liquids, molten materials, aqueous solutions, organic or aqueous slurries, gaseous materials or gas suspended solids can all be atomized in appropriate burners (with added liquid or gaseous fuel if necessary) and burnt in a controlled manner. Solid wastes can be similarly burnt using a two stage system in which the solid is first pyrolised in starved air conditions and the gases produced thermally oxidised with additional air. On a very large scale such systems can be continuous, but for the quantities of solid waste (noxious or bland) produced in most factory environments are such that batch loaded incinerators must be used. These give very variable off gas flow through their batch cycles and this makes heat recovery less easy and generally less effective. It also becomes difficult to control the off gas oxygen content and temperature closely so that more air and fuel have to be used to ensure the destruction of noxious constituents than would appear theoretically necessary. Further, solid incinerators are a great deal bulkier and more expensive, and subject to greater heat losses, than fluid fired units. There is consequently a considerable advantage in getting the noxious components into a form which can be burnt as a gas, liquid, melt or slurry. Even if this involves more fuel at the incinerator (eg as diesel fuel to suspend a noxious solid, or fuel to evaporate an aqueous slurry) the fuel value added can normally be largely recovered.

CONDITIONS REQUIRED FOR COMPLETE OXIDATION OF ORGANIC COMPOUNDS

If a thermal oxidiser is used to detoxify a waste the primary need is to achieve conditions which will destroy the noxious components. The destruction process is a mixture of thermal cracking and oxidation. Since what is needed is a vent in which all C-H, C-S, C-Cl bonds have been oxidised which is at the same time low in carbon monoxide the final clean up stages must be oxidations. These will be rate dependant on oxygen concentration provided the temperature is high enough to ensure a large proportion of the oxygen/contaminant molecule collisions produce a reaction. Low carbon monoxide and nitrogen oxides concentration is favoured however by low temperatures.

Lee et al (ref 1) showed that the destruction rates of dilute (but at the same time appreciable in vent concentration terms) organic fume followed first order reaction kinetics down to 2% of the initial concentration. Their measured k values in the equation:

$$f = e^{-kt}$$

(where f is the fraction of organic material remaining after t secs) for vinyl chloride are given in table 1.

TABLE 1

Decomposition of Vinyl Chloride

Temp, deg K	k, secs^{-1}	f after 0.4 secs	f after 2.0 secs
923	0.8	7.2×10^{-1}	2.0×10^{-1}
977	2.6	3.5×10^{-1}	(5.5×10^{-3})
1033	13.2	(5.1×10^{-3})	(3.4×10^{-12})
1061	35.1	(8.0×10^{-7})	(3.3×10^{-31})

Bracketed values of f calculated from k and t: unbracketed values measured.

Whilst these figures are for vinyl chloride, data and the suggested formula for the 99.99% destruction temperature for other organics in the paper indicate similar order of magnitude figures for many other organics.

The American EPA regulation for destruction of organics, which is 99.9% destruction ($f = 1.0 \times 10^3$), can thus be met by 0.4 secs at 1048 deg K, provided there is enough oxygen present for the degree of destruction not to become limited by too low an oxygen concentration. Even the extravagant otandards suggested for such materials as dioxin, eg $f = 1.0 \times 10^{-8}$ can be met apparently by 0.4 secs at 1068 deg K, 2.0 secs at 1043 deg K.

The product of oxygen concentration and time achieved by a given retention volume is much affected by temperature. If a typical hydrocarbon is burnt in air the oxygen concentration remaining at various flue gas temperature increases with lower temperatures: and the retention time represented by a given retention volume decreases linearly with temperature. Table 2 indicates typical oxygen concentrations and retention time ratios against retention temperature and shows the product of these as relative oxidation effectiveness of a given retention volume, assuming combustion air at 288 deg K.

TABLE 2

Effectiveness of Unit Retention Volume as Oxidiser

	Temp, (deg K)		
	(973)	(1023)	(1473)
Oxygen content in flue, vv%	15.6	14.9	11.7
Actual vol of flue gas ——————————— Vol at 15 deg C	3.4	3.7	5.4
Relative oxidation effectiveness of unit retention volume	$\frac{15.6}{3.4} = 4.6$	$\frac{14.9}{3.7} = 4.0$	$\frac{11.7}{5.4} = 2.2$

Temperatures in the 973-1023 deg K range thus give about twice the oxidation rate per unit retention volume compared with 1473 deg K at conditions when the rate is limited by organic molecule concentration, given that the temperature is high enough for the activation energy of the molecules to be such that most collisions result in reaction: and the figures of ref 1 indicate this energy level is generally achieved in the 973-1023 deg K temperature range.

Lower temperatures also offer smaller and cheaper incinerators, need less supplementary fuel and give longer refractory life.

A disadvantage of lower temperature is that the free halogens formed from burning halogenated materials is higher at lower temperatures: for chlorine, about 20 times higher at 973 deg K than at 1473 deg K (ref 2). However, tolerable free chlorine levels can normally be achieved at 1073-1173 deg K.

Given a correctly designed incinerator there seems therefore little point in using incineration temperatures above 1073 deg K to achieve contaminant destruction. Such incinerators will be smaller, cheaper to buy and run and more reliable than high temperature units built on the basis that if hot is good, hotter must be better.

An important design feature is that the gases must be well mixed and retained in a chamber with the walls close to gas temperature. This implies a refractory lining or metal walls with heavy external lagging. If the retention chamber walls are cooled reaction in the gas layers close to the wall will be slow and incomplete, a condition incompatible with the achievement of very high levels of contaminant destruction.

HEAT RECOVERY POSSIBILITIES

The prime design aim of an incinerator must be destruction of the contaminants. Within the degree of freedom available in selecting these conditions however the heat recovery possibilities need to be considered. Incinerators can generally be arranged to recover a proportion of the input heat which approaches the results achieved with conventional fuel burning equipment.

The following examples assume a discharge of cooled incinerator exhaust to stack at 533 deg K, that is a temperature which can be achieved by a simple waste heat boiler.

An incinerator burning 293 kW of waste (or waste plus fuel) operating at 1033 deg K will show an efficiency of 58%, at 1478 deg K 70% (Figs 1 and 2). Similar capacity incinerators with heat exchange between the incoming air and the incinerator, contrary to what would be experienced with a normal boiler, show lower thermal efficiencies (Figs 3 and 4) and need to be much larger, handling twice the flue gas flow of the units without heat exchange.

Particular installations can show extremely good thermal returns when considered against purchased fuel consumed. Incineration of organic laden air streams (eg paint oven exhaust, reactor vent gas) can give many times the heat content of the added fuel as recovered heat. Figs 5 and 6 show the flows and temperatures for a paint oven exhaust incinerator. Incinerated at 1023 deg K, recovered heat can be seven times the fuel heat content: higher incineration temperatures show a bigger heat recovery, but the recovered heat to fuel heat ratio down to 1.6.

If there is sufficient residue or material to detoxify more elaborate heat recovery can be contemplated, aiming for efficiencies more typical of large conventional boiler plants. One of the larger problems is that of landfill gas, an odorous gas of about half the calorific value of natural gas generated in rubbish dumps. Users for this gas are difficult to find economically close to the tipping sites, particularly as the gas is generated and must be burnt at a steady rate 24 hrs/day, 365 days/yr, unfailingly. Consequently much of this gas is flared.

Sites flaring £3,000,000/yr of calorific value of purchased as natural gas are not uncommon. Such a site could carry a simple 7.5 MW boiler and condensing turbine generator set costing about £2,500,000 and earning £1,600,000/yr (assuming a sale value of power to the Central Electricity Generating Board of £26.4/MWh).

Heat recovery from incineration can thus be efficient particularly when viewed in terms of supplementary fuel bought. In practice finding users for the recovered heat is frequently the difficult aspect. If the site has a continuous steam demand a straightforward waste heat boiler is the simple, economical answer. Lacking such a demand, users which can absorb the heat whenever the incinerator is running and can do without heat when the incinerator is idle are not easy to locate.

One solution to the problem is to arrange that the incinerator and its heat recovery plant are reasonably thermally efficient and to burn purchased fuel in the incinerator when waste is not available, making the incinerator into a "base load" unit. The slightly lower thermal efficiency of the incinerator is usually more than offset by the capital saved by not having to provide an alternative heat source for use when the incinerator is idle. A line diagram of such a system for chlorinated wste is shown on Fig 7. This plant operates at 1173 deg K and burns 227 kg/hr of chlorinated organics. Contractors charged $560,000/yr for disposal of this waste. The waste produces steam equivalent to $140,000/yr of purchased fuel and the system, when waste is not available, burns purchased oil at normal boiler efficiencies. Capital cost was $375,000 (prices as of 1980).

A line diagram of such a system applied to paint oven exhausts is shown on Fig 8B. As first proposed this unit would have burnt about 2500 kW (85 therms/hr) of gas and 1610 kW (55 therms/hr) of solvent in the oven exhausts at the incinerator to provide 1700 kW (58 therms/hr) to a hot water system and 1640 kW (56 therms net/hr) to the paint ovens. This seemed a reasonable result: 2500 kW, (85 therms/hr) of purchased fuel replacing 5360 kW (183 therms/hr) currently burnt (Fig 8A). However, modifying the ovens to reduce the fresh air ingested gives Fig 8C. This uses 1640 kW (56 therms/hr) of purchased fuel gas to provide 1640 kW (56 therms net/hr) to the ovens and 1438 kW (49.0 therms/hr) into hot water, a saving of 3460 kW (118 therms/hr) from present conditions.

CONCLUSIONS

Thermal oxidation of wastes can destroy all noxious organic constituents to acceptable levels at easily manageable temperatures and retention times. It can be done at good thermal efficiencies provided a use can be found for the heat in the oxidiser exhaust. Systems need to be examined as a whole and integrated with other heat users on the site. The waste generating step should also be examined as modifications there can often improve the economics of incineration. What is appropriate is very dependant on local conditions and because all or part of the heat is generated from nil value waste may differ markedly from conventional thermal system designs. On the scales normally encountered in factory operation it is very desirable to get the noxious waste into a fluid form as this makes the incineration operation more efficient and the plant needed cheaper to buy and run than if solids are to be burnt.

REFS

1 Lee K, Hansen J, Macauley D. June 24-29, 1979. Air Pollution Control Association Meeting, Cincinnati, Ohio. Paper 70-10-1.

2 Herpers E Th, Schweinsberg B, Ozer N, Bozcar J. April 1979. 3rd Int Symp on Control of Sulphur and Other Gaseous Emissions, Salford. EFCE Publication Series No 4 (Published by I Chem E).

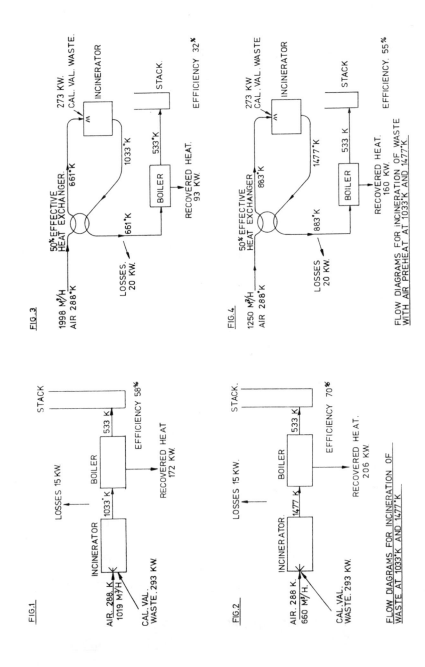

FIG.1

FIG.2

FLOW DIAGRAMS FOR INCINERATION OF WASTE AT 1033°K AND 1477°K.

FIG.3

FIG.4

FLOW DIAGRAMS FOR INCINERATION OF WASTE WITH AIR PREHEAT AT 1033°K AND 1477°K.

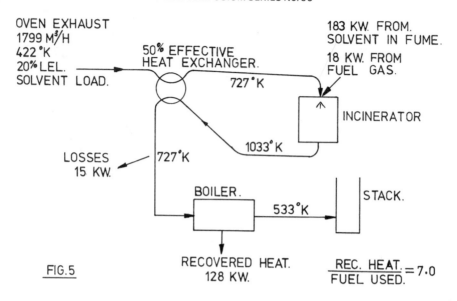

OVEN EXHAUST
1799 M³/H
422 °K
20% LEL.
SOLVENT LOAD.

50% EFFECTIVE
HEAT EXCHANGER.
727 °K

183 KW. FROM.
SOLVENT IN FUME.

18 KW. FROM
FUEL GAS.

INCINERATOR

1033° K

LOSSES
15 KW.

727°K

BOILER.

533°K

STACK.

FIG.5

RECOVERED HEAT.
128 KW.

$$\frac{REC.\ HEAT.}{FUEL\ USED.} = 7.0$$

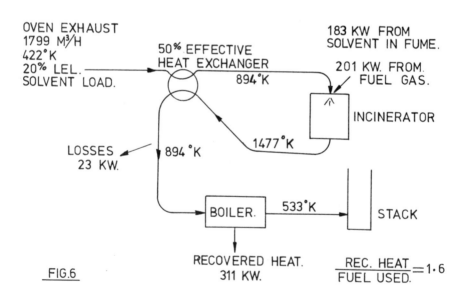

OVEN EXHAUST
1799 M³/H
422°K
20% LEL.
SOLVENT LOAD.

50% EFFECTIVE
HEAT EXCHANGER
894°K

183 KW FROM
SOLVENT IN FUME.

201 KW. FROM.
FUEL GAS.

INCINERATOR

1477°K

LOSSES
23 KW.

894 °K

BOILER.

533°K

STACK

FIG.6

RECOVERED HEAT.
311 KW.

$$\frac{REC.\ HEAT}{FUEL\ USED.} = 1.6$$

FLOW DIAGRAMS FOR INCINERATION OF
SOLVENT LADEN AIR AT 1033 °K AND 1477 °K

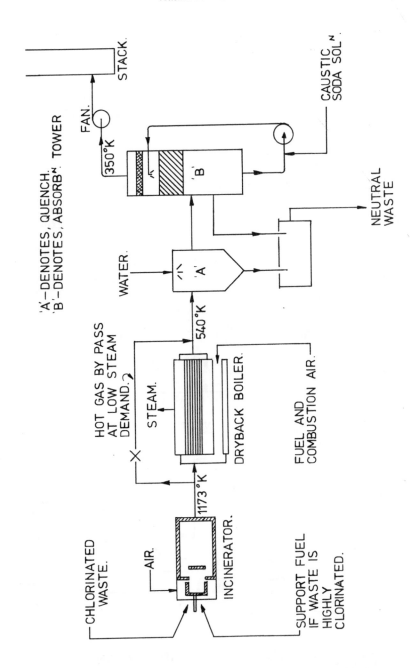

'A'–DENOTES, QUENCH.
'B'–DENOTES, ABSORB^N. TOWER

FIG.7   FLOW DIAGRAM FOR CLORINATED WASTE INCINERATION.

A) OVEN AS INSTALLED

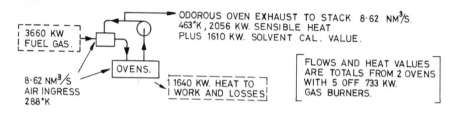

B) OVENS AT INSTALLED VENT FLOWS WITH INCINERATION AND HEAT RECOVERY.

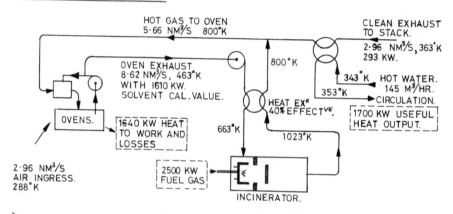

C) OVENS AT REDUCED VENT FLOWS WITH INCINERATION AND HEAT RECOVERY.

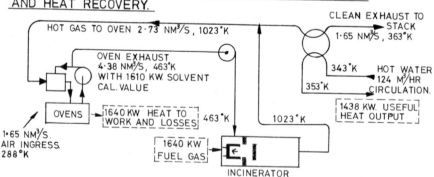

FIG 8. INCINERATOR AND HEAT RECOVERY APPLICATION TO PAINT OVENS.

APPROPRIATE SOLUTIONS TO AGRO-INDUSTRIAL POLLUTION ABATEMENT IN DEVELOPING

COUNTRIES.

Dr. B.S. Holmes* and M. Sane.*

The paper details the results of a pollution survey conducted in a beetsugar and alcohol plant in Turkey and discusses the various options for pollution abatement with energy and by-product recovery. The results of a similar investigation in a cane-sugar/alcohol plant is also presented and discussed.

APPROPRIATE SOLUTIONS TO AGRO-INDUSTRIAL POLLUTION ABATEMENT IN
DEVELOPING COUNTRIES

Introduction

The protection of water resources from the effects of accelerating population growth and industrial development is recognised as an essential duty on modern society. However, pollution protection costs money, and there is always a great deal of competition for any available financial resources. These pressures on financial resources are considerably greater in the developing countries and few of us whom have worked in these areas, cannot but be aware that pollution control is only one of the many social and economic problems in need of money and technical resources.

It is therefore incumbant upon the engineer to consider not only environmental protection by appropriate means, but also to be aware of the economic implications of his solution. In practice this means taking account of:-

- Availability of foreign exchange for initial purchase, spares and process chemicals

- Expertise for the operation, control and maintenance of plant

- Energy.

* W.S. Atkins & Partners., Woodcote Grove, Ashley Road, Epsom, Surrey

All of which may only be available at the expense of other equally desirable objectives. In addition the engineer should seek:-

- means of reducing the quantity and pollution loads disposed to treatment by workable water conservation and "good-housekeeping" techniques.

- to recover and/or separate materials which may be re-processed, sold or be more cheaply and effectively disposed prior to discharge to a waste treatment facility.

- to utilise the waste treatment process to combine pollution abatement with the production of a useable by-product or final residue.

The paper considers pollution control measures for a 6000 T.P.D. beet sugar processing plant and associated distillery in Turkey. Most crops in the country are served by irrigation systems so that water is at a premium and at the same time the country is a net importer of fuel oil and chemical fertilisers so that the production of energy from biomass in the form of methane or production of fertilisers would be most important by-products.

The general conditions above are also often found in factories producing sugar from cane so the authors have reported as a second part some results of studies carried out for a possible new factory of similar size based on cane.

Beet Sugar and Alcohol Plant

The investigation was undertaken as part of a study on improving the overall efficiency, energy utilisation and environmental pollution protection in the beet sugar/alcohol production industry in Turkey. The pollution study was principally aimed at abating wastewater pollution arising from the production of drinking quality alcohol from beet molasses produced at the countries four distilleries. The production processes and operating procedures are similar for all sites and therefore the brief confined the study to one particular plant designed to process 6000 TPD beet during a 160 day campaign and produce up to 64,000 litres per day alcohol in a 294 day campaign.

Location and Environment

Turkey is developing rapidly in both industry and agriculture and in consequence is suffering a shortage of foreign exchange and technical resources. Approximately 48% of the total land area is cultivated making the country virtually self-sufficient in most agricultural crops and a major exporter in some e.g. cotton and tobacco. However indigenous energy sources are confined to lignite and some coal whilst all oil products are imported. Water shortage is rare but almost all the rivers are used for irrigating a diversity of non-processed and re-processed crops.

Approximately 250,000 hecteres of land is used for growing sugar beet and, under local agreements, the sugar industry is committed to support the farmers in the supply of fertilisers with a consequent drain on foreign exchange.

The sugar/alcohol plant investigated is located on the outskirts of a city some 25Km from the beet fields and approximately 1Km from a major river which presently receives the sugar plant treated effluents and the untreated distillery wastewaters. The river also receives the untreated sewage discharges from the city and untreated industrial wastes from a textile factory immediately up stream of the sugar factory discharge together with the untreated wastes from a small abattoir down stream of the sugar factory outfall. Analaytical records maintained by the water authority on the river conditions indicates that the sugar/alcohol plant outfall raises the BOD load in the river by 146,000Kg/day to 543mg/l during the combined sugar and alcohol campaigns and by 88,000Kg/day to 139mg/l during the alcohol campaign alone. The average BOD concentration in the river upstream of the city through the year is in the order of 2.0mg/l.

Legislation to progressively reduce river pollution, is presently under review and it is expected that the initial standards for all outfalls will be.

Threshold value	Average/month	Maximum/day
pH	6-9	6-9
BOD (5) mg/l	150	375
Suspended solids mg/l	80	200
Kjeldahl Nitrogen -N mg/l	15	42
Oil mg/l	30	75
Temperature °C	30	30

It is also expected that this particular river will support coarse fish.

Sugar Plant Wastewater Generation and Treatment

Wastewater discharges from the beet sugar production facility arise from:-

- Beet washing and transportation systems
- Barometric condensers
- Filters
- Cooling water system bleed

Barometric condenser waters are recirculated as make-up to the beet washing and transport system and filter waste is separately dried in drying lagoons. The washing and transport system is a closed loop incorporating a solids settling tank (mud thickener) from which settled sludges are removed and discharged to large atmospheric treatment lagoons at a rate to match the barometric condenser make-up. The lagoons are sized to take advantage of the long periods between campaigns for natural treatment and a slow controlled rate of discharge from the lagoons to the river, to allow for settled mud removal prior to the start of the next campaign. Generally as indicated in Figure 1. The lagoons are sized up to contain the total surplus water generated for a period of up to 8 months. During this time natural aerobic treatment is expected to reduce the pollutants sufficiently to allow a controlled low flow discharge to the river over a 2 month period. In the remaining 2 months of the year the mud is allowed to dry for removal. Unfortunately, during the investigation the mud thickener plant was not working effectively and being by-passed by a direct flow to the river from the recirculating beet washing and transport system. Nevertheless analysis of the partly filled lagoon waters after some 39 days retention, indicated a 64% COD and 98% suspended solids removal. It is expected that given a full 8 months period for atmospheric treatment the lagoon effluents should comply with the discharge conditions. Cooling tower bleed water is discharged direct to the river.

It was clear from the investigations that the sugar plant waste treatment facilities could not be used to treat the alcohol plant wastewaters.

Alcohol Plant Wastewater Generation

A schematic flowsheet of the alcohol distillation plant is given in Figure 2. It will be noted that wastewaters arise from the vinasse (yeasty residue discharged from the stripping columns), from the once-through cooling and condenser water systems and from periodic floor washing of the yeast preparation and distillation areas. The average analysis of the vinasse discharged from the stripping columns of the alcohol plant are given in Table 1. The volume of vinasse flows was established from alcohol production mass balances.

TABLE 1 - TYPICAL ANALYSIS OF VINASSE

Constituent		Average	Max.
Volume of flow	m³/day	722	940
Rate of flow	m³/hr.	30	40
pH		4.9	4.9
COD load	Kg/day	47 030	70 130
COD concentration	mg/l	65 140	74 600
BOD load	Kg/day	27 436	43 240
BOD concentration	mg/l	38 000	46 000
Suspended solids load	Kg/day	7 560	12 135
Suspended solids concentration	mg/l	10 470	12 910
Total Nitrogen - N	Kg/day	2 166	3 760
Total Nitrogen - N	mg/l	3 000	4 000
Amm Nitrogen - N	Kg/day	62	106
Amm Nitrogen -N	mg/l	85	113
Total Dissolved solids	mg/l	74 410	81 820
Temperature	°C	91	93

The condenser and cooling water flow was established by pump duty and mass balance to be in the order of 300 m³/day.

Pollution Reductions

In a beet sugar factory it is normally expected that the water contained in the incoming beet should be sufficient for the process requirements.

Examination of the installed sugar and alcohol plant and operating procedures indicated that marginal reductions in water consumption were possible in the sugar plant to reduce the final discharges to more closely equate to the water content of the received beet but the cost of the work could not be justified. However it was recommended that the beet tailing screens, currently 10mm diameter perforated plate, be replaced with 5mm diameter screens to:-

-     remove more beet particles from the water flow quickly and thereby reduce the contact time for organic leaching to occur.

-     overcome problem of blanketing of the larger particles in the mud thickener which could periodically settle as a mass and cause difficulties for the mud extraction pumps.

Considerable reductions in the quantity of vinasse disposed from the distillation columns could be made by adopting vinasse recirculation techniques. Pilot plant work undertaken on this particular distillery some years previously by the client indicated that 40% recirculation of the vinasse could be practical without loss of quality and with insignificant effects on production rates. International practice in distilling beet sugar molasses suggests that recirculation up to 60% can be practical with sterilisation and contamination control. In discussion with the client it was agreed that the distillery would be operated with 50% recirculation but that further pilot plant work be undertaken to see if this could be increased. Adopting recirculation should improve yeast recovery and reduce demands for nutrients in the fermentation process and thereby reduce the organic loads discharged in the vinasse by about 25%. It was also recommended that initial dry cleaning of the yeast recovery floor area be practiced to reduce the quantity of dry yeast washed to drain. Taking account of these pollution reduction measures was expected to result in a vinasse and floor wash combined discharge generally as indicated in Table 2.

TABLE 2 - TYPICAL ANALYSIS OF ALCOHOL PLANT WASTEWATERS

Constitutent		Average	Max.
Volume of flow	m^3/day	360	480
Rate of flow	m^3/hr.	15	20
pH		5	5
COD load	Kg/day	35 000	53 000
COD concentration	mg/l	97 000	110 000
BOD load	Kg/day	20 500	25 000
BOD concentration	mg/l	57 000	52 000
Suspended solids load	Kg/day	5,800	9 000
Suspended solids concen	mg/l	16 000	19 000
Total Nitrogen - N	Kg/day	1 080	1 920
Total Nitrogen - N	mg/l	3 000	4 000
Amm. Nitrogen-N	Kg/day	30	55
Am Nitrogen - N	mg/l	85	115
T.D.S.	mg/l	110 000	120 000
Temperature	°C	91	93

Treatment Options

The vinasse treatment and disposal options considered for this distillery included;

- sub-soil injection of untreated waste.

- anaerobic digestion with disposal of the anaerobically treated effluent to irrigating water courses or land application and with biogas utilisation.

- anaerobic digestion first stage treatment with biological nitrification/denitrification second stage for final discharge to river and with biogas utilisation.

- evaporation and incineration of the vinasse with potassium recovery as a fertiliser.

Sub-soil injection

This disposal method is environmentally acceptable for the vinasse wastes since injection at depths of below 400mm below soil level virtually eliminates the odour problem which has precluded the use of spray irrigation system. The value of vinasse as an agricultural fertiliser and soil conditioner when applied at the correct application rates for the soil and crop is well documented. (1,2,3,4 & 5). The benefits reported include

- improvements in the chemical and physical properties of the soil.

- increase in the water retaining capacity of the soil.

- increase in the mineral salt retaining capacity of the soil.

- restoration and maintenance of soil fertility.

- increase in soil microflora.

Experience in Brazil indicates sugar cane crop yield improvement of 2 to 10 times that of areas not treated with vinasse. However the rate and frequency of applications for particular soil pH and crop conditions appears critical ranging from 1000m^3/hectare for soils of below pH4 to 650m^3/hectare at pH5 and over. In some instances figures as low as 90 m^3/hectare have been used and applications are required at 1 month to 4 year intervals depending on crop.

However, the viability of this disposal method is principally one of logistics governed by the quantity of vinasse to be disposed, and the transport costs to available sites. Unfortunately the remoteness of the beet fields from the distillery and the local soil conditions detracted from using this method for this particular distillery but could be appropriate for other sites.

Anaerobic digestion

Anaerobic digestion could reduce the BOD and COD of the alcohol plant wastes by 85-90% (1,2,6,7,8) but would not reduce the total nitrogen content significantly, converting most of the original organic nitrogen into ammonia nitrogen. Anaerobic treatment of the wastewaters given in Table 2 would be expected to produce an effluent containing in the order of 520mg BOD/l, 1650 mgCOD/l and 400mg total N/l. (320mg NH_3-N/l)

However the biogas produced from treatment would be in the order of 10,500 Nm^3/day containing about 60% methane and providing an energy equivalent to some 6 tonnes/day fuel oil (1800 tonnes/campaign year). The anaerobic process would also remove most of the odour associated with the vinasse and make the digested effluent acceptable for spray application to land.

Clearly the digested effluent does not comply with the proposed treated effluent standards for river discharges and the alcohol plant is too remote for land spray application. Therefore this solution was not acceptable for this particular alcohol plant but, in view of the potential energy recovery could be attractive to other alcohol plant sites.

Anaerobic digestion plus aerobic nitrification

Anaerobic digestion followed by a second stage aerobic nitrifying biological treatment plant, (9) can be expected to reduce the BOD and suspended solids to within the discharge limits but would only oxidise the ammonia to nitrites and nitrates without reducing the total nitrogen significantly. Utilising the available cooling and condenser waters for dilution would result in a final effluent containing some 400 mg/l total nitrogen. Further dilution in the river would still result in a rise in river water nitrogen of about 20mg/l which is too high to support fish life.

This process is not, therefore, suitable for installation at this particular alcohol plant.

Anaerobic digestion plus Nitrification plus Denitrification

Anaerobic treatment with secondary nitrification then denitrification treatment would be suitable for reducing the organic content of the wastes to below the required treated water standards, and reducing the total nitrogen to about 100mg/l and the ammonia nitrogen to below 5mg/l. Taking account of the minimum river water flows would raise the total nitrogen in the river by approximately 5mg/l to a maximum of about 7mg/l i.e within limits recommended by the EEC for support of coarse fish.

The two stage anaerobic/nitrification/denitrification treatment method could therefore provide the benefit of biogas generation and a river water condition suitable for the support of coarse fish and thereby be an acceptable solution for pollution abatement at this particular alcohol plant.

Evaporation with Incineration

This process involves the first stage evaporation of the vinasse from an initial total solids of about 15% to 60-65% total solids to ensure autothermic and stable combustion conditions with reasonable thermal efficiencies for steam generation in an incinerator. Evaluation of the various combinations of evaporator and incinerator types available suggested a 4 stage evaporator, a furnace equipped with steam atomising jets and burners, connected to a waste heat boiler and provided with electro-static gas cleaning plant offered the most effective solutions for this plant.
Incinerating the distillery vinasse will produce an excess of steam of approximately 5 T.P.H. which, together with a nominal steam saving in the rest of the sugar/alcohol plant will produce a coal saving of approximately 4725 tonnes/year at $58.2/tonne, and also produce approximately 14.5 tonnes/day of dry ash residue containing some 50% potassium (1,2,10,11) currently imported as a fertiliser at $225/tonne.

Evaporating and incinerating the wastes could therefore save approximately £216,500 p.a. in coal costs and produce fertiliser valued at some £745,000 p.a. The process would also meet the wastewater pollution abatement requirements since there would be no polluted water discharge and atmospheric pollution would be prevented by the gas cleaning plant.

Comparative Costs

The comparative costs for the options considered are shown in Table 3.

Of these options two namely anaerobic digester alone and anaerobic digester plus Nitrification do not meet the discharge conditions for the site under consideration. When considering a choice among the other three the local circumstances will be determinant. The financial advantage of sub-soil injection both in the first cost and operating cost is evident from the table but this will only be liable where the beet growing areas are close to the refinery and probably also where the land is owned by the refinery operator. Where this is not the case the choice will lie between direct incineration and gas production. The main advantage of gas production is lower capital cost but with limited storage and production only during part of the year a use would have to be found for the gas on the process plant. The direct incineration technique on the other hand provides a similar energy saving but produces a by-product which is dry and can be conveniently stored or sold. It is the value of this by product which produces the much shorter payback period shown in Table 3. The evident choice would be the incineration option but the large first cost must be recognised and where capital is limited the gas production system may be appropriate.

TABLE 3 - SUMMARY OF CAPITAL AND OPERATING COST ESTIMATES

Disposal Method	Capital Cost $£x10^3$	Plant [1] Operating Costs $£x10^3$	Revenues			Net Annual Operating Costs $£x10^3$	Capital Pay back Period Years
			Energy Saving $£x10^3$	By-Product Sale $£x10^3$	Total Revenue $£x10^3$		
Anaerobic Digester with Nitrification and Gas Holder	1690	66.8	270 (oil equivalent)	0	270	203.2 Profit	8.3
Anaerobic Digester with Nitrification/ Denitrification and Gas Holder	2074	71.3	270 (oil equivalent)	0	270	198.7 PROFIT	10.4
Evaporation with Incineration [2]	3653	81.2	215.7 (coal equivalent)	761.4	977.1	895.9 Profit	4.4
Land Disposal (Sub-soil Injection of Raw Slops)	264	18.2	0	338	338	319.8 Profit	0.8
Anaerobic Digester with Gas Holder	1274	14.85	270 (oil equivalent)	0	270	255.2 Profit	4.99

Notes:

1) Operating costs do not include for financing plant capital costs.

2) Capital costs do not include for ash storage, bagging or transport costs that would be necessary for distribution to growing areas for use as fertiliser.

Cane Sugar and Alcohol Plant

In a cane sugar plant bagasse (fibrous residue after sugar leaching) is used for boiler firing and this normally provides sufficient energy to satisfy the total demands of the production plant. Sadly sometimes plants supplement the bagasse with wood or oil burning which can contribute to the depletion of trees with possible serious ecological consequences.

TABLE 4 - TYPICAL WASTEWATER ANALYSIS FOR A CANE SUGAR PLANT

CONSTITUENT		VINASSE	COMBINED DISTILLERY AND COOLING WATER	BAROMETRIC CONDENSERS	MUD FILTER + FLOOR WASH
		Average	Average	Average	Average
COD	mg/l	140,000	5800	46	3240
BOD$_{(5)}$	mg/l	70,000	3900	41	2411
TOTAL NITROGEN (as N)	mg/l	2,000	144	1.65	22
AMMONIA NITROGEN (as N)	mg/l	300	25.2	0.59	4.7
SUSPENDED SOLIDS	mg/l	15,000	426	144	853
ORTHO PHOSPHATE as (PO_4)	mg/l	50	4.6	0.55	10.5
POTASSIUM (asK)	mg/l	5,000	270	9.9	39.2
TOTAL SOLIDS	mg/l	140,000			
PH		4.5	4.5	6.2	5.2

FLOW l/day per tonne cane crushed	120	200	1200	105
TEMPERATURE	98°C	Slightly over ambient	Ambient plus 5°C	Ambient
Colour	Brown	Light Brown	-	Black
Odour	Foul	Noticeable	-	Noticeable

In this type of plant the major water users are the barometric condensers of the sugar plant and a water supply system for a cane sugar and alcohol plant is shown in Figure 3.

Typically in a cane sugar plant the barometric condenser wastes are separately collected and all other wastes are collected in site surface water drainage channels for conveyance to disposal points as shown in Figure 4. Process wastewater discharges are so arranged that the relatively clean process water discharges are separated from the more highly polluted wastes.

Wastewater Generations and Pollution Loads

Site investigation has established the character of the waste discharges from the sugar plant and the distillery to be generally as indicated in Table 4. A pollution balance on the plant showed that approximately 20% of the organic load in the final distillery effluent arises from extraneous pollutant discharges from within the distillery which could be reduced by adopting the measures discussed below. Based on data previously collected and taking account of proposed yeast recovery and the proposed pollution reduction measures, the wastes discharged to the disposal points could be expected to be as shown in Table 5.

TABLE 5 - ESTIMATED WASTEWATER DISCHARGES FOR PROPOSED 6000 TPD CANE PLANT

Wastewater Source	Flow	C.O.D.		B.O.D.(5)		Suspended Solids		Total Nitrogen	
	Average M³/day	Mg/l	Kg/day	Mg/l	Kg/day	Mg/l	Kg/day	Mg/l	Kg/day
1. Disposed Direct to Pumping Station									
Vinesse Distillery Cooling,	700	136,000	95,200	65,000	45,500	15,500	10,850	2,300	1,610
Condensate & Floor Wash	6,000	40	240	15	90	70	400	2.0	12
Domestic Sewage	150	600	90	300	45	280	40	40	6
Composite Waste Direct to Pump Station	6,850	13,900	95,500	6,660	45,635	1,648	11,290	238	1,630
2. Disposed to Lagoon									
Mud Filter Wastes	17,850	3,200	57,100	2,400	42,840	850	15,170	22	390
(1) Cooling water, condensate, Blowdown, Floor wash, Cold water services, wastes etc.	31,000	40	1,240	15	460	70	2,170	2.0	60
Composite Waste to Lagoon	48,850	1,190	58,340	886	43,300	355	17,340	9	450
3. Combine waste pumped from waste pump station to final disposal (2)	55,700	2,600	145,100	1,480	82,435	265	14,760	37	2,080
4. Barometric Condenser Waters Disposed to Irrigation Canal	124,000	40	4,960	40	4,960	20	2,480	1.6	198

(1) Assuming pollution prevention measures recommended are implemented.
(2) Assumes 80% solids reduction and 15% B.O.D. reduction of wastes disposed to the lagoon.

Provision of a clarifier to treat mud filter wastewaters is assumed and this can reduce the suspended solids and BOD disposed from filters by approximately 80% and 10% respectively which will help significantly in final discharges.

Environmental Pollution Impact

In assessing the environmental impact of wastes discharged from the new site consideration must be given to:-

- health hazards
- effects on receiving waters
- effects on receiving soils, short and long term
- effects on local ammenities
- nuisance.

It will be noted from Table 5 that the principal polluting constituents in the wastewaters are COD, BOD, nitrogen compounds, potassium and suspended solids, and that the major source of pollution is the distillery and in particular the distillery vinasse. The mud filter wastes are also highly polluting. However, none of these constituents or wastes, in themselves present a health hazard although both the vinasse and the filter wastes, in particular the vinasse, smell abominably and are very real nuisances. In the presence of domestic sewage the organic matter and nutrients in the industrial wastes could accelerate and increase the growth of bacteria and pathogons and increase the health risks.

The environmental impact of wastes discharged to surface waters is related principally to the use of the surface waters and to the dilution available, and in this case the receiving waters are confined to providing irrigation waters with no intentions of fish cultivation or potable supply use. Therefore any solution which overcomes the odour problem could be acceptable to the surface water conditions.

Local amenities are an additional factor needing to be considered. In the authors experience irrigation canals are often used for bathing and washing in hot climates and sometimes for irrigation of domestic allotments as well.

Proposed Solutions

We were guided in our choices by the recommendations of the California State Department of Health for waters suitable for irrigating crops to be reprocessed and given as equivalent to "primary sewage treatment effluents" and by the World Bank Environmental Guidelines - Ethanol Productions" which suggests discharges should be limited to between 30 and 60 mg/l for both BOD and suspended solids.

The simple solution was straight forward viz:-

i)   Collect the "dirty" effluents from the sugar and alcohol plant and pump into the main canal via a submerged outlet. The submerged outlet will remove the odour problem and the very large dilution (30 times) together with the absence of domestic sewage produce a safe and acceptable water quality.

ii)   Discharge the barometric condenser waters direct to the irrigation canal.

313

The character of the canal waters at the proposed Plant resulting from adopting this disposal philosophy are shown in Table 6. It will be noted that the quality of both the main canal and irrigation canal waters containing the process wastes are within the required standards.

TABLE 6 - IMPACT ON RECEIVING WATERS OF PROPOSED PLANT

	Feed Waters	Irrigation Waters
Wastewater flow m³/hr	2000	5000
Dilution water	30 times	0
	Predicted concentration in mixed water	
COD mg/l	86	40
BOD$_{(5)}$ mg/l	50	40
Total nitrogen (as N) mg/l	1.2	1.6
Ammonia nitrogen (as N)mg/l	0.4	0.6
Ortho-phosphate(as PO4)mg/l	0.3	0.5
Suspended solids mg/l	9	20

The overall capital costs of implementing the pollution reduction, domestic sewage treatment and waste water collection and disposal systems outlined above have been estimated at £250,000.

It will be recalled that the objectives of these studies are energy conservation as well as pollution control and it is important that this objective be kept in mind. An alternative pollution abatement solution for the distillery would be to treat the distillery vinasse anaerobically and produce methane gas. From Table 5 it will be seen that the vinasse disposed would be in the order of 700m³/day containing approximately 96,000Kg COD/day. Treating these wastes by any of the conventional anaerobic techniques could be expected to generate approximately 29,000N m³/day of methane and equivalent to an oil saving of 2,500 tonnes of fuel oil per year. The overall capital cost of installing such a system would be in the order of £2.1m with an operating cost of about £60,000.

Skilled personnel would be required to operate and maintain such a facility and, since a cane sugar/alcohol plant should be self-sufficient in energy from bagasse, an external demand for the gas energy would need to be identified. Therefore whilst the cheap and simple solution to pollution abatement would be recommended for this site the cost effective benefits of the alternative solution should not be lost sight of. Again as was found in the first study the fact that the vinasse is not produced 365 days per year is a major handicap to finding effective uses for the gas.

Acknowledgements

The authors are grateful for the assistance given in conducting the site investigation by:-

The Turkish Sugar Factories Corporation, Ankara, Turkey, and in particular by Mrs. Mujgan Erturk, Projects Department.

References

1. Jackman E.A. 1977 The Chemical Engineer

2. Maiorella BL, Blanch H.W., Wilke CR. 1983, Process Biochemistry

3. Chen S, 1980 Hawaii Natural Energy institute

4. Costa Ribeiro C, Castello Branco JR, 1981, Process

5. Seminario Internacional Sobre Tratomento de Vinhote, 1976, Institute Nacional de Technologia, Rio de Janeiro

6. Sherratt A, Robertson A, 1984, Brewing and Distilling Int.

7. Nilsson M, 1981, Int. Sugar J

8. Sheehan GJ, Greenfield PF, Water Research Vol. 14

9. Boon AG. W.R.G., Stevenage Laboratories

10. Spruytenburg G.P., 1982, Int. Sugar J

11. Martin R.K., 1963 British Chem. Eng.

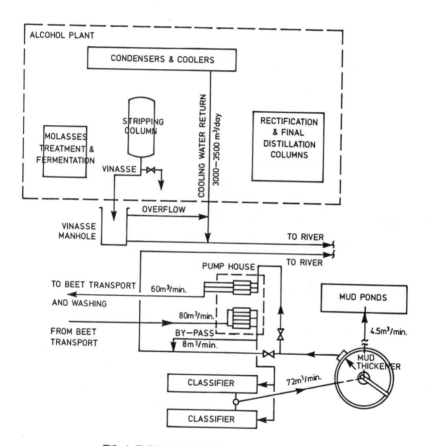

FIG. 1. TYPICAL BEET SUGAR WATER SYSTEM

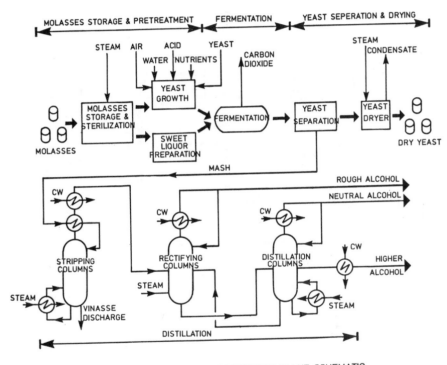

FIG.2. TYPICAL ALCOHOL PRODUCTION PLANT SCHEMATIC

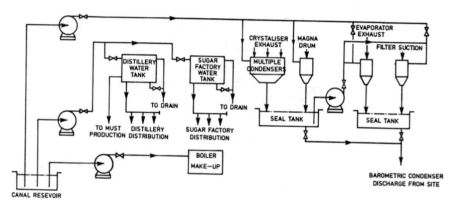

FIG.3. WATER SUPPLY FOR CANE SUGAR PLANT

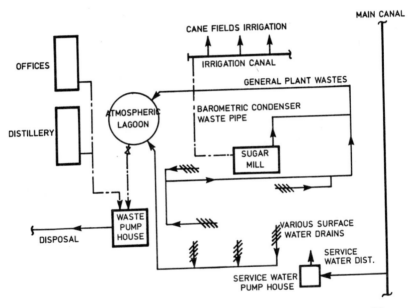

FIG.4. WASTE WATER DISPOSAL AT CANE SUGAR PLANT

BIOHYDROLYSIS OF UREA EFFLUENTS : A CONTINUOUS PROCESS WITH MIXED CULTURES *

G.Prabhakaran, M.R.Udayakumar, S.R.Ramakrishnan and
R.M.Krishnan **

A simple, versatile and economically attractive urea biohydrolysis process is developed. The process features include the use of mixed cultures of urease positive and urease negative bacterial strains, a mild alkaline pH, the ability to withstand high concentrations of urea nitrogen (4,000 to 15,000 mg/l) together with ammoniacal nitrogen concentrations of 2,000 to 10,000 mg/l. The hydrolysis is carried out under anoxic and non-sterile conditions. This process compares favourably with the energy-intensive thermal hydrolysis process.

INTRODUCTION

The ecological impact of industrial effluents is becoming a significant factor in most of the chemical process industries. In the case of nitrogenous fertilizers like urea this problem is all the more emphasised by the very chemistry of producing urea. For every mole of urea produced from ammonia and carbon-dioxide, one mole of water is produced simultaneously.

$$2NH_3 + CO_2 \rightleftharpoons CO (NH_2)_2 + H_2O$$

Subsequently in the concentration stages of urea processes, invariably a condensate containing ammonia and urea is separated and discharged. Although the presence of urea nitrogen in such an effluent does not pose any toxicity problem, urea is prone to hydrolyse both in the acidic and alkaline media and one of the hydrolysis products, ammonia, is toxic.

In fact, it is reported that one mg of ammoniacal nitrogen exerts an ultimate BOD of 4.5 mg of oxygen[1] . Apart from this there are two other problems viz., the oxidation of ammonia to nitrate posing a potential health hazard and the phenomenon of eutrophication caused by urea and ammonia which serve as nutrients for the development of algal blooms in surface waters. This latter problem creates a supplemental effect leading to accelerated fish mortality[2].

* Patent pending.
** R&D Centre, Southern Petrochemical Industries Corporation Ltd., Tuticorin-628 005, INDIA.

The permissible limits for total nitrogen in effluent streams are being made more stringent in many countries. In a developing country with intensive agriculture like India, the limit for ammoniacal nitrogen in effluents from the nitrogenous fertiliser industry discharged into inland surface waters has been set at 50 mg/l (IS : 2490 Part I - 1974). Currently there is a proposal to change this standard from ammoniacal nitrogen to total kjeldhal nitrogen. This proposal matches the US Environmental Protection Agency requirement for total nitrogen contained in treated effluent prior to disposal. Also, such a change will not affect the 50 mg/l limit numerically. In setting acceptable standards there are no specific limits laid down exclusively for urea nitrogen since its hydrolysis to ammonia very much depends on the environment. However, a value of 20 mg/l for urea nitrogen has been quoted in one reference[3].

THE EXISTING UREA HYDROLYSIS SCHEMES

The necessity to maintain the limits set by the various pollution control authorities forces urea producers to have a mandatory urea hydrolysis scheme before effluent disposal. To cater for these demands, many of the process companies have been offering urea hydrolysis schemes based on thermal decomposition[4]. Some of the companies such as DSM[5] and SNAM Progetti[6] have recently developed modified versions of thermal hydrolysis through extensive phase equilibria studies. These processes reduce the treated effluent concentration levels to less than 10 mg/l. However, there is a price to achieve such low concentration levels by way of substantial energy requirements. The treated effluent is said to be reusable as boiler feed water.

In addition to the thermal hydrolysis schemes various other schemes like reverse osmosis[7], oxidation with sodium nitrite and ion exchange have been tested at laboratory scale. However, the scale-up studies of these methods have not been reported. As an alternative to the thermal hydro-lysis, the microbiological approach has been tried up to commercial scale. In fact, a method based on the immobilised urease enzyme extracted from Bacillus pasteurii is offered by DSM of the Netherlands. Also, Geo Miller of India are offering a bioprocess for treating urea effluent. However, some fears have been expressed about this process being highly pH sensitive and that any slight deviation might throw the system out of gear.

WHY MIXED CULTURE?

Before we describe our bioprocess, it is worthwhile to explain the rationale behind the choice of a mixed culture.

Most of the ureolytic microbes are steno responsive[8]. They require free ammonia in addition to growth promoting substances[8]. It is also known that urea is a protein denaturant. Hence, if any microorganism is placed in an environment containing urea, the organism has to degrade urea in order to survive. Such a natural necessity exhibits itself through the presence of urease enzyme reportedly occurring in 200 species of bacteria, several species of yeast, in fungi and in large number of plants[9].

The ureolytic bacteria are just a special group which transform a survival mechanism into a growth promoting mechanism. This transformation is evident by the presence of exceedingly large amounts of urease up to 1% of the total weight of Bacillus pasteurii cells. In elucidating the effect of ammonium ions and alkaline pH, Wiley and Stokes[10] have suggested that the presence of ammonium ions may be required for substrate penetration at low substrate concentrations and not for internal metabolism. In other words these conditions only facilitate active transport. At high substrate concentrations the simple diffusion of substrates will facilitate growth.

One of the major observations noted in pure culture studies with ureolytic bacteria relates to the antagonistic aspects of ammonia vis-a-vis the urea concentration. The increasing ammonium ion concentration in the growth medium represses the biosynthesis of urease enzyme and further inhibits the urease activity which in turn impedes the urea transport across the cell membrane. Such a conclusion implies that the allowable ammonia concentration in biohydrolysis has to be very low. Such a severe constraint placed on the use of pure culture for treating urea effluent is a major draw-back in developing a microbial process.

If any microbiological process has to match the performance of thermal hydrolysis processes, it is essential to pretreat an effluent containing very high levels of ammonia and urea (2,000 to 10,000 mg/l and 4,000 to 15,000 mg/l respectively) which are present simultaneously. It is not possible to achieve this objective at present with pure cultures. For this reason, we chose to work with mixed bacterial cultures. The use of mixed cultures has often paid dividends in industrial preparations of cheese, wine and sauerkraut. Even in biological treatment of water and wastes (rumen, soil) mixed cultures have already proved to be effective.

BUILT-IN FEATURES OF MIXED CULTURE BIOHYDROLYSIS

Essential requirements for any effluent treatment process are ease of operation, cost effectiveness, flexibility etc. Accordingly, the following requirements may be set down prior to design of mixed culture biohydrolysis:

1. The selection of suitable carbon and nitrogen sources and design of growth medium for the mixed populations,

2. Achievement of non-sterile conditions,

3. Ability to withstand wide pH range of 8.0 to 11.2,

4. Oxygen insensitivity,

5. Treatment of an effluent containing high concentrations of urea and ammonia.

In order to achieve the above requirements both ureolytic and non-ureolytic bacteria and fungi were isolated from wet land soils. The resource was subsequently taken to enrichment. The members of mixed culture tailored for our specific needs are belonging to the genera Micrococcus, Corynebacterium, Bacillus, Proteus and Sarcina. The growth curve and the percentage hydrolysis vs time curve observed for the chosen mixed culture is represented in Fig. 1.

CARBON SOURCE AND NITROGEN SOURCE

Ureolytic bacteria are known to utilise glycerol, methanol, glucose, succinate and carbonates as carbon sources. Except for glucose, other sources of carbon are highly value-added substances. It has been reported that the utilisation of glucose as a carbon source has a bearing on the percentage of urea hydrolysed through its effect on urease enzyme activity[11].

In the present study various commercially available carbon sources were tried purely from the cost effective angle taking into consideration the heterogenity of the culture. Out of these studies sucrose was found to be the best carbon source. The use of disaccharide was made possible because of the presence of non-ureolytic bacteria in the mixed culture which facilitate the growth of the simultaneously existing ureolytic bacteria. This is also substantiated by the growth curve (Fig. 1) where the onset of exponential growth is delayed by a more than anticipated period. The effect of the sugar content expressed as a percentage of growth saturation value on the microbial growth and the percentage of urea hydrolysed is shown in Fig. 2.

During the course of developing the process, the peculiar requirement of organic nitrogen source as a growth promoting substance for the mixed culture was investigated. Although, the incoming effluent contained urea and ammonia, the culture could not sustain itself without additional organic nitrogen. The incapacity to utilise urea and ammonia as a source of nitrogen has been already demonstrated for ureolytic bacteria [12]. What is so unusual in the present mixed culture was the dominant behavioural pattern set up by these group of organisms over that of the non-ureolytic part. In other words, the non-ureolytic bacteria in the mixed culture seem to adapt their metabolic activities to aid cohabitation, eventually enhancing the activity of the ureolytic organisms.

Many of the commonly used nitrogen sources like corn steep liquor, poly-peptones and vitamin free casitone, either individually or in combinations, were tried and in each case, after a few generations, the mixed culture adapted itself and carried out the hydrolysis. The effect of the finally selected proprietory nitrogen source on the percentage hydrolysis and growth is presented in Fig. 2. For our continuous system, the optimum carbon and nitrogen nutrient concentrations were obtained from Fig. 2, as a compromise between hydrolysis and growth rates.

NON-STERILE CONDITION

When a mixed microbial population is grown in open systems the phenomenon of natural selection continuously occurs and determines which organism can survive and which will predominate in the ecosystem. Such selection can be influenced by certain external stimuli. In such cases, it is essential that the bacteria we have chosen predominate over the invaders. This selection was achieved by exploiting the alkaline pH conditions and high ammonia and urea nitrogen concentrations. Once again the approach to non-sterile conditions was dictated by the need to obtain an energy economy.

pH RANGE

The quality of urea effluent emanating from urea processes (unless discharged from a single source such as condensers) varies widely in terms
of constituent concentrations and hence in pH. This feature was also
taken into account in the selection and enrichment procedures. The mixed
culture thus selected is able to survive from a pH of 8.0 to 11.2. In
contrast, steno-responsive pure ureolytic strains are narrowly responsive
to pH. This feature of the pure culture is completely masked in the
mixed culture where the ureolytic organisms are made viable throughout
a wide range of pH. It is, however, observed that there is a gradual
decrease in the growth and hydrolysis rates as pH increases. Even so,
the process yields satisfactory rates at a pH around 11 (Fig. 3).

OXYGEN REQUIREMENT

The role of dissolved oxygen was studied for this mixed culture. The
results revealed that a mild variation in the dissolved oxygen content
originating in the untreated urea effluent (2.0 to 5.0 mg/l) does not
affect the percentage of urea hydrolysed and also the growth. This insensitivity enabled us to operate the process always under anoxic conditions.
The performance of the process under a dissolved oxygen range of 0 to
2.0 mg/l was not studied.

PROCESS REALISATION

Growth curves were determined by cultivating the mixed culture in nephe-
lometric flasks and measuring the turbidity with an ERMA photo electric
colorimeter model AE.11 equipped with red filter. A calibration curve
of absorbancy versus dry weight was constructed. For continuous cultures,
a chemostat was used. The temperature was maintained at 34°C. Ammoniacal
nitrogen was measured by Nessler's method and urea nitrogen by the
reaction using p-dimethylaminobenzaldehyde (PDAB) reagent. The physico-
chemical properties of the effluent samples (untreated and treated) are
given in Table-1.

Subsequent to the batch studies, a continuous arrangement with one continuously stirred tank reactor (CSTR) was tried initially. The residence time
was maintained at 20 hours, as adopted from the batch studies. On further
scale up through empirical analysis, it was found that a double CSTR
set-up with a residence time of around 10 to 15 hours per tank was economical with respect to the rate of hydrolysis, nutrient uptake and
agitation requirement. An analysis of the kinetics of the biohydrolysis
revealed that the entry of urea into the cell rather than its hydrolysis
may have been the rate limiting step. The process conditions (urea concentration, nutrient level and the residence time) were established
for each CSTR so as to obtain optimum hydrolysis and growth rates.
Nutrients were added intermittently; the carbon source requirement was
of the order of 0.1 to 0.2 kg per kg of urea treated. Similarly the
nitrogen source requirement ranged from 0.05 to 0.1 kg per kg of urea
treated. In this process approximately 75 % to 90 % hydrolysis takes
place in the first bioreactor. The growth rate in the first reactor

adequately compensates the dilution rate, so that there is no requirement to add fresh culture during continuous operation. A schematic
diagram of this process is given in Fig. 4. The urea effluent at the
exit of bioreactor 2 having suspended solids was subsequently treated
through an ammonia stripper and mixed with other plant effluents. Hence,
there is no need for a separate sludge removal and associated dewatering
units for this process. Eventually, the combined effluent is disposed
off.

The continuous process was demonstrated at bench scale and pilot scale
levels. For pilot plant operations, initial seeding was done to the
order of 10% of the hold-up volume with the mother culture prepared from
lyophilized cells. The cost of inoculant available in lyophilized form
is being worked out. A scale-up factor of 25 was adopted for each development stage. At present, commercial-scale bioreactors, capable of treating
the entire process effluent from a 1600 t/d urea plant, are being erected.

The cost of treatment using this bioprocess was estimated during each
stage of scale-up and the results compared with costs of existing thermal
hydrolysis processes. For a urea plant of capacity of 1500 tonnes/day
the energy requirement for the treatment plant is as much as 17.2×10^6
kJ/h in the case of thermal hydrolysis. This is equivalent to about
275,000 kJ/tonne of urea produced. Assuming an energy cost of 6 U.S.$
for 10^6 kJ, the variable cost of treatment through thermal hydrolysis
works out to about 1.64 U.S. $/tonne of urea produced. As opposed to
this cost, the bioprocess using mixed cultures developed by the R&D
Division of SPIC Ltd, requires only the nutrient addition and very low
electricity consumption for agitation and pumping. The estimated variable
cost of this bioprocess (not including ammonia stripping) works out to
around 0.6 U.S.$/tonne of urea produced. The ammonia removal can be
effected through conventional stripping methods. As seen from the schematic flow diagram of the process (Fig.4),there will also be a substantial saving in investment cost as compared to the thermal   hydrolysis
process.

CONCLUSION

The use of mixed cultures for effluent treatment was well demonstrated
in the case of urea effluent containing high loads of ammonia and urea.
This valuable technique is very useful in designing similar systems for
other treatments. In many cases, what is achieved at a prohibitive cost
through pure culture can be made more versatile and at a cheaper cost
through mixed cultures, with sustained research efforts. Finally the
biological processes carry an air of "environmental compatibility".
It is afterall a duplication of the naturally occuring processes, but
at a faster rate.

ACKNOWLEDGEMENT

The authors wish to acknowledge the encouragement and the necessary
facilities offered by the Management of SPIC Ltd. Our special thanks
go to Mr.P.Authimoorthi, Chief Manager (R&D) for his constant support
and motivation. Also the efforts due to our research assistants,
Mr.R.Hariharaputhran, Mr.P.Mohan, Mr.G.Jayaraj and all other colleagues
of our department are sincerely acknowledged.

REFERENCES

1) Bhatt BI and Joshi GC, Ammonia nitrogen in effluents from a nitro-genous fertiliser industry, Group discussion on ammoniacal nitrogen effluents in the fertiliser industry, FAI, India - September, 1981.

2) Gujral GS, Treatment of effluents from various plants at NFL, Panipat, Group Discussions on pollution control and monitoring techniques in fertiliser industry, FAI, India - July, 1979.

3) Natarajan R, Removal and recovery of ammonia/urea nitrogen from effluents of urea/complex fertiliser plants, seminar report on pollution control, Bombay, India - 1978.

4) Lagana V and Schmid G, SNAM Progetti's newest urea process, Hydro-carbon Processing, Vol. 54, No. 6, 1975, pp 102-104.

5) Bruls P et al, Purification of urea plant water to extremely low levels. 4th Int. Conference on Fertiliser Technology, British Sulphur Corporation, London - January, 1981.

6) Granelli F and Ellam R, Lower nitrogen effluents from urea plants. A progress report by SNAM - Progetti, Group discussions on ammoniacal nitrogen effluents in the fertiliser industry, FAI, India - Sept.1981.

7) Hedges RM and Pepper D, Reverse osmosis concentration and ultra-filtration separation in biochemical processes, Filtration and Separation - March/April, 1984, pp 112-114.

8) Bornside GH and Kallio RE, Urea hydrolysing bacilli I - A physio-logical approach for identification, J.Bacteriol, Vol.71, 1956 pp 627-634.

9) Sumner JB and Somers GF, Chemistry and Methods of Enzymes, 3rd ed., Academic press, New York, 1953.

10) Wiley WR and Stokes JL, Effect of pH and ammonium ions on the permeability of Bacillus Pasteurii, J.Bacteriol, vol. 86, 1963, pp 1152-1156.

11) Magna - Plaza I and Ruiz - Herrea J, Mechanisms of regulation of urease biosynthesis in Proteus rettgeri, J.Bacteriol, vol.93, No. 4, 1967, pp 1294-1301.

12) Gibson T, An investigation of Bacillus pasteurii group.II. Special physiology of the organisms, J.Bacteriol, vol.28, 1934, pp 313-322.

******

Table - 1

PHYSICO CHEMICAL PROPERTIES OF EFFLUENT SAMPLES

	Untreated Urea Effluent	Final Treated Urea Effluent
Colour	Colourless	Colourless
Odour	Ammonia smell	Odourless
Temperature	28 - 37°C	26 - 29°C
pH	9.0 - 10.4	6.0 - 8.0
Ammoniacal nitrogen	2,000 - 10,000	20 - 50
Urea nitrogen	4,000 - 15,000	Traces
Nitrate nitrogen	10 - 20	Traces to 2.0
Nitrite nitrogen	0.1 - 0.2	Traces
Total hardness as $CaCO_3$	60 - 80	About 60
Chloride as $CaCO_3$	29 - 40	20 - 40
Sulphate as $CaCO_3$	54 - 62	16 - 34
Iron	0.5	0.5
Oil	2.0 - 5.0	Traces
Total dissolved solids	30 - 55	30 - 70
Suspended solids	12 - 25	18 - 25
Dissolved oxygen	2.0 - 4.0	4.0 - 6.0
BOD_5	Nil	20 - 30
COD	85.0 - 163.0	Traces after ammonia stripping

(Values given in mg/l or as otherwise stated)

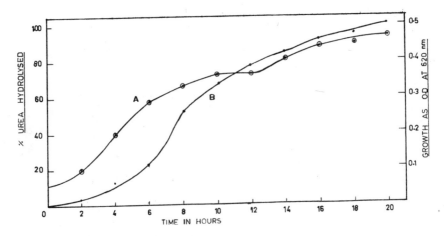

FIG. 1   The growth rate of mixed culture and the percentage of urea
hydrolysed vs time.
A : The growth curve.   B : Percentage of urea hydrolysed.
OD : Optical density measured at 620 nm corresponds to a
population of 1 million cells/ml.

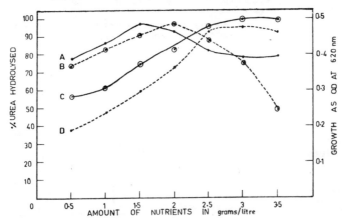

Fig. 2   Effect of carbon and nitrogen source on the percentage of urea
hydrolysed and growth.
A : Percentage of urea hydrolysed vs amount of nutrient as
organic nitrogen source (at constant carbon source concn.)
B : Percentage of urea hydrolysed vs amount of nutrient as
carbon source (@ constant organic nitrogen source concn.)
C : Growth vs amount of organic nitrogen nutrient (@ constant
carbon source concn.)
D : Growth vs amount of carbon nutrient (@ constant organic
nitrogen source concn.)
OD: Optical density measured at 620 nm corresponds to a
population of 1 million cells/ml.

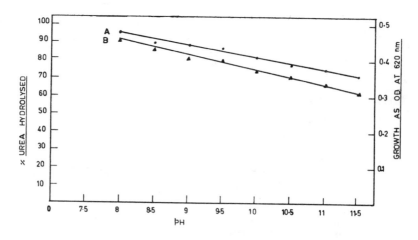

Fig. 3   Effect of pH on the growth and the percentage of urea hydrolysed
          in a lab-scale continuous bioreactor study.
          A : Percentage of urea hydrolysed vs pH.
          B : Growth vs pH.
          OD: Optical density measured at 620 nm corresponds to a
               population of 1 million cells/ml.

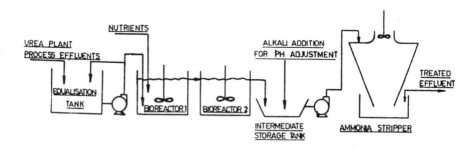

Fig. 4   Process flow diagram for biohydrolysis of urea effluent.

MICROBIOLOGY OF LANDFILL. IDENTIFICATION OF METHANOGENIC BACTERIA AND THEIR ENUMERATION

Elizabeth R. Fielding and David B. Archer

In a study of methanogenic bacteria in landfill sites the density of methanogenic bacteria was estimated in 6 different sites by dilution series methods. Species were obtained in pure culture for characterization and for investigation of the factors affecting their growth and methane production.

An assay for the fluorescent coenzyme F_{420}, found in all methanogenic bacteria, is being developed for use with landfill samples as an indirect measure of methanogenic biomass. Preliminary results are presented.

INTRODUCTION

Research into the microbiology of landfills should aim to understand the process of waste degradation and indicate ways in which landfill management can be adapted to improve the process. Two major problems requiring a microbiological solution are the production of acidic leachates and reduced methane yields. Acidic leachates pollute surrounding groundwaters and reduced methane yields make the installation of gas abstraction equipment economically unattractive. In this paper we confine attention to the microbiology of methane production from volatile fatty acids.

Public health aspects of landfill microbiology have been considered (Cromwell, 1965; Thompson, 1969) and some metabolic groupings of the microorganisms not of sanitary significance have also been investigated (Filip and Küster, 1979; Jones et al., 1983). Enzymatic activities, presumably of microbial origin, concerned with polymer hydrolysis have been estimated (Jones and Grainger, 1983; Grainger et al., 1984). None of these investigations have addressed the problems of methanogenesis from acidic leachates and only recently have approaches to tackling this area been described (Campbell et al., 1985).

The metabolic pathways of waste degradation in landfills are poorly understood. The bulk of the waste deposited in landfill is cellulosic (Rees, 1980) and it is a reasonable assumption that the pathways of methanogenesis from cellulose are similar to those established in better studied systems (Bryant, 1979). The degradation of volatile fatty acids to methane requires species of acetogenic bacteria together with H_2/CO_2- and acetate-utilizing species of methanogenic bacteria (Archer, 1983, 1984). The activities of the methanogenic bacteria are, therefore, central to successful landfill

AFRC Food Research Institute Norwich, Colney Lane, Norwich NR4 7UA, U.K.

management. Knowledge of the physiological properties of landfill methanogens, and determination of their ideal growth conditions would enable landfill management to be directed to ensure optimum conditions for methanogenesis. Isolation and enumeration of methanogenic bacteria is made difficult by the strictly anaerobic nature of these bacteria and so we describe methods for the indirect estimation of methanogenic biomass by assay of a coenzyme found in all methanogens, coenzyme F_{420} (Eirich et al., 1979). Such techniques do not require specialist microbiological laboratories, and, consequently, a routine analytical laboratory, by assay of coenzyme F_{420}, should have a means of estimating the methanogenic potential of landfill samples. In this paper we describe results of preliminary studies to identify and enumerate methanogenic species in landfills and discuss some aspects of conditions within landfills which can be expected to affect the activities of methanogenic bacteria.

MATERIALS AND METHODS

Landfill samples were all supplied by members of the Waste Research Unit, Harwell. In order to maintain anaerobic conditions during transfer to Norwich landfill samples were packaged tightly into a sealed container. This method was found to be as effective in maintaining numbers of methanogens as transporting and storing samples in nitrogen-filled containers.

Isolation and cultivation of methanogenic bacteria. The composition and preparation of media for the growth of methanogenic bacteria at 37°C have been described elsewhere (Kirsop et al., 1984). The growth of non-methanogenic species was inhibited by supplementing media with the antibiotic cefoxitin at a final concentration of 0.1 gl^{-1}. Cefoxitin inhibits growth of non-methanogenic species by inhibiting peptidoglycan synthesis; because methanogens do not contain peptidoglycan their growth is unaffected by cefoxitin. Methanogenic species were obtained in pure culture by picking single colonies on medium solidified with agar into liquid medium not containing cefoxitin. Purity was assessed by microscopic examination. Enumeration of methanogenic bacteria utilizing H_2/CO_2 or acetate was by 10-fold dilution series of landfill samples in liquid medium. Samples for the dilution series were taken from the soil surrounding refuse. The highest dilution producing methane, estimated by gas chromatography (Kirsop et al., 1984), was recorded.

Identification of methanogenic bacteria.
    Species obtained in pure culture were determined to be methanogenic bacteria by their ability to produce methane as their major metabolic product and by autofluorescence under near ultraviolet light. Phase contrast and fluorescence microscopy by incident light excitation was performed with a Leitz Ortholux II microscope (E. Leitz Ltd., Luton, U.K.). Filter block G was used to provide incident light of 350-460 nm (E. Leitz, Ltd.). They were then characterized according to their properties described by Balch et al. (1979). Briefly, the characterization to genus level relied upon morphology determined microscopically and the ability of the isolates to utilize particular methanogenic substrates. Confirmation of our assignation of an isolate was obtained by serological typing (results not shown) by A.J.L. Macario (New York Department of Health, U.S.A.).

Estimation of coenzyme F_{420}.
    Two methods were used to estimate the concentration of coenzyme F_{420} in landfill samples. Initially an isopropanol extraction method followed by fluorimetric monitoring was used. 1 g of landfill and 9 ml of glass-distilled water were boiled for 10 minutes. After cooling the sample was centrifuged at

10,000 g for 10 minutes at 4°C. 3 ml of isopropanol and 0.1 ml of 1N KOH was added to 1 ml of the supernatant. The mixture was shaken vigorously and centrifuged at 10,000 g for 10 minutes at 4°C. The fluorescence of the supernatant was measured at 425 nm excitation and 472 nm emission (Perkin-Elmer Luminescence Spectrophotometer Model LS-5) (Delafontaine et al., 1979).

The second method employed acetone-extraction and reversed-phase high-performance liquid chromatography to separate the coenzymes of methanogenic bacteria from landfill samples or pure cultures of methanogenic bacteria (van Beelen et al., 1983a). 40 g of landfill and 10 ml of glass-distilled water or 40 ml of culture was boiled for 5 minutes. 10 ml of acetone was added after cooling and the mixture vigorously shaken and centrifuged for 10 minutes at 10,000 g. The supernatant was concentrated 10-fold by rotary evaporation and then analysed by reversed-phase high-performance liquid chromatography.

High-performance liquid chromatography.

The methods were similar to those of van Beelen et al. (1983b). The column was 15 cm x 0.46 cm internal diameter packed with 5 μ C_{18} ODS material (HS-15 C_{18}, Perkin-Elmer Ltd.). The column was held at 25°C with a mobile phase flowrate of 0.8 ml/min. The solvent delivery system was a model 3B pump (Perkin-Elmer Ltd.) fitted with a Rheodyne injector (10 μl loop). The detectors were the model 3000 fluorimeter (Perkin-Elmer Ltd.) set to excitation/emission wavelengths of 398 nm and 468 nm respectively, and the Pye Unicam model PU 4021 multichannel detector (Phillips, U.K.). set to an absorbance wavelength of 254 nm. The excitation/emission wavelengths were slightly different to those used above but were optimal at the pH used in this chromatographic system. The mobile phases consisted of methanol:water (1:1 v/v solution A) and 25 mM acetic acid set to pH 6 with 2 M NaOH (solution B). The concentration of solution A in the mobile phase was increased linearly from an initial value of 2% up to 36% over 15 min, then linearly to 98% over 10 min followed by a period of 15 min at 98%, a linear reduction to 2% over 10 min and an equilibration period of 15 min.

Standard Curve.

For calibration of the fluorescence detector a standard curve of concentration versus response was obtained using coenzyme F_{420} purified from Methanobacterium thermoautotrophicum (supplied by G. Vogels, University of Nijmegen, The Netherlands).

RESULTS

Isolation of methanogenic bacteria in pure culture
Mesophilic species of methanogenic bacteria were isolated in pure culture from different landfill sites (Table 1). In all sites examined Methanobacterium spp. were predominant although other genera, recognised by their morphologies, were seen in enrichment cultures. One Methanosarcina sp. and a coccoid methanogen, probably a Methanogenium sp., were isolated from Aveley landfill site.

Direct enumeration of methanogenic bacteria
A wide variation in the numbers of methanogenic bacteria utilising either H_2/CO_2 or acetate as energy substrates was seen in samples from different sources (Table 2) and from different depths within the same landfill (Table 3). Many methanogenic species form clumps or filaments during growth (Balch et al., 1979) thus affecting the results of the dilution series method for direct enumeration. An indirect method for enumeration, based on assay of

coenzyme F_{420}, was therefore developed.

Assay of coenzyme F_{420}

The direct fluorimetric assay of coenzyme F_{420} (Delafontaine et al., 1979) was inadequate with landfill samples because fluorescent compounds other than coenzyme F_{420} were also determined. Reversed-phase high-performance liquid chromatography (HPLC) was found to be effective at separating coenzyme F_{420} from other compounds and at separating coenzyme F_{420} molecules with structural variations.

A standard of coenzyme F_{420} purified with Methanobacterium thermoautotrophicum gave a single peak on the chromatograph allowing construction of a calibration curve (Fig.1). Response was linear for concentrations in the range 0-10 μM coenzyme F_{420} but became non-linear at higher concentrations. Samples were therefore diluted to the linear range for quantitation.

Coenzyme F_{420} molecules from different genera of methanogenic bacteria exhibit slight structural differences (van Beelen, et al., 1983a) with a variation in the number of glutamic acid moieties in the side chain. The structure of coenzyme F_{420} from Methanobacterium thermoautotrophicum and its excitation/emission spectra are shown in Fig .2. Differences in structure of coenzyme F_{420} alter the retention times of the molecules in the HPLC column, limiting the use of retention time for identification of peaks due to F_{420}. An acetone-extraction of Methanobacterium thermoautotrophicum produced several peaks which absorbed light at 254 nm (Fig.3); those due to the presence of coenzyme F_{420} (A), (B), were identified by their excitation/emission spectra.

DISCUSSION

Methanogenic bacteria are responsible for the terminal stages of anaerobic digestion; they convert metabolic end-products of other bacteria (H_2/CO_2, acetate, methanol, methylamines and formate) to methane and carbon dioxide. In many landfill sites anaerobic digestion is incomplete, resulting in acidic leachates due to a build up of volatile fatty acids which are produced by acidogenic and acetogenic bacteria. Removal of acetate by methanogenic bacteria, and removal of higher chain fatty acids by mutualistic associations of acetogenic and methanogenic bacteria would alleviate this problem and increase yields of methane, making the installation of gas abstraction equipment economically attractive.

Of the two genera, Methanothrix and Methanosarcina, known to produce methane from acetic acid only the latter was seen in enrichment cultures from landfill samples and one strain of Methanosarcina barkeri was obtained in pure culture. Species of Methanobacterium and a coccoid methanogen, probably a Methanogenium sp., were isolated from landfill samples using H_2/CO_2 as the enriching substrate. Methanobacterium spp. were the most common H_2-utilizing species in enrichment cultures although other methanogens may have been present in lower numbers in the same landfill samples. For example, in a sample from Aveley landfill, the density of Methanobacterium spp. exceeded that of the coccoid methanogen by two orders of magnitude.

The densities of methanogens present in landfill samples varied according to the landfill site studied and the substrates (H_2/CO_2 or acetic acid) employed. Such estimations can be inaccurate because of the difficulties in obtaining a representative sample and the tendency of methanogenic bacteria to form clumps or filaments. An indirect measure of methanogenic biomass was therefore investigated. Assay of coenzyme F_{420} has been used by others to estimate methanogenic biomass in anaerobic digesters but the simplest method of estimating levels of coenzyme F_{420} (Delafontaine et al., 1979) was found to be unsuitable with landfill samples.

Techniques similar to those published by van Beelen et al. (1983a,b) are therefore being developed for use with landfills and we describe progress to date in this paper. It is our view that assay of coenzyme F_{420} can become a useful analytical tool in monitoring methanogenic biomass within landfills.

What practical value is there in knowing what species of methanogens are present in a landfill and at what densities? The simplest answer, that degradation of wastes in a landfill is a biological process and must therefore benefit from an improved understanding of its biology, is probably correct but is too vague to have any impact on landfill management practices. We have already argued that the methanogenic bacteria are crucial to the degradation of volatile fatty acids under anaerobic conditions. So, any landfill practice which is likely to be inhibitory to the methanogenic bacteria should be discouraged and, conversely, conditions which favour the development of methanogenic communities should be encouraged. In order to establish the properties of the methanogenic bacteria present in landfills it is helpful to examine isolates in pure culture. Monitoring their numbers by direct or indirect methods in conjunction with knowledge of methane production rates enables their specific activities to be estimated.

We consider, briefly, some properties of the methanogenic bacteria of relevance in landfill management. Methanogenic bacteria generally require a pH of between 6 and 8 and a range of nutrients for their growth and methanogenesis (Balch et al., 1979). Levels of nitrogen in landfills would not be expected to limit methanogenesis (Rees and Grainger, 1982; Thompson, 1969) particularly as methanogens can fix atmospheric nitrogen (Murray and Zinder, 1985; Bomar et al., 1985). The carbon:phosphate ratios are generally very high in landfill leachates (Robinson et al., 1982; Bull et al., 1983) and may limit the growth of methanogenic bacteria (Archer, 1985). The availability of carbon, phosphorus and the many other requirements, e.g. metal ions, of methanogenic bacteria must be considered together with the effects of toxic compounds upon their methanogenesis if methanogenic activity is to be optimised.

The methanogens isolated by us are all mesophiles with temperature optima of approximately 40°C. How might landfill management be conducted to achieve such temperatures in a temperate climate when the degradation of wastes by anaerobic bacteria releases very little heat? Aerobic decomposition is exothermic and, in order to raise the temperature of the anaerobic methanogenic regions within a landfill, it may be appropriate to devote more attention to the extent and proximity of aerobic decomposition.

In summary, we have presented some preliminary data on the numbers and species of methanogenic bacteria in landfills and have described the development of an analytical method for indirectly estimating methanogenic biomass. The need to develop such methodology and gain information on the methanogenic bacteria in landfills was discussed in relation to landfill management practices.

ACKNOWLEDGEMENTS
The authors would like to thank the Department of the Environment and AERE Harwell for funding this work and providing the landfill samples. We are grateful to A. Hobson-Frohock for advice on reversed-phase high-performance liquid chromatography.

REFERENCES

Archer, D.B. (1983) Enzyme and Microbial Technology 5, 162-170.

Archer, D.B. (1984) Biochemical Society Transactions 12, 1144-1146.

Archer, D.B. (1985) Applied and Environmental Microbiology 50, 1233-1237.

Balch, W.E., Fox, G.E., Magrum, L.J., Woese, C.R. and Wolfe, R.S. (1979)
Microbiological Reviews 43, 260-296.

Bomar, M., Knoll, K. and Widdel, F. (1985) FEMS Microbiology Ecology 31,
47-55.

Bryant, M.P. (1979) Journal of Animal Science 48, 193-201.

Bull, P.S., Evans, J.V., Wechsler, R.M. and Cleland, K.J. (1983) Water
Research 17, 1473-1481.

Campbell, D.J.V., Fielding, E.R. and Archer, D.B. (1985) Proceedings of the
3rd EC Conference, Energy from Biomass, in press, Elsevier.

Cromwell, D.L. (1965) M.Sc. Thesis, West Virginia University.

Delafontaine, M.J., Naveau, H.-P. and Nyns, E.J. (1979) Biotechnology
Letters 1, 71-74.

Eirich, L., Vogels, G.D. and Wolfe, R.S. (1979) Journal of Bacteriology
140, 20-27.

Filip, Z. and Küster, E. (1979) European Journal of Applied Microbiology and
Biotechnology 7, 371-379.

Grainger, J.M., Jones, K.L., Hotten, P.M. and Rees, J.F. (1984) In:
Microbiological Methods for Environmental Biotechnology, pp.259-273, Academic
Press, London and New York.

Jones, K.L. and Grainger, J.M. (1983) European Journal of Applied
Microbiology and Biotechnology 18, 181-185.

Jones, K.L., Rees, J.F. and Grainger, J.M. (1985) European Journal of
Applied Microbiology and Biotechnology 18, 242-245.

Kirsop, B.H., Hilton, M.G., Powell, G.E. and Archer, D.B. (1984) In:
Microbiological Methods for Environmental Biotechnology, pp.139-158, Academic
Press, London and New York.

Murray, P.A. and Zinder, S.H. (1984) Nature 312, 284-286.

Rees, J.F. (1980) Journal of Chemical Technology and Biotechnology 30B,
161-175.

Rees, J.F. and Grainger, J.M. (1982) Process Biochemistry 17, 41-44.

Robinson, H.D., Barker, C. and Maris, P.J. (1982) Water Pollution Control
81, 465-478.

Thompson, F.C. (1969) M.Sc. Thesis, West Virginia University.

van Beelen, P., Dijkstra, A.C. and Vogels, G.D. (1983a) European Journal of Applied Microbiology and Biotechnology 18, 67-69.

van Beelen, P., Geerts, W.J., Pol, A. and Vogels, G.D. (1983b) Analytical Biochemistry 131, 285-290.

TABLE 1

Methanogenic bacteria isolated in pure culture from landfill sites

Landfill site and depth	Genus
Aveley (4 m)	Methanobacterium
Aveley (4 m)	Methanogenium
Aveley (4 m)	Methanosarcina
Stangate Quarry	Methanobacterium
Enderby Warren Quarry	Methanobacterium
Blue Circle landfill	Methanobacterium
Refuse fraction 3	Methanobacterium

TABLE 2

Estimation of the numbers of methanogenic bacteria from 6 different landfill sites by ten-fold dilution series. The inverse of the dilution factors given are an order of magnitude estimation of the number of methanogens per g wet weight of landfill

Landfill site and Depth	Dilution producing methane from H_2/CO_2	Dilution producing methane from acetate
Aveley landfill (4 m)	10^{-6}	10^{-4}
Stangate Quarry landfill (7 m)	10^{-3}	10^{-1}
Enderby Warren Quarry landfill (7.3 m)	10^{-6}	10^{-4}
Refuse fraction 3	10^{-10}	10^{-8}
Judkins Quarry landfill (4 m)	10^{-1}	10^{-1}
Blue Circle landfill (2-3 m)	10^{-7}	10^{-5}

TABLE 3

Variation in numbers of methanogenic bacteria producing methane from H_2/CO_2 and total anaerobic bacteria with depth in Stangate Quarry landfill. Numbers per g wet weight of landfill can be estimated from the dilution factor given (see legend to Table 2).

Sample Depth (m)	Dilution producing methane	Dilution showing visible growth
0.9	10^{-3}	10^{-8}
3	10^{-3}	10^{-8}
5	10^{-4}	10^{-8}
7	10^{-3}	10^{-8}
9	10^{-3}	10^{-8}
11	10^{-1}	10^{-8}
12.5	10^{-1}	10^{-8}

FIGURE LEGENDS

Figure 1. Calibration curve of standard coenzyme F_{420}. Detector sensitivity x10.

Figure 2. Excitation/emission spectrum, and structure, of coenzyme F_{420}.

Figure 3. HPLC chromatogram of an acetone-extraction of <u>Methanobacterium thermoautotrophicum</u>. 10 μl injected.
x = point of injection of sample; → = chromatogram direction; (A),(B) = peaks due to coenzyme F_{420}.
Bottom trace - fluorescence detection; top trace - ultra-violet absorption at 254 nm.

Figure 1.

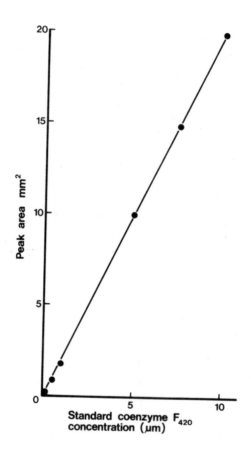

Figure 2.

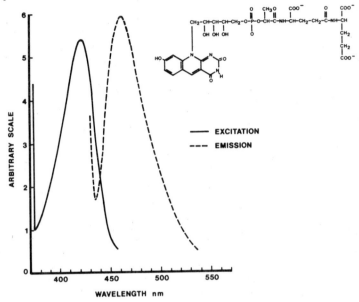

Figure 3.

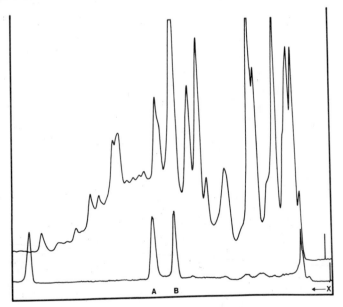

BULK INCINERATION AND ENERGY RECOVERY FROM SOLID WASTES

by   B Mills*
      A A B Pickles*

*Peabody Holmes Limited

1._____INTRODUCTION

Energy recovery from solid wastes is normally associated
with domestic refuse, although other forms of solid waste do
arise e.g. tyres, textile wastes, paper. Refuse disposal
has been for many, many years just DISPOSAL. Because there
is a statutory requirement on Local Authorities to collect
and dispose of refuse, the simplest means has traditionally
been adopted.

In the past, this has generally meant dumping in holes in
the ground which has, incidentally, also been the most
economical method.

In recent years there has been much more awareness of the
value of refuse as a fuel and, although there are problems
in incineration and recovery of the energy value from the
combustion products, several projects have been implemented
and are operating successfully, generating steam and power
from refuse.

2._____REFUSE QUALITY

Let us now consider the nature of this material which we
call refuse. Refuse may arise from domestic premises (our
own dustbins), from light industrial premises (plastics,
paper) or from heavy industrial premises (anything).

However, when considering the design of a system a typical
value of refuse is required against which to produce a
specification. An analysis, although varying from area to
area, generally regarded as typical for the UK, is shown in
Table 1.

TABLE 1

TYPICAL UK REFUSE ANALYSIS

	% w/w	Moisture content % w/w
Paper	31	10
Putrescibles	23	76
Plastics	7	2
Rubber/Textiles	3	10
Metals	8	5
Glass	10	2
Dust, cinder	14	12
Unclassified	4	10
	100	25.5

Truly a mixture!!

But what of the energy values in such a diverse material?
Table 2 gives the energy values for each component as
Calorific Value (CV) in kilojoules per kilogram.

TABLE 2

CALORIFIC VALUE OF UK REFUSE

	CV dry kJ/kg	CV wet kJ/kg	Heat Contribution to refuse kJ/kg
Paper	17600	15840	4910
Putrescibles	20900	5016	1153
Plastics	33500	32830	2298
Rubber/Textiles	18800	16920	508
Metals	0	0	0
Glass	0	0	0
Dust, cinder	0	0	0
Unclassified	16000	14400	576
			9445

The value of approximately 9500 kJ/kg refuse compares with
that for a good quality, industrial coal of 29000 kJ/kg or a
power generation coal of say 20,000-24,000 kJ/kg.

Possessing an energy value of about a third of the solid
material used by CEGB for generating steam and power, refuse
is obviously a major source of energy (some 30 million tons
per annum in the UK) - and it is apparently free.

3.   ENERGY PRODUCTION

So how do we tackle the problem of releasing this energy
mountain in a useful form?

Well, assuming that the refuse has been collected from
numerous back gardens or industrial premises, it is taken to
a central location where it is tipped into reception hoppers
or concrete pits. This is where the problems begin. As an
aid to understanding these difficulties we will consider the
historical situation regarding refuse incineration.

Many refuse incinerators were built in the 1960's. However,
the motivation in those days was one of straight disposal.
Few units were fitted with energy recovery.

Problems on these early units centred mainly on:

1. Refuse feeding from the reception pit into the incinerators;

2. Poor refuse and air distribution control to the grates, which resulted in inefficient burn out of carbon and high particulate emissions to pollution control equipment;

3. The incinerator chambers were lined with massive refractory sections which incurred high maintenance costs, due to the erratic manner in which refuse incinerators then tended to be operated;

4. Incinerators which were fitted with heat recovery exhibited problems such as corrosion and/or erosion of boiler tubes.

Most of these early incinerators are, however, now working well.

We can see now that recovering energy from refuse is not easy. This is why, in our opinion, the most cost effective incineration system on a long term basis is that which is designed using this long available experience, all of which is based on mass burning grate type boilers.

To recover energy from refuse implies that we have a use for the resultant energy. Prior to the Energy Act, 1983, any power generated from refuse incineration could only be used privately.

The effect of the Energy Act was that any power generated from refuse could now be sold to the Electricity Authority, thus generating revenue for the waste disposal operator even when energy could not be disposed of in, for example, a district heating scheme.

Energy recovery from refuse incineration is, therefore, now an economical proposition, particularly if a Combined Heat and Power Scheme can be installed generating power and using the resultant low pressure steam for district heating or a similar purpose.

4.   THE PROCESS

Figure 1 shows the flow diagram through the combustion and boiler system.

4.1   Reception Hopper and Feed Preparation

Refuse is such a diverse material that in energy recovery, steps must be taken to try to ensure a consistent feed quality. In practice, refuse is dumped from trucks into a common refuse bunker. Using an electrohydraulic, overhead crane potentially hazardous material is extracted whilst high calorific value waste is premixed with general waste before transferring the mixed feed to the incinerator feed chute.

Hydraulically operated rams feed the material onto the grate at a rate controlled by steam production. Isolating dampers are strategically positioned in case of overheating of material in the feed chute.

4.2   The Combustion System

Refuse is progressed at a controlled rate along the horizontal grate. The grate bars are made of lightweight alloy and have an underside labyrinth for air cooling. Every alternate bar is fixed whilst the intermediate moving bars are operated by hydraulic levers. The action of the grate is that the bars move in a straight line relative to one another so as to provide minimum wear.

A unique feature of the grate is that some bars are moving backwards whilst others traverse forwards. This opens and mixes the refuse to provide efficient combustion. (See Figure 2).

Primary air is supplied through the grate; a high pressure drop is maintained to ensure that variations in refuse flow or depth do not affect the closely controlled ratio of combustion air to refuse.

Reference to Figure 3 shows that the primary air is zoned so that different flows are used for drying, burning and cooling. Some 55% - 60% of total combustion air is used at this point to give a low velocity and hence low particulate carryover. Combustible gases and volatiles are then thoroughly mixed above the grate with secondary air to ensure complete combustion.

The furnace chamber is designed to contain minimum refractory and uses a welded gas-tight water tube construction. Side walls are designed to absorb lateral thermal expansion and to keep the grate flat and free moving.

4.3   The Boiler Section

Hot gases from the combustion chamber pass through three, empty water-wall radiation zones to promote maximum fall out of entrained dust and limit the gas velocity into the boiler tubes, thus reducing erosion. Normal tube banks for superheater, evaporator and economiser complete the boiler.

Gases leave the boiler and are cleaned using an electrostatic precipitator. All ashes are conveyed to a single quench tank from whence the ashes go to landfill.

Quality of steam generation and power produced is very much site specific and depends on the requirements of the ultimate client.

For the purposes of providing typical details it will be assumed that some power is required to be generated and that the client has a use for a proportion of the low pressure steam for district heating purposes or for sale as process steam.

In this situation, steam will be generated at a pressure of 40 bar and a temperature of 400°C. Electrical power would be generated using a back pressure turbo alternator. Low pressure steam would be used to supply a calorifier generating hot water for district heating at 130°C or alternately the steam may be sold as process steam. Surplus steam under any conditions would be condensed in an air blast condenser system and condensate returned to the boiler through the water treatment system.

5.   PROCESS PERFORMANCE

As an example to produce typical economic data it is assumed that the throughput of refuse would be 200 tonnes per day providing 465 tonnes per day of steam at 40 bar and 400°C.

The unit would operate continuously 24 hours per day, 7 days per week, 46 weeks per year (7700 hours).

Automatic control would maintain refuse throughput relative to steam demand.

Based on the typical UK refuse analysis but using conservative figures, chemical composition of the refuse on a dry, ash free basis is shown in Table 3.

TABLE 3

	% w/w
Carbon	52.1
Hydrogen	6.7
Nitrogen	0.9
Oxygen	38.8
Chlorine	1.0
Sulphur	0.5
Moisture	= 23.3% w/w
Ash	= 33.8% w/w
Combustibles	= 33.8%
Net Calorific Value	= 8000 kJ/kg

From this refuse, energy may be generated as follows:

Steam	= 19.4 te/h
Pressure	= 40 bar
Temperature	= 400°C
Power	= 1950 kW

6. ECONOMICS OF INCINERATION

6.1 Income from Incineration Process

Power Generation

Power generated	= 1.95 MW
Power consumed	= 0.35 MW
Net production	= 1.60 MW

Typical sales value for
power (average over year) = 2.5p/kWH

Income from power = £7700 x 1600 x $\frac{2.5}{100}$ p.a.

= £308,000 p.a.

Charge against Refuse Disposal

Typical cost attributable to refuse disposal is £5-7 per tonne refuse. Credit against refuse disposal at say £6 per tonne for 200 tonnes per day = $\frac{200 \times 7700 \times 6}{24}$

= £385,000 p.a.

Steam Supply

Low Pressure Steam production = 19.4 tonnes/h

Costing steam at £8 per tonne and 80% usable time

Income from steam = 19.4 x 7700 x 8 x 0.6

= £717,000

Total Income becomes £1,410,000

6.2 Charges against the Refuse Incineration Installation

At 200 tonnes per day of refuse incinerated, capital costs for the plant fully installed and operational would be approximately £7 million.

Operational costs for the plant including power, water and maintenance would be approximately £300,000 p.a.

Capital charges (depreciation plus interest) would be approximately £1,000,000 p.a.

Total charges: £1,300,000 p.a.

The economics for the plant can be seen to be approximately in balance at 200 tonnes per day sizing.

Most applications are likely to be around 300 tonnes/day refuse or higher which improves the economic balance. The income against disposal of the refuse is based on current charges for landfill operation. This will become increasingly more expensive in future, if indeed, landfill sites can be found.

Incineration of the refuse instead of using landfill improves the environment and reduces pollution. To utilise the energy values in the refuse instead of simply throwing it away must make economic sense for the country.

We look forward to the day when the majority of our refuse will be treated in this way.

ACKNOWLEDGEMENT

The authors thank the Directors of Peabody Holmes Ltd for permission to publish this paper and thank colleagues for much of the information enclosed.

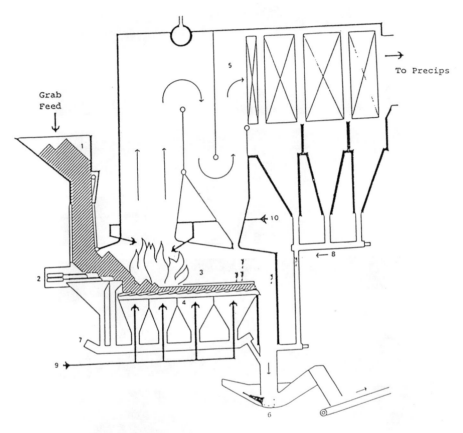

To Precips

Grab
Feed

1.   Refuse feed chute
2.   Hydraulic feed rams
3.   Combustion chamber
4.   Incinerator grate
5.   3-Pass radiation/mixing chambers
6.   Ash quench vessel
7.   Undergrate ash conveyor
8.   Boiler ash conveyors
9.   Primary air
10.   Secondary air

Figure 1   Flow Diagram – Refuse feed through boiler

351

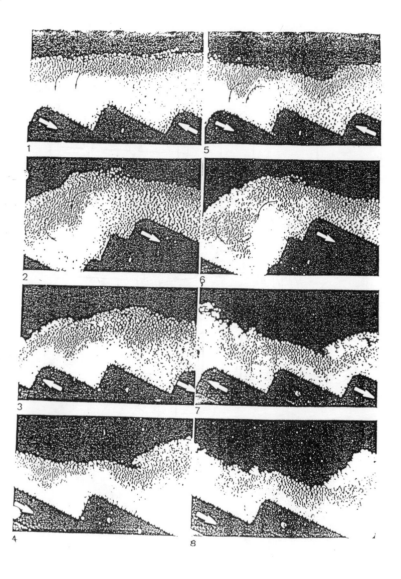

Figure 2   Solids Mixing on the Double Motion Transvection Grate

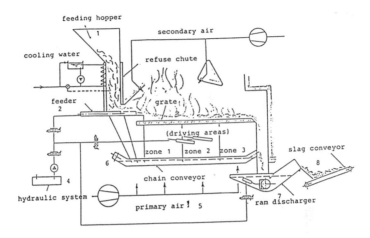

The combustion system comprises the following:

1) feeding hopper/refuse chute
2) feeder
3) combustion grate
4) hydraulic station with control
5) combustion air system
6) chain conveyor
7) ram discharger
8) slag conveyor

Figure 3   Refuse Combustion System

COMPOSTING OF ORGANIC WASTES

A.J.Biddlestone*, J.D.Cooper* and K.R.Gray*

Composting in heaps using straw as a bulking agent has been investigated for the disposal and treatment of two types organic waste, dewatered sewage sludge and celery/leek wastes from vegetable packing operations. The temperature and carbon dioxide levels reached in the heaps were measured and it is concluded that provided the aeration requirements are met the process offers a simple means of stabilising these wastes.

INTRODUCTION

Many environmental problems arise because local accumulations of organic wastes are too great for the basic degradation process inherent in nature. Composting offers a means of both a production process for an end product of value and a waste treatment process to render low grade organic waste less obnoxious to the environment. The end product quickly equilibrates with the ecosystem in which it is placed without causing the major disruption associated with raw wastes.

Composting is the decomposition of organic material by a mixed microbial population in a moist, warm, aerobic environment. By gathering suitable mixtures of wastes into heaps and conserving some of the heat of fermentation, the temperature rises and rates of degradation result which are far higher than those achieved under ambient conditions. The process offers a means of stabilising organic wastes, providing a high level of pathogen destruction and resolving odour problems. The microbiology, biochemistry, process factors and applications of composting have been reviewed extensively by the authors (1-3).

This paper describes briefly some of the results of an extensive programme of work on the conjoint composting of organic wastes with straw (4).

*Department of Chemical Engineering, University of Birmingham, UK.

EXPERIMENTAL

Dewatered sewage sludge and straw

Dewatered sewage sludge was supplied by Severn-Trent Water Authority and was a mixture of primary and secondary sludge from a conventional treatment works which had been dewatered to about 75% moisture content. This was mixed with approximately 5% by weight of straw in a specifically designed mixing machine, the ARMIX Processor (3). The machine produced an intimate mix of the two materials, projecting the mixture in straight well shaped heaps. Two heaps were constructed on a concrete pad, each containing 5 tonnes sludge combined with straw. The dimensions of the heaps were approximately 6m long by 3m wide by 1.0 to 1.5m high.

Thermocouples for measuring temperature were wound around 2.5m long bamboo canes and inserted into the heaps. The concentration of carbon dioxide was also measured at certain times and positions in the heaps using an Orsat gas analyser.

After 18 days the two heaps were combined and remixed by passage through the ARMIX Processor to give a new combined heap. There was no forced aeration of this heap; air ingress was by natural diffusion except for the single remixing when combining the two heaps.

Celery waste and straw

Celery waste was supplied from a large commercial vegetable processing and packing plant and was mixed with straw using the same machine as for the sewage sludge trials. Two separate heaps were initially formed, each containing approximately 3 tonnes of celery waste and 7.5% by weight of straw. After 18 days the two heaps were remixed and combined to form a third heap. A single row of wooden sleepers were placed around the edge of this heap to prevent the 'flow' downwards and outwards of the material.

A fourth celery heap was constructed using fresh celery waste and straw. This heap contained 9.4 tonnes of material of which 12.5% by weight was straw. It was built alongside a wooden sleeper wall with a single row of sleepers on the other side to prevent slippage.

Temperature was measured using thermocouples and carbon dioxide levels with an Orsat gas analyser; forced aeration was not used.

Leek waste and straw

Leek waste was obtained from the same source as the celery waste and two different heaps were initially constructed using the mixing machine. The first heap contained 4.1 tonnes of material including 10% by weight of straw; the second heap contained 6.0 tonnes of material of which 5% by weight was straw. After 1 month of composting the second heap was rebuilt over an aeration pipe placed centrally at the base of the heap and extending to the length of the heap. Aeration was intermittent, air being supplied by a fan delivering 2.8m^3/min at 160mm water head. The heap was blown for 7 minutes every hour.

A third heap was constructed containing 10.8 tonnes of material including 4% by weight of straw. This heap was allowed to heat up and collapse for 6 days. The material was then remixed by passage through the mixing machine and a new heap formed over an aeration pipe. Forced aeration was applied in the same manner as for the rebuilt second heap.

Temperatures and carbon dioxide levels were measured similarly to the sewage and celery heaps.

RESULTS and DISCUSSION

Sewage sludge heaps

Temperatures rose quickly in the two sludge/straw heaps to over $60^{o}C$ in the hottest region within four to five days. Carbon dioxide concentrations in the lower regions of the two heaps built up to 20% by volume in one heap and 50% in the other by 8 days from heap construction. The lower regions also became very wet. The rate of composting was obviously slow, being limited by poor oxygen penetration. Nevertheless, when the heaps were broken up after 18 days and spun out together through the mixing machine again, there were no severe anaerobic odours.

When amalgamated into the new combined heap the mixture regained its high temperature as shown in Figure 1. High carbon dioxide levels again developed as indicated in Figure 2 which shows the carbon dioxide and temperature profiles in the combined heap 6 days after its construction. The highest level of carbon dioxide occurred in the middle at the bottom of the heap, suggesting an area of anaerobicity. This was further suggested by chemical analyses of samples taken from the centre and bottom of the heap; the level of low molecular weight volatile acids, especially acetic acid, was double in the bottom of the heap, consistent with anaerobic conditions.

It is clear that with a fairly dense material like dewatered sewage sludge, forced aeration is an advantage. Reaction rates would be increased and more of the material in the heap would be subjected to the highest possible temperatures. This is important in relation to pathogen destruction (5,6). Straw has been used as the bulking agent in these experiments and does have certain advantages in maintaining an open matrix for several days; its presence does not impose any process or product restraint. It is possible, however, to use other bulking agents such as refuse (2,6), wood chips (7,8), sawdust or low moisture content recycled compost.

Celery waste heaps

Temperatures quickly rose in the first two heaps of celery waste and straw. The first heap reached centre temperatures of $61^{o}C$ after 3 days and $66^{o}C$ after 6 days, whilst the second heap reached $65^{o}C$ after 3 days and $68^{o}C$ after 10 days. In other respects, however, the behaviour of these heaps was different from the sewage sludge heaps. Even though the moisture content of celery is very high, 93%, the water is bound up in plant tissue and is only slowly released. The result was a stiff porous matrix so that air penetration was good and carbon dioxide levels were well below those with sewage sludge. An unexpected feature of these heaps was their tendency to collapse with the material "flowing" down and outwards, a phenomenon that we had not encountered previously.

After 18 days the two heaps were remixed and combined to form a third heap with a single row of surrounding wooden sleepers. The centre temperature-time pattern of this combined heap is given in Figure 3 (the curve showing 75% by weight of straw). The maximum carbon dioxide level measured was 6.4% by volume; the single row of sleepers successfully prevented the heap flowing outwards. By the time the heap had cooled down the celery structure had entirely disappeared.

The largest celery heap was the fourth one containing 9.4 tonnes of material including 12.5% by weight of straw. The temperature-time pattern at the centre of the heap is also shown in Figure 3. Higher levels of carbon dioxide were found in this larger heap, some isolated values of 25% by volume being measured. However, these areas of anaerobicity were small and no putrid odours were noticed. Perhaps the most significant feature of the composting of celery waste is the volume and weight reduction. The reduction in height of this large heap was 44% after 8 days and 65% after 2 months. After 4 months the weight reduction was 51%, after 9 months it was 75%. The volume reduction over the composting period was even greater.

The very significant volume and weight reduction should be considered in relation to the original disposal problem. A single processing factory can produce 5000 tonnes/year of celery and leek wastes. When stacked high as at present the mass goes anaerobic, very little breakdown occurs and highly polluting leachates are produced. Composting offers a simple but significant means of dealing with the problem.

Leek waste heaps

Three leek heaps were constructed containing differing total amounts of material, differing straw content and means of aeration. The resulting temperature-time patterns are shown in Figure 4. Each heap will be separately considered.

The heap containing 10% by weight of straw was not force aerated at any time. It sank very quickly with a height reduction of 58% after 6 days. High levels of carbon dioxide developed in the central lower region of the heap, a maximum of 27% by volume being measured. There was no liquid run off from the heap. Weight reduction after 4 months was 39%.

The second heap containing 5% by weight of straw also sank significantly with a height reduction of 38% after 4 days. This heap developed a maximum level of 44% by volume of carbon dioxide in the centre at the bottom and also produced significant amounts of leachate which smelled putrid and anaerobic. After 25 days the temperature of this heap had fallen to ambient. The heap was then reformed and forced aerated. The temperature did not rise again but the carbon dioxide levels were reduced to 4% by volume in the lower central region after the second period of blowing. Weight loss after 4 months was 48%, a greater loss than the first heap due to evaporative water loss with the forced aeration.

The third heap was the largest one and contained the lowest percentage of straw (4%). This heap was allowed to heat up and collapse for 6 days. By this time steam was rising from the top of the heap. It was then remixed and formed into a new heap for which the intermittent forced aeration system was used. Carbon dioxide levels were markedly reduced, falling from 30% by volume to 3% by volume in the lower central region of the heap. The temperature pattern was particularly good, as shown in Figure 4, with high temperatures being sustained. There was no leachate run-off problem with this forced aerated heap.

CONCLUSIONS

Experiments have been described in which two types of organic waste have been mixed with a third organic waste, straw, for the purpose of composting in heaps. The results have shown that these wastes can be successfully composted at moisture contents far in excess of the 55% normally regarded as optimum when handling urban refuse. This is because cereal straw can maintain an open matrix for many days, even at moisture contents over 80%.

Dewatered sewage sludge was composted with straw added at 5% by weight. Large heaps, and the lower regions of small heaps, will develop anaerobic regions at this level of straw addition if the process relies on natural aeration. Anaerobic conditions suppress the temperature which reduces pathogen kill and results in less efficient degradation. Anaerobicity also results in odour problems. Increased straw content would help but would increase costs. It is concluded that forced aeration is desirable when composting sewage sludge.

The vegetable wastes and straw heaps composted well at the higher levels of straw used in the experiments. To reduce straw levels, or increase the size of heaps, it is again recommended that forced aeration be considered. A short period of consolidation, up to 10 days, is advantageous before the material is remixed and prepared for aeration. Because of the low energy content of these vegetable wastes forced aeration would need to be controlled, balancing air requirements and moisture evaporation against fermentation heat release. From a disposal consideration the composting of these wastes is attractive because of the very substantial volume and weight reduction.

The addition of fresh organic wastes to any ecosystem can create problems; these can include the high oxygen demand of the wastes, competition for nitrogen, the effects of intermediate compounds and the release of malodours. Composting provides a means of obtaining a stable product by biological oxidative transformation. The compost product comes quickly into equilibrium with the ecosystem in which it is placed without causing the major disruption associated with raw wastes. The temperatures achieved in composting are significant in regard to pathogen kill.

REFERENCES

1. Gray, K.R and A.J.Biddlestone. 1971, 1973. A review of composting. Process Biochemistry. 6(6): 32-36. 6(10): 22-28. 8(10): 11-16.

2. Biddlestone, A.J., D.Ball and K.R.Gray. 1981. Composting and urban waste recycling, p191-224. In J.T.Manassah and E.J.Briskey (ed). Advances in food producing systems for arid and semi-arid lands. Academic Press, London and New York.

3. Biddlestone, A.J., K.R.Gray and D.J.Cooper. 1985. Development of straw based techniques for composting organic wastes. Environmental Health. 93(3): 67-71.

4. Cooper, J.D. The conjoint composting of organic wastes with straw. Ph.D.thesis (in preparation). University of Birmingham.

5.   Stentiford, E.I., T.J.Pereira-Neto, P.L.Taylor, D.D.Mara, J.Lopez-Real and E.Witter. 1985.   Sanitisation potential of composting for sewage sludge and refuse in a static pile system.   In   T.H.Y.   Tebbutt   (ed). Advances in Water Engineering. Elsevier, Amsterdam.

6.   Pereiro-Neto, J.T., E.I.Stentiford and D.D.Mara. 1986.   Pathogen survival in a refuse/sludge forced aeration compost system.   In Effluent Treatment and Disposal. Symposium Series No.96, Institution of Chemical Engineers.

7.   Finstein, M.S., F.C.Miller, P.F.Strom, S.T.MacGregor and K.M.Psarianos. 1983.   Composting ecosystem management for waste treatment. Bio/Technology 1(4): 347-353.

8.   Singley, M.E., A.J.Higgins and M.Frumkin-Rosengaus. 1982.   Sludge composting and utilization: a design and operating manual.   New Jersey Agricultural Experimental Station, Rutgers University, New Brunswick, New Jersey 08903, USA.

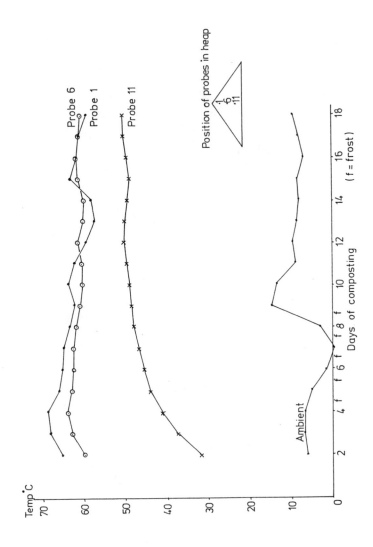

Figure 1.   Temperature-time pattern for sewage sludge and straw (remixed combined heap)

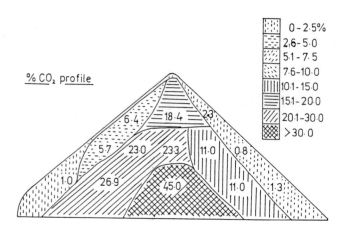

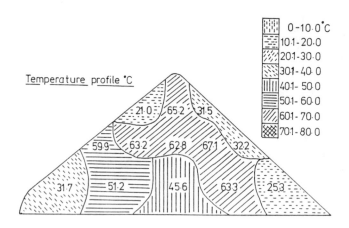

Figure 2.   Temperature and Carbon Dioxide profiles.
Day 6 of remixed combined sewage sludge heap.

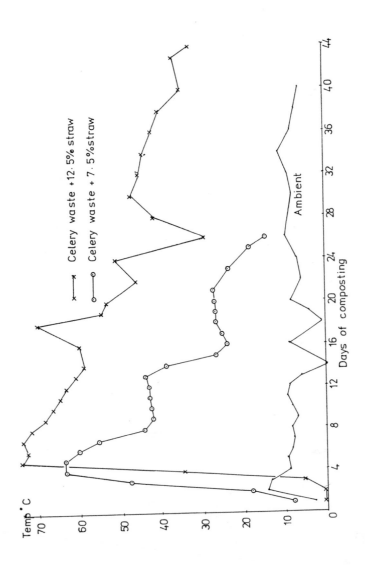

Figure 3.   Centre temperature-time pattern of celery waste and straw composting heaps.

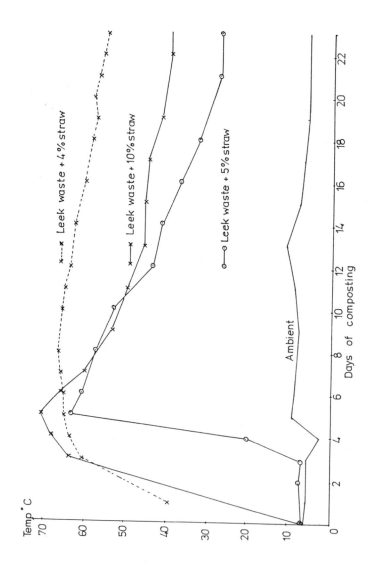

Figure 4. Centre temperature-time pattern of leek waste and straw composting heaps.

WASTE DISPOSAL BY INCINERATION ON LARGE INDUSTRIAL SITES

J. A. J. Clark[*]

This paper considers generally the problems of liquid,
fume and solid waste incineration and highlights some
successful approaches to such problems.

Wastes can of course be variable and thus it is implicit
that for a design to be successful it must also be flexible.

Cost savings from waste heat recovery are given for
specific examples but care should be taken in applying
such data across the board. In waste treatment each
system should be treated on its merits in terms of the
waste itself, its quality, site circumstances an alternative disposal means available.

The chemical industry today produces many and varied forms of waste. These
may be gaseous, liquid and solid wastes.

The objective of this paper is to review the current state of the art of
waste combustion systems, this being illustrated by reference to sites where
various forms of incineration are practiced. In most cases incinerators for
fume and solid wastes, and aqueous wastes require auxillary fuel. It is
therefore a necessity to incorporate heat recovery to give economic operation.

The application of incineration as a form of waste disposal is not universal,
the route chosen will inevitably depend on economics and other factors such
as product security or safety and it is fair to state that smaller sites
usually practice contract off-site disposal by various means.

Arguably the difficulty of the problem of effectively combusting wastes is
varied according to the density, that is to say gases and fumes are the
simplest followed by liquids and then solids.

Dealing with the easier problem first a typical crude fume incinerator is
shown in Figure 1.

The essentials for efficient combustion are well known, adequate temperature,
turbulence for mixing the fuel and fume stream with air and a sufficiently
long residence time. It is possible for the crude unit shown in Figure 1 to
operate reasonably effectively.

[*]Robert Jenkins Systems Ltd., Combustion Division, Rotherham, S61 1LT

By applying more thought it is possible to improve the design, especially in plants which are essentially air streams laden with solvents diluted to 25% of the lower explosive limit. Such a design is shown in Figure 2.

This design is capable of using the contaminated air stream as combustion air. Since no external air is required to support combustion great fuel savings can be made when compared to the unit shown in Figure 1 which uses an external supply of air for the burner.

Additionally, because of the inherently 'flat flame' profile given by the burner design, in this case a HYGROTHERM unit, extremely efficient mixing results and the mean incineration temperature is reached very quickly. This enables short residence periods of 0.4 to 0.5 seconds to be used, even when burning fume streams containing such compounds as mercaptans which have probably the lowest odour threshhold of any gaseous effluents. The burner will operate on oxygen contents in the fume stream as low as 12%.

A further development of the plant shown in Figure 2 was the "two chamber" low "Nox" incinerator designed specifically for burning gas streams containing high amounts of chemically fixed nitrogen such as ammonia.

The plant, patented by Hygrotherm Engineering Limited, is shown in Figure 3.

Heat recovery on fume incinerators can be achieved in many ways. The simplest method and often most useful is to use the hot combustion products to preheat the incoming fume stream. Preheat values of $400^{\circ}C$ can be achieved. Residual heat in the flue gases after the heat exchanger can be removed by heating a thermal fluid or water to produce steam. Some very complex yet effective systems have been devised, one of which is shown in Figure 4.

Turning to liquid wastes, again it is possible to use a modification of the previously described fume incinerator to burn liquids. These may be either combustible as is the case with waste solvents or can be aqueous mixtures.

Again because of the design of the burner, which uses a matrix of venturi burner ports to give a flat flame profile, it is possible to fit a number of liquid injection guns or atomisers.

It is possible to burn liquid and fume waste simultaneously, indeed one plant has been successfully commissioned burning streams from 23 sources on site.

The criteria for successful combustion of liquid wastes if whether the waste can be effectively atomised or broken into droplets, the size of which is small enough for complete combustion.

Even wastes such as actactic polypropylene have been burned by preheating prior to atomisation.

Heat recovery on a plant of this type is highly rewarding financially if the liquid waste has a significant calorific value.

For high calorific value wastes a firetube waste heat boiler would be used as shown in Figure 5.

There is absolutely no case for preheating combustion air on a high calorific value incinerator since no support fuel other than a pilot is required.

In the case of disposal of wastes with a high water content the converse applies and air preheat is often used in the form shown in Figure 6.

To incinerate any aqueous waste stream requires energy input. Many different routes have been tried such as preconcentration, which requires heat followed by incineration of the concentrated liquor. The latter mentioned systems are costly, complicated and often require a separate fume incinerator to treat the lighter fractions which are released with steam during concentration.

The economics of solvent incineration with one user was that an annual disposal cost of £75,000 for contaminated solvents was turned into a revenue earner by providing heat to generate approximately 4000 kg/h of steam.

Summarising the step forward from burning a liquid as opposed to a gas or fume is that we have, by atomisation, producing small droplets with a large surface area, made the liquid behave like a fume stream.

The last waste form, solids, is a very different problem although it is analagous to the burning of a liquid waste.

The rate at which a solid material burns is largely dependent on its surface area available for reaction with oxygen. Most wastes such as general industrial refuse consisting of waste paper, packaging, pallets, plastic containers and the like have adequate area. Items such as tightly wound paper reels, dense wads of computer paper, packs of files and drums of solid residues do not and require pretreatment by hogging or shredding prior to burning.

Over the past 20 or 30 years the burning of solid wastes has been transformed from what was a 'black art' to something with a semblance of both science and common sense.

Early industrial incinerators were little removed from a bonfire in a refractory enclosure featuring a grate through which copious amounts of air were driven in an effort to give high rates of burning and completion of combustion before the stack.

There is much truth in the cynical view that man, after discovering fire spent the next 4000 years trying to make it burn faster. Whilst he succeeded with liquids and gases the problem of combustion of solids persists even today.

The early forms of incinerator typified in Figure 7 were plagued with excessive emission of grit, flyash and smoke coupled with short refractory life caused by high temperatures.

This was attributable to the clear intention of the design to drive large amounts of air through the grate and firebed.

After some relatively radical thinking the starved air, two chamber design of incinerator emerged, often referred to as the partial pyrolysis incinerator. The design first found favour in the U.S.A. The first successful application of this type of plant in the U.K. was the CONSUMAT plant typified in Figure 8.

This form of incinerator now accounts for the majority of plants installed in Britain and Europe in the size range up to 2 tonnes/h.

Its performance is such that it can meet most national pollution codes without any form of gas cleaning.

With the exception of halogenated plastics some plants will burn up to 100% plastics continuously.

Because the flue gases produced by the incinerator contain low levels of grit and dust it is possible to recover heat from the flue gases by using a conventional firetube type shell boiler.

This boiler is similar in its control functions and safety features to most steam and hot water boilers commonly found in industry.

One major difference between a fired boiler and an incinerator/waste heat boiler combination is that in a situation requiring shutdown of the boiler it is necessary to divert the heat input to atmosphere or 'dump' it rather than extinguish the burner on a conventional boiler.

In this manner it is possible to continue the disposal of waste without the recovery of heat. This is of particular importance in the case of hospitals or research centres when the incineration facility is always required. It should be remembered that a waste heat boiler like any other boiler requires an annual shutdown and inspection.

A typical arrangement of a plant with heat dumping is shown in Figure 9.

WASTE HEAT RECOVERY SYSTEM

In terms of overall performance and thermal efficiency it is important to point out that an incinerator and waste heat boiler will not be as efficient as a normal fired boiler.

This is so for two reasons, firstly incineration is a process which often requires an excess of combustion air when compared to normal burners. Secondly the smaller incinerators, operating for one shift per day, require a significant amount of heat to bring the refractory and structure of the plant up to normal working temperature.

Despite this the overall savings realised by the plant are still worth the investment.

To illustrate the economics of an industrial solid waste incinerator the case of an International Company in the North West is a good example.

This factory produces household detergents and other consumer products on a large scale. The waste produced consists mainly of packaging wastes, broken pallets, cardboard, paper and significant quantities of polythene bottles.

The plant is capable of burning up to 900 kg/h of waste depending on calorific value. In return the waste heat boiler has been shown to give in excess of 25 tonnes/day of high pressure steam at 17 Bars pressure from cold feedwater. The plant is operated by one operative who is also responsible for collection and management of all waste on site.

The value of the savings in energy by not burning fuel oil can be equated to £65-70,000 per annum at present oil prices. Additional to this the savings in contract waste disposal costs, given a disposal cost of £15-20/tonne would be of the order of £35-40,000/annum for a plant of this size.

To conclude it can be stated that with modern technology it is possible to treat fume, liquid and solid waste streams economically in an environmentally acceptable manner.

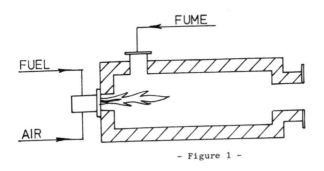

- Figure 1 -

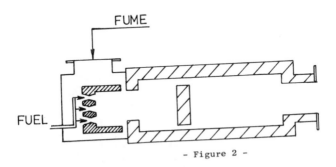

- Figure 2 -

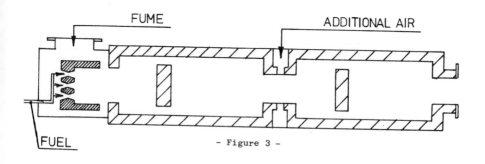

FUME

ADDITIONAL AIR

FUEL

- Figure 3 -

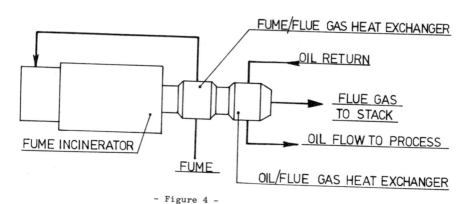

FUME/FLUE GAS HEAT EXCHANGER

OIL RETURN

FLUE GAS
TO STACK

OIL FLOW TO PROCESS

FUME INCINERATOR

FUME

OIL/FLUE GAS HEAT EXCHANGER

- Figure 4 -

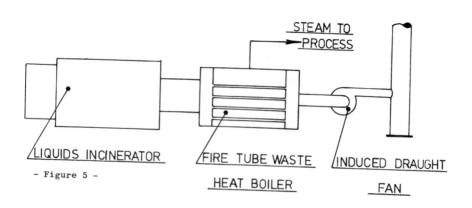

STEAM TO
PROCESS

LIQUIDS INCINERATOR

FIRE TUBE WASTE

INDUCED DRAUGHT

- Figure 5 -

HEAT BOILER

FAN

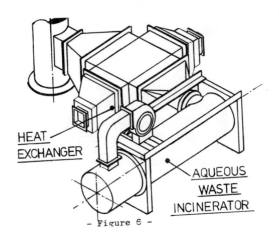

HEAT EXCHANGER

AQUEOUS WASTE INCINERATOR

- Figure 6 -

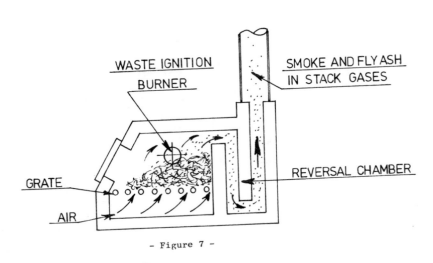

WASTE IGNITION BURNER

SMOKE AND FLY ASH IN STACK GASES

GRATE

AIR

REVERSAL CHAMBER

- Figure 7 -

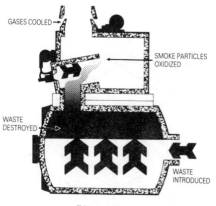

- Figure 8 -

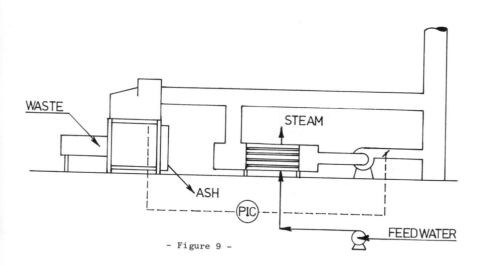

- Figure 9 -

PATHOGEN SURVIVAL IN A REFUSE/SLUDGE FORCED AERATION COMPOST SYSTEM

J.T. Pereira-Neto*, E.I. Stentiford* and D.D. Mara*
Department of Civil Engineering, University of Leeds, U.K.

A major concern in the use of compost made from refuse and sewage sludge is the presence of potential pathogenic organisms. The effectiveness of static piles in producing a sanitised compost is considered relative to the faecal indicators E.coli, faecal streptococci, C.perfringens and salmonellae. A range of operating conditions were evaluated using 8 piles each containing 20-30 tonnes of material. Under the conditions studied substantial indicator reductions ($< 10^2$ cfu/g.ww) were aeration phase with all but the anaerobic sporeformer C.perfringens. Its numbers significantly reduced during the maturation phase.

INTRODUCTION

In recent years wherever composting has been used to treat human wastes a high level of pathogen destruction has been considered essential. Many plants have been designed and are operated with this as their primary objective with other aspects of product quality being secondary. The relevant literature leaves an impression that pathogens, widely present in these wastes, can be destroyed in properly operated plants [1],[2],[3],[4] and [5].

The mechanisms which bring about this destruction of pathogenic organisms during the composting process are: heat, competition, antibiosis and the depletion of nutrients. These factors are usually present in a composting process as a consequence of the complex microorganism populations involved and the ecological behaviour of the whole system. Of these mechanisms, competition and antibiosis, are difficult to monitor directly on a daily basis, whereas the temperature/time profile for a particular process which, reflects heat generation, can be readily measured and related to pathogen destruction. In a forced aeration composting system, pathogen destruction can be achieved by maintaining the appropriate temperature/time profile during composting. However, a pathogen control strategy requires routine monitoring of the final material to ensure a safe product.

The best method to determine the success of a process in destroying pathogens would be to monitor the pathogens themselves, but these procedures are too difficult for routine application [6]. To overcome this problem, analyses can be carried out for so-called indicator organisms. These organisms are generally used as a model to express the behaviour of related pathogens under certain conditions.

*Department of Civil Engineering, The University of Leeds, Leeds, U.K.

The use of pathogen indicator organisms in composting serves two basic purposes:

i)   to reflect the microbial population condition and the potential for further contamination; and

ii)   to monitor the performance and the stage of degradation reached in the composting process.

It is important to realise that the significance, for the final product, of a particular indicator organism result from a spot sample is closely related to the control exerted over the process. Consequently the relationship between indicator organism densities and health risks is very much process dependent(7)

The indicator organisms used in the reported work in this paper were: Escherichia coli, faecal streptococci, Clostridium perfringens and salmonellae. Each experimental trial involved two compost piles operating under similar conditions, making a total of approximately 50 tonnes per run. Work on this scale is essential since the non-homogeneous nature of the material and the difficulties of scaling-up make most laboratory studies non-representative.

The work reported in this paper refers to trial numbers 13 to 17 which constitute part of a five year research programme on composting.

MATERIALS AND METHODS

Raw Materials

This work used domestic refuse from the South Manchester Waste Plant (which employs a Dano drum for grading purposes, typical analysis in Table 1) and a mixture of primary and secondary sewage sludge from Sandall Sewage Treatment Works in Doncaster (this employs a conventional activated sludge system). A typical sludge analysis is given in Table 2.

Sampling

Throughout the composting process it was necessary to sample material at various stages during the aeration and the maturation phases. In both phases samples were collected from the pile at different positions depending on the objective of each particular run.

A 100mm diameter soil auger (holding approximately 1kg of material) was used to collect the sample for analysis. Three replicate samples, from similar cross-sectional positions along the length of the pile, were bulked, and after sieving, through a 6mm sieve, in order to remove large pieces of glass, metal, plastic etc., were used for analysis. Prior to bacterial analysis the samples were thoroughly mixed and 1g of material was added to 99ml of Ringer's solution. Serial dilutions were made from this solution and then examined by membrane filtration and/or the MPN technique.

Enumeration of bacteria

Sodium lauryl sulphate broth (SLSB) was used to enumerate faecal coliforms.(8) Plates were incubated at $30^{o}C$ for 4hrs followed by $44.5^{o}C \pm 0.25$ for 18-24hrs. All yellow colonies were counted and presumed to be E.coli. The identification tests used included: the Catalase test, the Oxidation-fermentation (OF) test, the Carbohydrate utilization and Urease test.(9)   In some cases the AP120E test was used as recommended by the manufacturers.

Faecal streptococci were enumerated on membranes incubated on KF streptococcus agar.(10)   Incubation was at $37^{o}C$ for 4hrs followed by $44^{o}C$ for 44hrs.(11) All dark maroon or pink colonies were counted as faecal streptococci. The confirmation test involved plating a representative number of presumptive colonies onto MacConkey agar.   The plates were incubated at $37^{o}C$ for 24hrs. Faecal streptococci grew as small red colonies.   Further confirmation was done by direct microscopical examination of these colonies for typical short-chained gram positive cocci.

C.perfringens was enumerated on membranes incubated on SFP agar (Shahidi Ferguson Perfringens agar, DIFCO), incubated anaerobically in Gaspak jars in the presence of hydrogen and carbon dioxide.   C.perfringens appeared as greyish colonies with black centres or totally black colonies.   Litmus milk was used for the confirmatory tests.(12)

Salmonellae enumeration, which excluded only S.typhii was carried out using the method employed by the Yorkshire Water Authority for sewage sludge.(13) Confirmatory tests were made using the API system or serological tests.

Process Operation

Mixing

Refuse and sludge were mixed by placing the refuse in a ring and pumping the liquid sludge (4-6% dry solids) into the central recess. The material was then mixed using a rubber-tyred front end loader, which proved to be effective and practical in this role.   In most cases 3 to 4 hours proved to be adequate to mix 50 tonnes of material to the desired uniformity.   The mixing ratio was based on the moisture content of the mixture being between 55-60% of the wet weight.

In the case of a refuse/sludge mixture, the refuse (main source of carbon) forms a part of the substrate as well as acting as a bulking agent, the sludge (main souce of nitrogen) provides a substrate and the liquid to produce the final moisture content.

Pile Construction

The mixture to be composted was piled over a perforated aeration pipe (100mm in diameter) as shown in Figure 1.   A layer of straw was used to assist air distribution through the mass and to prevent the composting material blocking the perforated pipe supplying air.   A layer of matured compost (100-150mm thick) was normally used as a cover material to provide thermal protection, ensuring optimal composting conditions.   Pile temperature was maintained in the range $50-60^{o}C$ by means of temperature feedback to maximise both pathogen inactivation and bioxidation of substrate.

Typical initial pile dimensions were: 4m wide at the base x 1.5m high x 15m in length with a triangular cross-section.   Subsequently a combination of physical settling and solids breakdown produced substantial changes in the pile dimensions.   Previous pile heights have reduced from 1.70m to 1.1m in 30 days. (14)

Aeration Systems

Three alternative methods of aeration were employed during this work:

i)   positive pressure (blowing into the pile);

ii) negative pressure (sucking through the pile); and

iii) a hybrid system ((ii) followed by (i))

A single perforated aeration pipe previously described, connected to a 0.5HP fan by means of an unperforated pipe, constituted the aeration equipment used.

Control

A basic control concept in static pile composition is to maintain an optimal operating temperature to maximise both bioxidation and pathogen elimination. This can be achieved by controlling the aeration cycle based on temperature feedback.

The aeration demand during the composting process is highest between the 5th and 20th days and lowest during the first 5 days and the last period of the aeration. This demand reflects the rate of decomposition within the pile (Figure 2). Previous experimental runs were monitored and controlled by a computer using both temperature and oxygen feedback control. These runs showed that the amount of air necessary to control the temperature at a desired level was more than sufficient to supply the oxygen required by the aerobic microbial population. This fact gave greater flexibility in operating the system at a lower level of technology, i.e. wihout the need for oxygen monitoring. Details of the control system, aeration mode used and the amount of material involved during the experimental period are given in Table 3.

Maturation

Compost undergoes further, relatively slow, biochemical changes following the initial rapid biooxidative phase. In the case of compost derived from refuse and sewage sludge a period of 2 to 4 months of maturation appears to be necessary to produce a general purpose material. Maturation was accomplished in the work reported by storing the material in conical heaps 1.5 to 2m high; aeration or turning was not necessary in this phase.

RESULTS AND DISCUSSION

Trials 13 and 14

Trials 13 and 14 were carried out as identical experiments, to assess the aeration system performance (positive and negative pressure), and its effectiveness with respect to the pathogen elimination. Particular attention was paid to the pile core from where samples were taken for analysis (three replicates from three different positions along the length of the pile core). See position 1 in Figure 1.

The piles using positive pressure aeration were characterized by more even temperature distribution with a maximum amount of the pile subjected to a temperature in the range 45-60°C. This increases the overall sanitisation effectiveness of the process.

The piles using negative pressure aeration showed a different behaviour with high peaks of temperature ($67-75^{\circ}$C). In this case, the fan worked continuously once the control temperature was reached because it was unable to hold the temperature down at the set point of 55°C.

Figure 3 shows the pile core temperature variation for positive and negative pressure systems during trials 13 and 14. Note the completely different temperature distributions for each aeration mode. In addition the temperature distribution in the pile cross-section has different characteristics for each system (figure 4) These temperature distributions produce different results in terms of pathogen indicator organism reduction during the composting process (figure 5).

At the end of the aeration period (28-32 days) all piles registered a significant reduction in <u>E.coli</u> and streptococci to less than 10^2 cfu/g of material.

<u>C.perfringens</u>, a very resistant anaerobic spore forming organism, was significantly reduced only during the maturation process, when the material was stored in large conical heaps after the initial aerobic composting phase. The reasons for this reduction are not fully understood and work is progressing in this area. Figure 6 shows the typical reduction in <u>C.perfringens</u> during maturation.

Trial <u>15</u>

The main objective of trial 15 arising from the results of trials 13 and 14, was to evaluate a system which achieved a high temperature in the pile in the first 6 days before reducing the temperature to the set point.

Again samples were taken from three different core positions during the aeration phase and any significant reduction in faecal indicators during this period were monitored. The idea was to use negative pressure to provide a high temperature zone near the aeration pipe in the early stage and switch to positive pressure aeration, thus progressively moving the high temperature zone to the outer section of the pile.

Two piles were built; one of which used a fixed aeration rate (15 minutes on, 45 minutes off), and the other a computer based control system using temperature feedback only. The hybrid aeration system used in both piles involved 6 days of negative pressure aeration followed by positive pressure aeration throughout the remaining aeration phase. The temperature variation during run 15 under the hybrid aeration mode is shown in figure 7.

Figure 8 confirmed that this mode of operation produced a more rapid initial reduction in indicator organisms. In some cases a reduction of 5 to 6 logs with <u>E.coli</u> was found during the first 6 days. In addition at the end of the aeration period a very significant reduction was maintained. <u>C.perfringens</u> numbers were hardly affected during this initial composting phase but numbers were significantly reduced during maturation.

Trial <u>16</u>

In trial 16, the objective was to assess the simple control system s effectiveness in keeping the piles under close temperature control, which is required to ensure conditions necessary to eliminate the pathogenic organisms.

The intention was also to observe any microorganism regrowth after the aeration phase. Pile two worked with a variable timer where the aeration rate could be adjusted to suit the composting phase. The pile exibited a high core temperature which was effective in significantly reducing the pathogen indicators; a reduction of 6 logs was found (figures 9 and 10).

Following the aeration phase, pile two was dismantled, re-mixed (using only water to adjust the moisture content, 58%), rebuilt and operated using the same aeration system. The temperature increased again, as shown in figure 11, E.coli and streptococci increased during the first 4 days from <10^2 to 10^4 cfu/g w.w of material (figure 11). Other researchers have reported that microorganism populations increase during the initial composting phase.(5), (16), (17) The temperature peak was found around day 8 and after day 10 started to decrease. On day 16 the pile core temperature was 35-45°C and the indicator levels were again <10^2 cfu/g w.w.

It is very difficult, from the practical point of view, to find a compost pile configuration which brings all parts of the pile, i.e. bottom, sides, corners etc., under the same ecological environmental conditions throughout the process. Re-invasion by microorganisms from cooler outer-layers of the pile could occur if the nutritional conditions and moisture content of the compost mass were still suitable. During maturation, when the pile material is undergoing stabilisation, some complex molecules are still breaking down biochemically forming humic compounds and the nutrient concentration is diminished. It is this phase where competition and antagonistic effects are thought to be the predominant mechanisms involved in pathogen inactivation. During all experimental runs a 3-4 month period was necessary to produce a well-stabilized material (for general purpose use) with no indicator organisms being detected (<10 cfu/g w.w.).

Trial 17

The main objective of trial 17 was to monitor two more specific areas of the composting piles (e.g. the apex and corners), since in the previous trials the core position had been studied. Thus, three replicate samples of material along the length of the pile were taken separately from positions 1, 2 and 3 (see sample positions in figure 1). An additional pathogen indicator – Salmonellae spp – was included with the previous indicators in this trial as had been suggested and used by other researchers.(18),(3) In addition a different controller was tested, which used temperature feedback.

A similar reduction in faecal indicators was achieved in this trial as in previous trials. Figure 12 shows the average temperature variation with pile age where temperatures of 50-60°C were maintained for a sufficient period to produce a considerable pathogen indicator reduction. (Figure 13). The salmonellae growth was very clearly defined during the first four days where the initial count of 54 organisms/g increased to 350 organisms/g for samples taken near the surface (position 2). However, on day 8 complete elimination of this organism was recorded for samples taken from positions 1 and 2. Salmonellae present in position 3 were eliminated only by day 16, when no organisms were found (<2 org./g). Similar results for salmonellae growth and subsequent elimination in composting have been found by other researchers, (6),(17),(19), and (20). Effective E.coli inactivation was found in both piles where this organism was completely undetectable in samples taken from positions 1 and 2 on day 14. Streptococci, which were generally more resistant than other indicators, were eliminated only during the last days of composting (25-31 days).

C.perfringens was only monitored in positions 1 and 2, both of which showed a similar small reduction at the end of the aeration phase.

CONCLUSIONS

(i)   All the control systems used from the sophisticated computer based to a simple fixed timer produce a high core temperature (58-65°C), for a period of 10-15 days and this was sufficient to significantly reduce the pathogen indicator organisms E.coli, streptococci and salmonellae.

(ii)   The three different aeration modes used, (positive and negative pressure aeration or a combination of the two), showed different indicator organism destruction patterns.   Some eliminated indicators more in the early phase of the process and others more in the latter phase, but all brought about a high degree of elimination over the whole composting process. However, in a practical composting installation some other additional objectives must be achieved, i.e. ease of operation, required end product characteristics and operational economy, and in these respects the positive pressure mode of aeration (blowing) showed better overall performance with this type of material.

(iii)   Microorganism regrowth between the aeration and maturation phase will generally occur if the material has sufficient moisture content (>35%), C/N ratio (>15:1) and nutrient availability.   This results from the practical characteristics of the static pile configuration, where it is impossible to maintain high temperatures in the whole pile, and remixing of the material from the cooler zones (with possible lower indicator inactivation) occurs when setting up maturation piles.   However, during the maturation period microbiological competition and some antagonistic effects will reduce substantially the number of organisms to a very low level, producing a sanitised material.

(iv)   Amongst the indicators used, the most thermolabile were the coliform bacteria E.coli and Salmonellae spp.   Faecal streptococci were shown to be the most important resistant indicator bacteria.   C.perfringens, as an anaerobic spore forming organism, is not a good indicator of the performance of an aerobic process;   however its numbers are reduced during the composting phase but perhaps more significantly so during maturation.

ACKNOWLEDGEMENTS

The project, of which this work forms a part, was funded by the Science and Engineering Research Council. The research would not have been possible without the enthusiastic and active support of the Yorkshire Water Authority and the Greater Manchester Council (Solid Waste Division).

REFERENCES

1. NELL, J.H., Sterr, A.G. and Rensburg, P.A.J. (1983) Wat. Sci. Tech. 15: 181-194, IAWPEC/Pergamon Press Ltd.

2. SHUVAL, H.I., Gunerson, C.G. and Julius, D.S. (1981) World Bank, Vol.10.

3. WILEY, B.B. and Westerberg, S.C. (1969) Appl. Microbiol. 18(6): 994-1001.

4. KRIGE, P.R. (1964) Jour. Inst. Sewage Purification, 215-220.

5. GOTAAS, H.B. (1956) W.H.O., Geneva, Switzerland - 205pp.

6. BURGE, W.D. (1983) BioCycle, March-Apr. 24(2) pp. 48-50.

7. PEREIRA-NETO, E.I. Stentiford and D.D. Mara (1985) ABES conference - AL. Brasil.

8. STARFIELD, G. and Irving, T.E. (1981) Water Research, 15, pp. 469-474.

9. COWANS, S.T. (1974) Manual for the Identification of Medical Bacteria, 2nd Ed., Cambridge University Press.

10. KENNER, B.A. (1961) Applied Microbiol., 9, pp. 15-20.

11. ORAGUI, J.I. (1982) Ph.D Thesis, University of Leeds, U.K.

12. YORKSHIRE WATER AUTHORITY (1981) Methods of Analysis, Leeds.

13. VASSILIADIS, P. (1983) Jour. of App. Bacteriology, 54, pp. 69-76.

14. STENTIFORD, E.I. (1985) Composting of Agricultural and Other Wastes, Elsevier Applied Science Publishers, London, pp. 42-55.

15. GOLUEKE, C.G. (1983) BioCycle, August, pp. 50-57.

16. WILLSON, G.B., Parr, J.F. and Casey, D.C. (1978) In: Proceedings of National Conference on Design of Municipal Sludge Compost Facilities, Chicago.

17. EPSTEIN, E, Taylor, J.M., and Chaney, R.L. (1976). J. Env. Sci. 5(4), pp. 442-426.

18. BURGE, W.D. (1983) BioCycle, Mar-Apl. 24(2) pp.48-50.

19. RUSS, C.F. and Yanko, W.A. (1981) Appl. and Env. Microb. 41(3) pp.597-602

20. De BERTOLDI, M. and Zucconi, F. (1980) Ingenerie Ambientale No.3, Italy.

TABLE 1: TYPICAL ANALYSIS FOR MANCHESTER REFUSE

COMPONENT	VALUE
<20mm	15*
Vegetable & Putrecibles	22*
Papers	35*
Metals	8*
Textiles	3*
Glass	10*
Plastic	4*
Unclassified	3*
Compostable (approximately)	57-72*
pH	6.5
Conductivity ($\sim^{-1} \times 10^{-5}$)	8
Moisture content (%w.w)	40
Dry solids (%w.w)	60
Volatile solids (%d.w)	68
Ash (%d.w)	32
Carbon (%d.w)	38
Total nitrogen (%d.w)	0.5
Total phosphorus (%d.w)	0.06
F. coliforms (cells/g w.w)	10^7
F. streptococci " " "	8×10^5
C. perfringens " " "	5×10^4

* percentage of wet weight

TABLE 2: TYPICAL ANALYSIS FOR SANDALL (DONCASTER) SEWAGE SLUDGE

PARAMETER	LIQUID SLUDGE
pH	5.7
Moisture content (%w.w)	96
Total solids (%w.w)	4
Volatile solids (%d.w)	75
Ash (%d.w)	25
Total Kjeldahl Nitrogen (%d.w)	4.0
Total Organic Carbon (%d.w)	41.4
Iron (Fe) (%d.w)	0.69
Calcium (Ca) (%d.w)	2.73
Potassium (K) (%d.w)	0.17
Total Phosphorus (%d.w)	1.71
Zinc equivalent mg/kg	1250
F. coliforms (cells/gm w.w)	4×10^6
F. streptococci " " "	6×10^5
C. perfringens " " "	2.5×10^6

TABLE 3: DETAILS OF EXPERIMENTAL RUNS

Run No.	Pile No.	Refuse (tonnes)	Sludge[a] (tonnes)	Control System	Aeration Mode[b]
13	1	25	3)	Temp and O_2 using	positive
	2	25	3)	computer	negative
14	1	25	2)	Temp and O_2[c]	positive
	2	25	2)	using computer	negative
15	1	19	6	Fixed rate aeration .)	negative for first 6 days then positive
	2	19	6	Temp only-computer)	
16	1	–	data not included in this paper		
	2	26	6	Variable rate timer	positive
17	1	20	4	Temperature Feed back controller	positive
	2	–	data not included in this paper		

Notes: (a) These figures are calculated using a moisture balance for the mixture based on the actual tonnage of refuse and refer to liquid sludge.

(b) Positive pressure indicates "blowing" into the pile, and negative pressure "sucking" from the pile.

(c) Failure of control system between days 4 and 16 meant a period of fixed rate aeration.

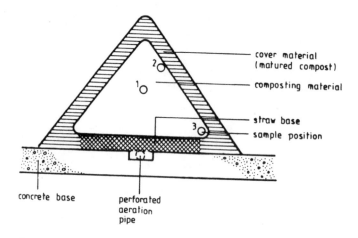

Fig. 1   Cross-section through a typical static pile showing the sampling positions

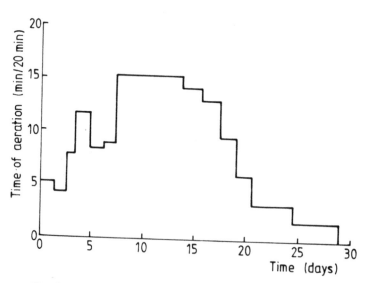

Fig. 2   Typical aeration variation with pile age

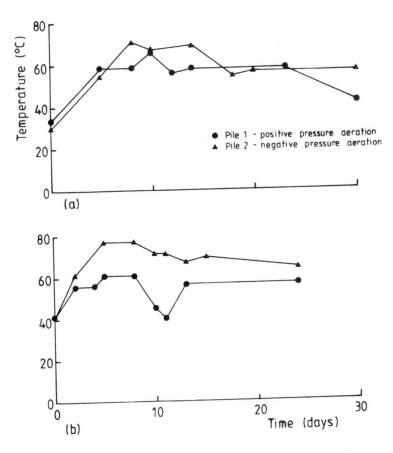

Fig. 3   Pile core temperature variation, with time, during runs 13 (a) and 14 (b)

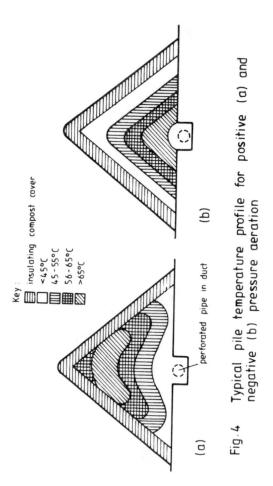

Key:

insulating compost cover

<45°C
45 - 55°C
56 - 65°C
>65°C

perforated pipe in duct

(a)

(b)

Fig. 4   Typical pile temperature profile for positive (a) and negative (b) pressure aeration

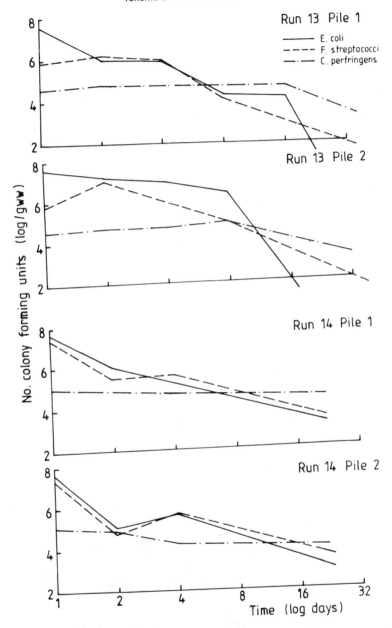

Fig. 5   Reduction in E. coli, Streptococci and C. perfringens during run 13 and run 14

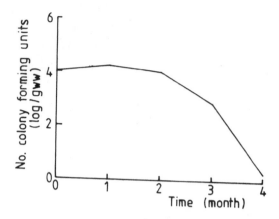

Fig. 6   Reduction of Clostridium Perfringens
during the maturation

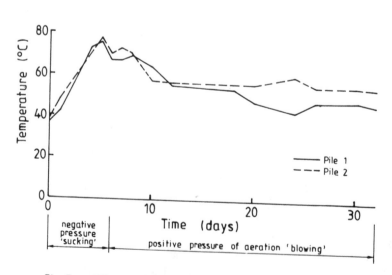

Fig. 7   Pile core temperature variation with time
during run 15

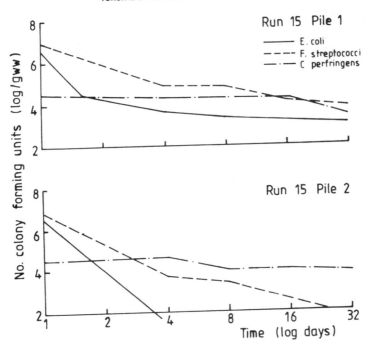

Fig. 8   Reduction in E.coli, Streptococci and C.perfringens during run 15

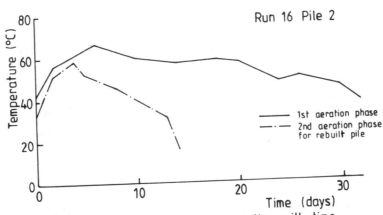

Fig. 9   Pile core temperature variation with time during run 16

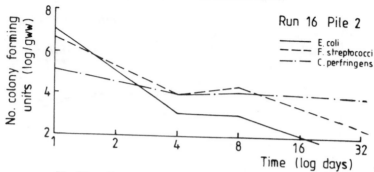

Fig. 10   Reduction in E.coli, Streptococci and C. perfringens during run 16

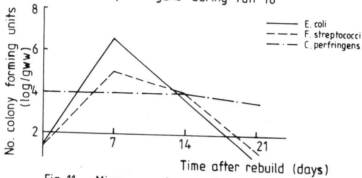

Fig. 11   Micro-organism re-invasion during a second aeration phase after rebuilding pile during run 16

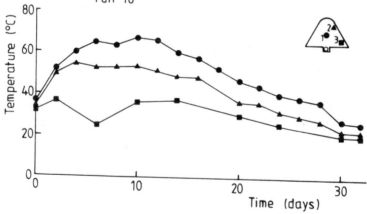

Fig. 12   Pile core temperature variation with time during run 17

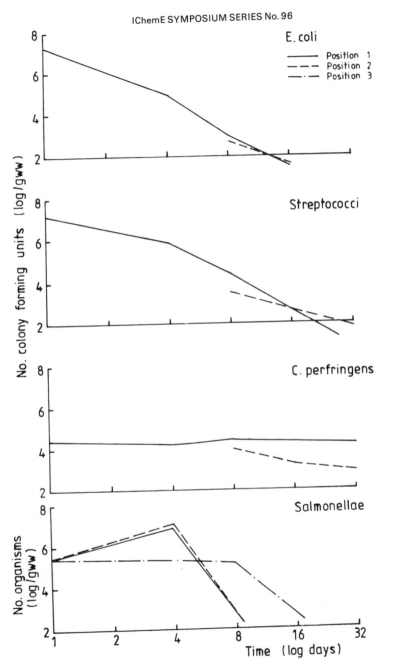

Fig. 13   Reduction in E. coli, Streptococci, C. perfringens and Salmonellae during run 17, pile 1

THE DESIGN OF AN AEROBIC THERMOPHILIC SLUDGE DIGESTION SYSTEM

S. F. Morgan*, R. Winstanley*, M.H. Littlewood* and H.G. Gunson**.

The design of an air operated full scale aerobic thermophilic sludge digester is described. Details of previous
work, and general design aspects are followed by process
specification and description of hardware in the present
plant. The 420 m³ reactor is designed to process up to 5
tonnes DS per day, to achieve a temperature lift of at
least 60°C, to render sludge stable and pasteurised, to
lose significant water volume by evaporation. Full mass
and thermal balances, cost appraisals, pathological and
virological studies will be conducted.

INTRODUCTION

The first full-scale purpose-built aerobic thermophilic sludge digestion
system in the UK is now under construction at Ponthir STW in South Wales.
This new system is designed to produce a fully stabilised pathogen free sludge
and is the product of design and operating experience gained over many years.
This paper describes the background to the present study, details aspects
important in the design of an aerobic thermophilic system, lists the objectives
of the present development, and presents a process specification and description of the new plant. The economics of aerobic thermophilic sludge digestion
are discussed and its value as an alternative to conventional sludge treatment
is considered.

In an aerobic biochemical process, the oxidation of organic material,
ultimately to carbon dioxide and water, is accompanied by a release of heat
energy. In aerobic wastewater treatment the liberation of heat energy is
dwarfed by other factors and is seldom obvious. In aerobic digestion of
a sludge, the heat flux is much greater and provided that pure oxygen is
used or an efficient aeration system is employed, the sludge temperature
will rise. If the rate of dissipation of heat energy is limited, the temperature will rise steadily. At about 43°C, naturally occurring thermophilic
micro-organisms become increasingly important and mesophilic activity begins
to be reduced. Also about that temperature, a visible change occurs as the
sludge becomes more dispersed and less flocculant. Viscosity is also much
reduced. In an air-operated system, a layer of foam will develop on the
sludge surface.

The rise in sludge temperature continues until a thermal balance is
obtained. In a well designed system it should be possible to routinely remove
40-50% of the organic and volatile sludge solids and achieve operating

* The Electricity Council Research Centre, Capenhurst, Chester, CH1 6ES.
** Welsh Water Authority, Brecon, Powys, LD3 7HP.

temperatures of at least 60°C.

The broad objectives of aerobic thermophilic sludge digestion are like those of anaerobic digestion : to render sludge odourless, stable and inoffensive, and suitable for disposal at an acceptable cost. But aerobic thermophilic digestion has two additional attributes which must influence any comparative appraisal.

First, particularly in air operated systems, evaporation losses account for a significant reduction in the volume of treated sludge for disposal. Secondly the high sludge temperatures render the sludge effectively pasteurised and hence ideal for safe land spreading. This attribute may have no assessable value in the UK at present, but should circumstances require it, the existence of an inexpensive and effective method of sludge pasteurisation would have great comparative value. In the present study the Welsh WA will monitor the fate of certain bacterial pathogens and viruses.

BACKGROUND TO THE PRESENT DEVELOPMENT

The interest of ECRC in aerobic digestion began in the early 1970's at the beginning of the development of the VO2 aeration system. While attempting to mix and aerate agricultural sludges and slurries with acceptable power efficiency, it became apparent from the rapid rise in reactor temperatures that an opportunity existed for the parallel development of process and hardware. Consequently, the requirements of a viable aerobic thermophilic sludge digestion system; high oxygen transfer, high power efficiency and excellent mixing became design objectives. As these attributes have general appeal, the VO2 aerator, now licensed to Tom Maguire and Company Limited, is used in a wide variety of effluent treatment and chemical applications apart from aerobic thermophilic sludge treatment (1).

Co-operation between ECRC and Welsh WA began in 1975. At that time WWA staff were among the few in the UK who had aerobic thermophilic operating experience. Using commercially available oxygen, a Wimpey-Unox pilot plant had operated at Ponthir STW and a full scale trial undertaken in an anaerobic digester at Llanfoist STW had achieved an operating temperature of 63°C. This system proved uneconomic, but provided the stimulus for the joint development of an alternative less expensive system operating with air.

At that time it was commonly asserted that thermophilic operation could be achieved with oxygen but not with air (2), but in addition to the present authors, research groups in the US and West Germany also believed that a viable system employing air could be devised (3,4).

Pilot developments at Ponthir

The first thermophilic reactor to operate successfully on air at Ponthir was a 9 m³ pilot plant constructed by ECRC. A peak sludge temperature of 61°C was achieved in 1979 and the reactor operated for two years producing high oxygen transfer figures (5). As a small research tool this reactor had a relatively high electrical input and only 60% of the sludge thermal energy was of biochemical origin.

Thereafter, an open uninsulated 100 m³ concrete tank was operated for a further 2 years as a thermophilic digester by installing a free standing VO2 aerator on the tank base. The sludges produced at temperatures up to 55°C were stable and inoffensive.

Full-scale retro-fit experience Ponthir

In 1981 the WWA decided to treat all of the sludge from Ponthir STW, in an aerobic thermophilic sludge digestion process. Ponthir serves 93,000 people and associated industry.

The system was installed with minimal capital outlay by employing an existing 1000 m³ uninsulated below ground concrete sludge holding tank as the reactor. Typically about 110 m³/d of sludge at about 4.5% solids were fed to a reactor volume of 890 m³. Sludge depth was 4.85 m and foam depth 0.5-1.0 m. An airflow of 650-2000 m³/h was delivered by 3 x 15 kW VO2 aerators and 2 x 22 kW low pressure air blowers. One blower was powered by a Tasc-Oulton variable speed drive unit which responded to an oxygen probe and later to a redox electrode situated in the sludge. Installed power was 89 kW, but absorbed power ranged from 42 to 76 kW depending upon demand.

Over the period of operation, Summer 1982 - Spring 1985, typically 45-57% of the COD, 28 - 42% of the total solids and 36 - 51% of the organic sludge solids were destroyed (6). The sludge temperature ranged from 39°C to 65°C depending upon the ambient air temperature and was very stable on a week to week basis.

A limited number of series of investigations for Salmonella & E.coli indicated that temperatures in excess of 50°C are required to eliminate these species in a continuous flow system with a mean retention of 8 days. This agrees with other workers (7) and with the US EPA guideline that sludge for land spreading should have been held at 55°C or above for at least 3 days.

The costs of this retro-fitted installation were £50,000 in June 1982 and energy costs have ranged from £15,000 to £20,000 per annum depending upon the mode of operation. During optimum operation the plant required an electrical input of 210kWh/tonne of dry solids treated.

The system installed in 1982 revealed that full scale continuous operation of aerobic thermophilic digestion was a practical proposition and demonstrated that many of the benefits of this very robust process could be obtained in a simple retro-fitted system. However, it was equally evident that the benefit which makes the system qualitatively different from anaerobic digestion, i.e. the possibility of reliable pathogen kill, was attainable only if continuous high temperature operation could be ensured. This implied an insulated reactor vessel, and at that time other workers in the UK were also investigating thermophilic operation with air, and temperatures of up to 67°C were achieved by WRC in an insulated above ground 28 m³ reactor volume at Palmersford STW Wessex WA (7,8).

OBJECTIVES OF THE NEW DEVELOPMENT

The objectives which underlie the design of the new aerobic thermophilic sludge digestion system are as follows.

(1) To treat all the sludge from Ponthir STW in an above ground insulated vessel and produce a stable inoffensive product.
(2) To effect a minimum reduction of 40% in volatile solids and a 50% reduction in COD.
(3) To raise the sludge temperature by at least 60°C.
(4) To record the destruction of pathogenic species.

(5) To achieve a significant reduction in sludge volume by evaporation.
(6) To explore possible fruitful uses of surplus heat energy from the digester.
(7) To compare the capital and running costs with those from alternative systems.

The achievement of these main technical and financial objectives is assisted by pre-thickening the feedstock sludge so reducing the reactor size and the heat losses from it; by further increasing the power efficiency of the VO2 oxygen transfer system; by employing existing package plant technology in the design of the reactor.

DESIGN CONSIDERATIONS

Biochemical heat release

The potential release of heat energy during an aerobic oxidation is determined by the reductive status of the substrate, fats for example being more energetic than carbohydrates. However, heat release in terms of oxygen consumption is much less dependent on substrate type and can conveniently be taken as 460 KJ/mol of oxygen consumed or 4 kWh/kg of oxygen consumed.

In a suitably designed system, a VO2 aerator can transfer 3 kgO_2/kWh, and consequently 12 kWh of biochemical energy can be released for each unit of electrical energy used. Oxygen transfer is frequently dependent upon scale of operation, and ratios of only 1.5 and 2.03 have been obtained in 9 m^3 and 28 m^3 reactors (5,8).

It has been suggested that the theoretical oxygen demand of sludge organic solids is 1.42 KgO_2/Kg VS oxidised (7). Results at Ponthir however indicated that COD removal was 2 - 2.6 Kg/Kg VS oxidised or 0.9 - 1.1 Kg/Kg VS fed at a volatile solids removal rate of 36-51%. As sludge solids exhibit a range of reductive status and ease of oxidation, it is important when quoting specific oxygen consumption that the percentage oxidation expected or attained is also stated.

Oxygen transfer

The oxygen transfer efficiency of traditional aeration devices varies greatly and is frequently low, but the VO2 aerator has been designed to be able to transfer more than 30% of the oxygen in air into solution in a single pass at 20°C and optimum depth. As a result, for a given weight of oxygen transfer the gas volume is small, the heat released while the system is still at low temperature is not dissipated in an excessive airflow and the sludge temperature begins to rise. During the oxidation of hot sludges, oxygen transfer figures of up to 55% by COD removal have been obtained at Ponthir, and higher figures have been reported by others.

By severely restricting the airflow in a high temperature system it is possible to obtain oxygen transfer efficiencies of 100% (8), but this reduces the percentage of organic solids which can be oxidised to below the acceptable limit which a practical system must seek to achieve. This total transfer does however illustrate that the biochemical demand for oxygen at these elevated temperatures renders inappropriate the purely physical methods of calculation of oxygen transfer commonly employed in dilute effluent studies (9,10).

Sludge strength and reactor insulation

The strength of the feedstock sludge has been found to have great effect on the temperature attained in the reactor. The available carbon flux influences microbial oxygen demand and all water must be heated as it passes through the digester. Consequently a sudden reduction in sludge strength will produce a relatively rapid drop in reactor temperature (11). If however the sludge is thickened prior to treatment, the digester can be smaller and heat losses in the treated sludge and through the walls will be reduced.

In the uninsulated retro-fitted systems previously reported, when sludges of 2-6% solids were used, a thermal balance was typically achieved at about 40°C above ambient air temperature, half of the heat being lost through the tank walls and the remainder shared between the treated sludge and the exhaust saturated air.

But to ensure high operating temperatures all the year round requires a purpose built, well insulated system treating a pre-thickened sludge, and this has been specified in the present study. By improving insulation, the heat loss through the reactor shell is reduced and the sludge temperature rises until a new equilibrium is reached at least 60°C above ambient. At this point most of the heat goes to evaporate water from the sludge, this resulting in a significant reduction in volume for disposal.

Stoichiometry and mathematical modelling of sludge oxidiation

The ECRC Biochemical Oxidation Mathematical Model, (BOMM), has been developed to increase the effectiveness of VO2 design and installation studies including the present aerobic thermophilic sludge digestion development. By providing all relevant data relating to physical aspects of the reactor, site data, sludge data, air data, physical constants, and the stoichiometry of the particular oxidation, a complete mass balance and thermal balance under steady state conditions is obtained by successive iteration (Figure 1). Alternatively, by fixing desired steady state conditions or results, particular aspects of the reactor design, or required sludge strengths or air rates can be determined.

PROCESS SPECIFICATION

The new above ground aerobic thermophilic digester receives pre-thickened sludge from a settling system designed by WRC. This thickens a nominal flow of 120 m³/d at 4.5% solids and produces a feedstock flow of 60 m³/d at 8% solids. The reactor volume was fixed at 420 m³ and nominal retention is therefore 7 days, but as the flow is expected to vary between 48 and 72 m³/d, retention time may be from 5.83 days to 8.75 days.

4.8 tonnes/d of dry solids represents about 3.6 tonnes/d of volatile solids and about 7.2 tonnes/d of COD. The plant is designed to effect a 40% reduction in volatile solids and a 50% reduction in COD. The latter target requires an oxygen transfer of 150 kgO_2/hr. This should produce a biochemical power output of more than 600 kw which will be sufficient to raise the temperature of the sludge flow by 60°C as it passes through the system. In consequence the treated sludge will be rendered stable and destruction of pathogens will occur.

Considerable loss of water by evaporation will occur during the process, and by reducing the volume for disposal by about 18 m³/d or 30% will substantially defray the operating costs of the process.

Maximum air delivery will be 1500 m³/h, an airflow of 3.6 m³/m³ of reactor volume/h, or 27 m³/h/m² of sludge surface. Air delivery will thus be less than in the previous system but the flux in the reactor will be substantially increased.

A simple heat exchange system is designed to transfer heat at a rate of at least 20 kW from the overflowing treated sludge to the cold untreated sludge. The reduction in temperature in the treated sludge may aid a future settlement programme. A much greater heat loss, perhaps in excess of 390 kw, is carried in the hot saturated exhaust gas stream. This will be cooled in a system which in the first instance will use clarified effluent as a heat sink as it leaves an adjacent primary sedimentation tank. Traces of organic or other odiferous compounds will then be removed from the partly cooled exhaust gas stream by passing it through a scrubbing system. Regular de-gritting, as necessary, is provided for in the design.

DESCRIPTION OF PLANT

The new installation at Ponthir briefly comprises a sludge thickener, a buffer tank, and a digester complete with aeration system, heat exchangers and gas scrubbing equipment (Figure 2). All three tanks are of bolt-up pre-formed vitreous enamelled steel construction and are mounted on a common, steel reinforced concrete base. All tanks are roofed to reduce smells and both buffer tank and digester are vented through the heat exchanger/gas scrubber arrangement.

The sludge thickener has been designed by WRC to provide sludge at 8-10% solids. This allows the size of the digester to be reduced, and improves the heat balance by reducing the surface area and the amount of ballasting water flowing through the system. Automatic desludging pumps feed thickened sludge into the 50 m³ buffer tank which also provides an additional 15 m³ capacity for the collapse of excess foam. The buffer tank has a conical base outlet from which variable speed positive displacement pumps feed the digester. The digester tank roof, supplied by Macbar Ltd, is formed from a double GRP foam filled laminated section and the shell wall is clad in panels of similar construction giving a thermal rating of 0.034 w/m²K. The digester shell, supplied by Tank Systems Ltd., is required to operate at temperatures up to 80°C. The digester tank will sit on a conical concrete base designed with an angle of slope of 30°C to the horizontal. It is expected that this will be adequate to permit regular degritting as necessary, and that the combination of slope and high turbulence in the system will prevent grit bridging problems. Heat losses in the concrete floor are between 10 and 20 w/m²K.

The digester is equipped with 4 Maguire VO2 aeration units mounted at floor level and firing into the tank from around its base (Figure 3). Each pump and nozzle can be independently isolated and removed for maintenance without interrupting treatment. The reactor has been designed around the particular immersion depth, 6.5m, at which the VO2 system exhibits optimum oxygen transfer with respect to electrical consumption.

The oxygen requirement of 150 Kg/h can be supplied by three of the aerators, the fourth unit providing a stand-by function. Air is supplied by two Roots type air blowers housed in weather proof acoustic enclosures adjacent to the digester. One blower runs at constant speed and provides the base air demand. The second unit, fitted with a Tasc-Oulton variable speed drive, is controlled by a signal from a redox probe, allowing the system to operate at peak efficiency whatever the oxygen demand.

Each aerator is fitted with a 7.5 kW motor and power consumption is 5.5 kW. Both air blowers are supplied with 22 kW motors and power consumption is up to 18 kW. Total installed power is thus 66.5 kW, but power consumption is expected to be 45-50 kW. Air from the blowers is piped around the digester above sludge level to prevent flooding, and this line is fitted with an anti-siphon valve.

The treated sludge is passed through a jacketed pipework system so that some energy can be recovered and used to pre-heat the incoming sludge. However by far the greatest rate of energy loss from the system occurs in the hot saturated spent air leaving the digester. There is expected to be almost 400 kw of latent and sensible heat contained in this air flow. A jet condenser in the exhaust duct recovers the majority of this energy by cooling the flow before it is presented to the gas scrubber column. This heat is then carried by the cooling water. In the future it is intended to install an alternative indirect heat exchange system which may be employed in the heating of buildings. Before the spent gas is vented, a multi-stage spray/packed column gas scrubber removes over 90% of chemical carry over, and a final mist eliminator prevents water-borne carry over.

Fig. 1 shows the heat balance of the system. It is anticipated that up to 30% of the water in the sludge presented to the digester will be evaporated, to be condensed by the outlet heat exchanger. The saving in disposal costs thus obtained will make a significant contribution to the running costs of the system.

THE COSTS OF AEROBIC THERMOPHILIC SLUDGE DIGESTION

The joint development of the present aerobic thermophilic sludge digestion system as described above is being undertaken within a total approved capital budget of £362,000. This sum includes an approved capital allowance of £110,000 for the WRC sludge thickening system, its foundations and ancillaries. The capital sum directly attributable to the aerobic thermophilic system is thus £252,000.

Some aspects of the costs of design, commissioning and instrumentation are associated with the developmental nature of this particular installation and would not necessarily be expected to recur in future installations. Be that as it may, capital costs of the present development are thus £3.89 per capita for the total development and £2.71 per capita for the aerobic thermophilic digestion package. The projected energy cost is derived from an expected power requirement of 50 kW. Electricity consumption will then be about 438,000 units per annum or 240 kWh/tonne of dry solids treated. Electrical energy costs at Ponthir will be about £15,200 p.a. or £8.33 per tonne of dry solids treated.

Losses due to evaporation will be up to 30% of the sludge volume treated or 18 m³/day. Assuming a disposal cost of £5.18/tonne of treated sludge at Ponthir, this represents a potential saving of £34,000 p.a. which can be set against energy costs. It is appreciated that disposal costs on other sites may be less than the Ponthir figure.

At this stage it is not possible to predict the quantity of heat which can be exported from the process and usefully employed elsewhere. For certain sites a financially attractive use could be envisaged.

Finally, it is important that the benefit of pathogen control in sludges is not entirely eliminated from the financial balance sheet. When the capital costs of a new process are less than those of conventional treatment and the differences in running costs are marginal, the choice of the superior process becomes sensible even before the beneficial effects of that process become mandatory.

CONCLUSIONS

For many years it has been the goal of the authors to develop a viable aerobic thermophilic sludge digestion system which would make use of the positive attributes of the VO2 Aeration System to economically transfer oxygen from air while conserving the biochemically derived heat energy in the sludge.

The development has already progressed logically through several pilot stages to a full-scale retro-fitted installation. While that system, as previously described, may be the preferred option on many sites, the advantages of the exceptionally low capital cost are traded against an acceptance of limited technical performance.

In the present study, however, a higher specification and improved performance is demanded. This has been made possible by a more systematic design engineering approach. As a result, the interactions and interdependencies of the process are successfully exploited in a system which offers several areas of potential benefit to the user.

Briefly, these are as follows:- the sludge is rendered stable and inoffensive; the sludge is substantially pathogen free; the volume of sludge for disposal is reduced; the system has a low capital cost; the process has an acceptable energy cost; the process offers future opportunities for the export of heat energy.

REFERENCES

1. Morgan S.F., Winstanley R. and Littlewood M.H., 1985. C.M.E. 32, (6), 27-29.

2. Gould, M.S. and Drnevich, R.F., 1978, Envir. Engng. Div., Proc. A.S.C.E. 104, No. EE2.

3. Jewell, W.J. and Kabrick R.M., 1980, J.W.P.C.F. 52, (3), 512-523.

4. Fuchs, H., and Fuchs L., 1980, Korrespondenz Abwasser, 27, (4), 241-244.

5. Morgan, S.F., and Gunson, H.G., 1981, Water Industry '81, Brighton, 482-487.

6. Morgan, S.F., Gunson, H.G., Littlewood, M.H. and Winstanley, R., 1983, in Sewage Sludge Stabilisation and Disinfection, 278-292. Ellis Horwood, Chichester.

7. Booth, M.G. and Tramontini, E., 1983, in Sewage Sludge Stabilisation and Disinfection, 293-331, Ellis Horwood, Chichester.

8. Wolinski, W.K., 1985, Wat. Pollut. Control 433-445.

9. Aiba, S., Humphrey, A.E. and Millis, N.F., 1973 Biochemical Engineering, Academic Press, New York and London.

10. Morgan, S.F., Winstanley, R., Littlewood, M.H. and Gunson, H.G., 1984, Bio Energy '84, World Conference, Gothenburg.

11. Vismara, R., 1985, Water Res. 19 (4), 441-447.

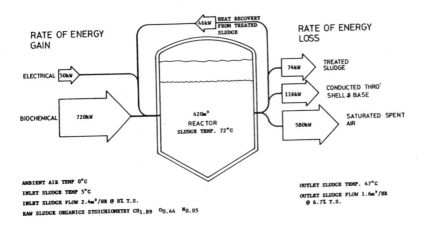

RATE OF ENERGY GAIN

ELECTRICAL 50kW

BIOCHEMICAL 720kW

HEAT RECOVERY FROM TREATED SLUDGE 46kW

420m³ REACTOR SLUDGE TEMP. 72°C

RATE OF ENERGY LOSS

74kW TREATED SLUDGE

116kW CONDUCTED THRO' SHELL & BASE

580kW SATURATED SPENT AIR

AMBIENT AIR TEMP 0°C
INLET SLUDGE TEMP 5°C
INLET SLUDGE FLOW 2.4m³/HR @ 8% T.S.
RAW SLUDGE ORGANICS STOICHIOMETRY $CH_{1.89}$ $O_{0.44}$ $N_{0.05}$

OUTLET SLUDGE TEMP. 47°C
OUTLET SLUDGE FLOW 1.6m³/HR @ 6.7% T.S.

FIG. 1   ENERGY FLOW RATE DATA FROM ECRC BIOLOGICAL OXIDATION MATHEMATICAL MODEL (BOMM)

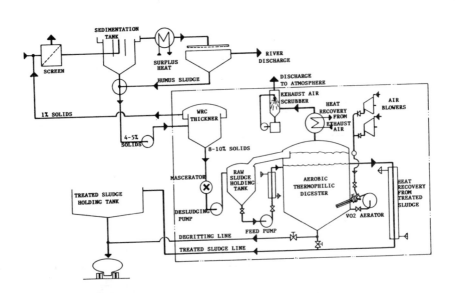

FIG. 2   FLOW DIAGRAM - PONTHIR STW

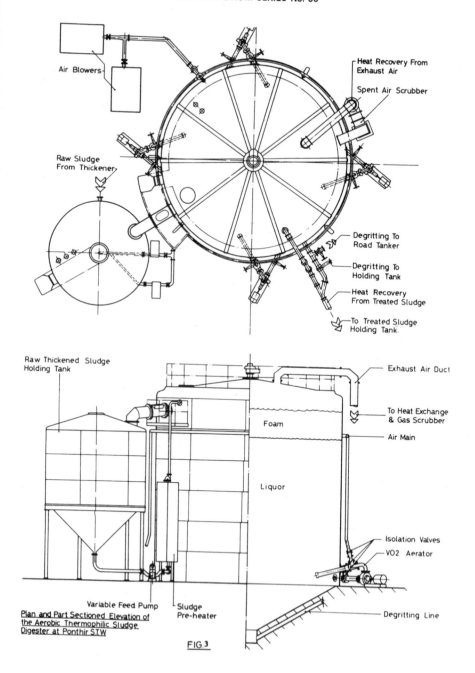

Plan and Part Sectioned Elevation of the Aerobic Thermophilic Sludge Digester at Ponthir STW

FIG.3

MEMBRANE SEPARATION TECHNIQUES FOR AQUEOUS EFFLUENT & PRODUCT RECOVERY

P.H.Fergusson *

Membrane processing offers potential for the economic recovery of by-products and valuable materials otherwise lost in waste streams and effluents. At the same time, effluent loadings and disposal problems are alleviated. Examples where this technology has been applied are given for the following industries : textile, printing, tannery, dye, latex, biotechnology, egg, dairy and brewing. The general principles of membrane filtration are discussed - terminology, membrane configuration, system engineering - and some basic concepts regarding the use of membrane systems in effluent treatment and product recovery are reviewed.

1. PRINCIPLES OF MEMBRANE PROCESSING

1.1 Terminology

The three main membrane technologies that we come across are hyperfiltration (reverse osmosis) , ultrafiltration and microfiltration . They may be distinguished by the size of the particle or molecule they are capable of retaining. Definitions vary, but for present purposes the following will be used :-

1.1.1 Hyperfiltration (pore size = 0.0001 - 0.001 microns)

Here the pore size is the smallest of the three systems under consideration, and even small dissolved molecules (e.g. salts) are retained by the membrane. At this molecular level, osmotic forces come into play and for this reason relatively high pressures are necessary (e.g. 10 - 50 bar). Hyperfiltration systems are most often used for dewatering purposes - where the concentrate is the valued stream, and perhaps thermolabile - or for water purification duties e.g. desalination or depyrogenation.

1.1.2 Ultrafiltration (pore size = 0.001 - 0.1 microns)

Ultrafiltration is a selective separation process in which

* APV Membrane Processes Ltd.,Manor Royal, Crawley, W. Sussex.

suspended solids, colloids (e.g. protein), emulsified solids (e.g. paint) and dissolved macro-molecules (generally those with a M.W. of over 1000 - 10000, depending on the membrane) are retained by the membrane. This retained stream is called the concentrate or retentate. Lower molecular weight dissolved materials such as solvents, salts, sugars and water will pass through the membrane under a driving force of relatively low hydrostatic pressure (e.g. 1 - 10 bar. This stream is called the permeate or filtrate.

1.1.3 Microfiltration (pore size = 0.1 - 10 microns)

In this instance, only very large macromolecular groups (e.g. large fat globules) and suspended particles (e.g. microbial cells) are held back by the membrane, the remainder of the components in the solution filtering across.

1.2 MEMBRANE CONFIGURATION

The whole array of commercially-available module designs can be classified into two quite fundamental configurations : tubular and narrow channel. For example, the tubular configuration includes the capillary or hollow fibre type, having internal diameters of between 0.001 and 1.2 mm, and membrane tubes of between 12 - 25 mm internal diameter. Similar variations hold true for the narrow channel modules which includes the flat plate membrane design and the spiral wound-membrane.

1.3 SYSTEM ENGINEERING

For efficient operation and minimal fouling, the fluid must be passed over the membrane surface at high velocities. For most geometries, this means that the total volumetric flow is high, and very much higher than the rate of permeation through the membrane. In consequence, the fluid is usually continuously recirculated. Based on this requirement, there are two main methods of operation : -

1.3.1 Batch Operation

The process fluid is pumped continuously from a holding tank into the membrane modules and directly back to the tank. As more and more water is removed by permeation, the level in the tank falls and the product concentration increases to the desired or limiting value.

1.3.2 Continuous Operation

Otherwise known as 'feed and bleed'. In this processing mode the concentration takes place entirely within the recirculation loop and none of the concentrate is returned to the feed tank.

Initially, the concentration within the loop is allowed to increase to the desired level. At this point, a proportion of the concentrate is bled from the system and fresh feed is added to the holding tank : the quantity of feed added must equal the amount of permeate flowing out of the loop plus the amount of concentrate being bled from the system.

Multi-stage operation is achieved by linking two or more 'feed and bleed' stages in series. Each stage operates at a constant concentration, which increases from the first to the last stage, the latter then operating at the desired product concentration. A feed pump is required to supply the process liquid to the first stage but subsequent stages are fed from the preceding stages by small pressure differences as they lose liquid by permeation and transfer.

2. THE USE OF MEMBRANE SYSTEMS IN EFFLUENT TREATMENT & PRODUCT RECOVERY

The potential of membrane technology in the treatment of waste streams is, in technical terms, very large. As can be seen from the initial remarks, a wide range of particles, suspended solids and dissolved components - in fact, virtually anything of a size below 10 microns - can be recovered, and where required, reprocessed. (Above this size range, conventional filtration takes over.)

However, it is obvious that economics play a major, and probably overiding role in deciding the viability of a particular application and hence whether it will ever see the light of day in terms of commercial, full-scale plant. Normally it is a question of calculating the operating costs and comparing these with the value of the recovered by-product. The difference is the net benefit, and it is this that has to justify the capital investment in membrane technology.

One area where another consideration has to be evaluated is when reverse osmosis/hyperfiltration is the appropriate route. Then it usually necessary to evaluate evaporation as an alternative dewatering method, and here we are really talking about the respective energy requirements and costs.

One useful comparison between hyperfiltration and evaporation is carried out by Hansen (1). The first point that is made is that when comparing various forms of energy (evaporation consumes primarily steam whilst hyperfiltration uses electrical energy), it must be borne in mind that there are different efficiencies of energy generation, depending on the type of energy and its source. Secondly, although it is possible to calculate, using thermodynamic principles, the minimum theoretical energy input necessary to separate water from its solutes, this value is fairly meaningless in practice, particulary with complex materials e.g. food products. The following table shows the relative energy requirements :

Type of plant	Direct Energy Input		Energy Cost	
	Steam kg/kg	Power kWh/kg	(a) DM/kg	(b) FF/kg
TVR - 3 effects	0.22	0.003	0.014	0.031
- 7 effects	0.10	0.003	0.0066	0.014
MVR	0.02	0.020	0.0052	0.0085
RO	-	0.010	0.0020	0.0029

(TVR = Evaporator with thermal vapour recompression)
(MVR =   "   "   mechanical vapour recompression)

Because of varying fuel prices in different countries, the table above shows costs for both West Germany and France. (Unfortunately the authors did not quote U.K. figures.)

3. APPLICATIONS.

The following section considers a selection of application areas for membrane processing.

3.1 Textile Industry

In many textile factories where cloth is sized with synthetic sizing agents such as CMC or PVA, money is often wasted at the desizing stage in that all of the PVA or CMC applied to the warp yarn in the slasher is usually discharged to drain in the finishing operation. By using ultrafiltration, it is possible to achieve some or all of the following benefits : (i) recover almost all the sizing agent from the desize waste stream, (ii) concentrate the PVA or CMC to levels suitable for direct recycle to the slasher, and (iii) return hot water to the washer or desize range for reuse.

The financial savings realised from reduced sizing agent purchases and lowered thermal energy requirements will often pay for the system in 12 - 18 months. Product quality is not forfeited because loom efficiencies are at least as high with recovered size as with fresh CMC or PVA.

The ultrafiltration system takes its feed from the desize washer or the washing stage of the desize range, passes it through a vibrating screen filter to remove lint, then pumps the filtered desize waste to a storage tank. From the tank, the waste is pumped through successive stages of ultrafiltration modules. In each stage, water is removed by the membranes,

406

increasing the concentration of sizing agent in the process fluid. At the exit of the last stage, the concentrated PVA or CMC is at slasher strength, ready for reuse. The water removed in each stage is collected in a second tank from which it can be recycled directly to the washer or range.

3.2 Flexographic Ink

Cleaning flexographic presses produces large volumes of wash water containing a small percentage of printing ink. Unlike chemical treatment and evaporation, ultrafiltration can recover and concentrate these diluted inks for reuse. Moreover, the remaining water can be reused.

Thhe wash water from cleaning a flexographic press may contain between 1% and 2% printing ink, and a typical mass balance for ultrafiltering this material containing 1% printing ink is :

FEED	=	CONCENTRATE	+	PERMEATE
(wash water)				
1000 gpd		40 gpd		960 gpd
1% ink		25% ink		

3.3 Tannery Wastes

There are two main applications for membrane technology in tanneries :

3.3.1 Sulphide Recovery

The spent unhairing bath waste stream from a beamhouse contributes from 40 - 70% of the total tannery BOD and COD loading, as well as essentially 100% of the waste water sulphide loading. Ultrafiltering it instead of mixing it with other process wastes eliminates this particular effluent from the overall beamhouse effluent, without the need for added chemicals or phase changes. It thus acheives a BOD reduction of up to 70% and a drop in COD by up to 60%. The ultrafiltration plant itself produces a permeate high in sulphides, suitable for recycling, and a high-protein concentrate with potential as a fertilizer or animal feed.

3.3.2 Vegetable Tannin Recovery

Ultrafiltration can increase the tannin to non-tannin ratio in the spent light liquor from vegetable tanning operations. The resulting product is a reuseable tannin solution. With only a two-fold concentration, the ratio of tannin to total soluble solids (i.e. purity) can be increased from, say, 52% to 59%; tannin concentration from 2.7% to 4.1%. Ultrafiltration can also be used with certain tannages until a commercial purity tannin (70%) is achieved.

3.4 Dye Industry

One conventional route for dyeing cloth involves, in simplified terms, passing the undyed cloth into a vat of dye (e.g. indigo), then through an air oxidation step before passing to the rinse stage. This consists of series of rinse tanks, the rinse water passing from one tank to the next in counter-current mode. The resultant rinse water obviously contains a low level of dye, which if passed through an ultrafiltration unit can be concentrated and then used as part of the make-up water in preparing fresh dye. The permeate will be free of dye, and can be reused (e.g. rinse water).

3.5 Latex

The general applications of membrane systems in the polymer latex industry are :- (i) the concentration of the latex as an in-process step, (ii) the purification of emulsions by washing out impurities, and (iii) the concentration of latex as a waste treatment technique.

Many different types of latex emulsions and slurries can be processed using this technology.

3.5.1 Latex Concentration

A portion of the PVC latex manufactured is produced by emulsion polymerisation. The polymer has a smaller and more uniform particle size than that formed in the more common suspension polymerisation technique, but unfortunately it is more difficult to remove water from an emulsion latex than a suspension polymer slurry. Usually the emulsion PVC must be taken from about 30-40% solids to dryness using a spray dryer, which is obviously a capital and energy-intensive route.

An ultrafiltration unit can be installed between the blend tank and the spray dryer, where it can take the solids from, say, 30% to 55%.

3.5.2 Latex Purification

During the manufacture of certain lattices (e.g. for coating applications), an inorganic salt is produced which interfers with the coating's properties. While dialysis had been used in the laboratory, it was not feasible on a commercial scale. When ultrafiltration was tried, it was found that the salt passed through the membrane with zero rejection, whilst the polymer was completely retained. By adding further water to the concentrate side of the membrane (a technique known as diafiltration), the salt can effectively be diluted out. For example, in one particular installation, the initial salt concentration of 13,300 ppm was reduced to 1,500 ppm.

3.5.3 Latex Waste Treatment

One interesting application of membranes is the recovery of a reuseable latex from waste streams. By way of example, a styrene-butadiene rubber latex factory loses some 1 to 5% of the latex in effluent (storage tanks, filters, washings, spillages, etc.). Chemical treatments are possible, but they often generate their own by-products which have to be disposed of. Concentrating the waste with ultrafiltration reduces these effluent treatment costs whilst at the same time producing a saleable product. A number of plants are operating in Europe, and a typical installation has a feed stream containing latex at 0.5% solids. The latex is concentrated to 20% solids prior to passing to an evaporator where the solids are taken up to 40%, at which point the material is saleable.

3.6 Biotechnology

As would be expected, a broad range of applications exist here :-

3.6.1 Whole Broth Separation

The overall cell separation problem has been considered in depth by BIOSEP (2).

3.6.2 Enzyme Concentration and Purification

On an industrial scale, enzymes are usually obtained from animal, plant or microbial tissues. In the latter case, the enzymes may well be extracellular; otherwise the cells will need macerating, as will be the case with plant and animal material, in order to release the enzymes. The next stage is often the removal of suspended solids and particulate matter - possibly by cross-flow microfiltration. Steam-sterilisable inorganic membranes are well suited to this application. The clarified liquor can then be further purified and concentrated by ultrafiltration and/or hyperfiltration.

A number of enzymes, including pectinases, proteinases and carbohydrases are presently processed using ultrafiltration.

3.6.3 Blood

Whole blood is the largest single by-product of the meat industry, and most of it is still wasted. The use of blood products in foods is generally nutritionally sound, although its use is limited because of the red colour (which usually deteriorates to brown), and also a metallic flavour, both problems imparted by the haemoglobin in the red cells.

In recent years, methods to separate blood into plasma (i.e. blood minus cells) and cellular fractions have been developed, and they include microfiltration and ultrafiltration.

Microfiltration is of interest as an alternative to the use of a centrifuge as a means of removing the cell component, and offers two main potential advantages over the centrifuge. Firstly the level of shear damage can be significantly reduced - this is important as damage to the red cells causes release of unwanted haemoglobin into the plasma fraction - and secondly the use of membranes offers the chance to increase the level of sterility at which this operation takes place - particularly so if an inorganic membrane (steam sterilisable) is used. Practical experience shows that the microfiltration of blood is complex in that the presence of cells (red, white and platelets) means that the viscosity of blood is anything but straightforward. The selection of membrane pore' size, pump type and performance are critical to an efficient separation.

The ultrafiltration of plasma, which is essentially a protein solution, is relatively simpler and better understood. The main motive behind employing membranes here is to replace evaporation, which traditionally has been the only large scale method available for plasma concentration. The relatively low temperature regimes found in ultrafiltration gives it an advantage over evaporation, because plasma proteins are heat sensitive, coagulating at temperatures around 40 - 50 deg C. Another potential attraction of following the membrane route is that whilst evaporation only removes water, ultrafiltration allows some loss of sugar and salts : a reduction in the level of blood sugar in plasma would enhance its microbiological stability.

3.6.4 Fermentation Processes

Some typical examples of fermentation products where membrane technology has been used include (i) antibiotics, (ii) alcohol, (iii) citric acid, and (iv) vinegar.

3.6.5 Pyrogen Reduction/Removal

Pyrogens are defined as chemical or biological agents that cause a rise in temperature when injected parenterally. The main group of pyrogens are lipoplysaccharides deriving from the breakdown of bacterial cell walls and having a molecular weight ranging from about 10000 to aggregates of 0.1 micron in diameter. However there is significant evidence to suggest that the basic sub-unit of lipopolysaccharides has a molecular weight between 10000 and 20000.

Because of the chemical nature of the lipopolysaccharide, many so-called "conventional" methods of sterilisation are ineffective in pyrogen removal. For instance, the molecule is usually thermostable and exposure to dry heat at 250 deg C for periods of up to one hour are required to destroy it. In addition the molecule is relatively insensitive to changes in pH, although high concentrations of acids and bases may deactivate it.

Membrane filtration offers significant potential in pyrogen removal. Whilst it is known that pyrogens will pass through a 0.2 micron sterilising grade cartridge, they will be retained by a conventional RO membrane (nominally rated at 10 Angstroms). However, since the unaggregated sub-unit has been shown to be of the order of 10000 - 20000 in molecular weight, a membrane in the UF range would appear to be suitable. This has to be borne out in practice, as the unaggregated sub-unit is seldom seen in aqueous solutions since the hydrophobic groups have a strong tendency to associate, resulting in aggregates of large numbers of lipoploysaccharide molecules.

Water, either pure or with low molecular weight solutes (such as dextrose or antibiotics) have been de-pyrogenated on a commercial scale with the use of a 10000 molecular weight cut-off ultrafilter. It is also believed that the depyrogenation of higher molecular weight parenteral solutions is possible.

3.8 Egg Industry

The normal processing route for eggs involves washing, rinsing, sanitising, flash-candling and then passing them to the egg breaking machine. Here the eggs are either separated into yolk and white or left as whole egg.

There are three basic forms of egg products : liquid, frozen or dried. Each product requires specific treatment prior to transportation, storage or introduction to food processing.

Typical treatments are :-

- Pasteurisationn
- Evaporation
- Spray drying
- Freezing

Ultrafiltration has successfully been used as an alternative to evaporation as a means of removing water from the egg because as well as being less energy intensive than evaporation, the relatively low temperature found in ultrafiltration systems results in far less thermal, and shear, damage to the protein fraction. Hence the functional properties of the egg (e.g. emulsification, foam formation, tenderising, moisture retention and flavour) are preserved.

Membrane units have also been installed in some factories to recover egg components from the various effluent streams generated in the processing of eggs.

3.9 Dairy Industry

A wide range of applications for microfiltration, ultrafiltration and hyperfiltration have been found in the dairy industry. Points of use for membranes include :

- the manufacture of hard, semi-hard and soft cheeses,
- the production of fermented milks (e.g. yoghurt),
- the processing of liquid milk for retail sale,
- the concentration of cream,
- the recovery of rennet from cheese whey,
- concentration of whey or whey permeate,
- on farm ultrafiltration of milk,
- production of whey protein concentrates,
- recovery of milk solids from dairy rinse water.

3.10 Brewing Industry

Membrane technology finds application in the brewing industry in three main areas :

- beer recovery from tank bottoms
- clarification of beer
- low-alcohol beer

3.11 Other Application Areas

3.11.1 Treatment of wool scouring liquids,
3.11.2 Separation of water/gasoline mixtures,
3.11.3 Concentration of magnesium hydroxide from sea-water,
3.11.4 Removal of hydrocarbon oils from laundry wastewaters,
3.11.5 Re-use of waste water from ammunition manufacture,
3.11.6 Re-use of wastewater containing firefighting agent,
3.11.7 Recovery of asbestos from asbestos-cement industry effluents.
3.11.8 Removal of suspended solids and/or heavy metals and hydroxides from lead-acid battery manufacture.
3.11.9 Treatment of electrophoretic paint,
3.11.10 Purification of mineral acids,
3.11.11 Clarification and concentration in the beet sugar, cane sugar and molasses industries.
3.11.12 By-product recovery from corn milling,
3.11.13 Production of soy protein.

4. REFERENCES

1. Hansen, R. (ed.) (1984) "Evaporation, Membrane Filtration and Spray Drying". North European Dairy Journal.

2. BIOSEP (1984) "State of the Art Report on Primary Solid-Liquid Separation and Biochemical Downstream Processing - The Recovery of Micro-organisms from Fermentation Broths". BIOSEP, the Biological Separations Club, Harwell Laboratory.

UPGRADING TREATMENT FOR EFFLUENT RE-USE

M.M.G. Bell* and K.H. Allum**

Various methods were considered for upgrading an effluent from an existing treatment plant serving a military camp in the Middle East to a standard suitable for unrestricted irrigation. On the basis of the study the ozone/activated carbon filtration process was selected. The process was compact; easily prefabricated and automated; did not require regular supply of chemicals and was cost competitive.

INTRODUCTION

The study examined methods for upgrading sewage effluent from a treatment plant serving a military camp in an Arabian Peninsula State to a quality that would be acceptable for "unrestricted" irrigation use without risk to public health.

Draft legislation under consideration at the time of the study set out standards that, in terms of irrigation methods, only apply to buried drip feed systems and then only where there would not be public exposure. No standards exist for unrestricted applications i.e irrigation by flood, hose, spray or sprinkler. Any such method would require the special consent of the controlling authority. In order to satisfy the authority that there would be no risk to public health it was considered that the upgrading treatment processes would have to produce an effluent of a microbiological quality approaching that of drinking water.

A number of treatment options were reviewed in terms of process reliability, operational factors, ease of integration with the treatment plant already under construction, as well as capital and operating costs. The options considered and described in the study included high-lime or alum coagulation and clarification, reverse-osmosis, maturation pond treatment with dissolved-air flotation to remove algae, and ozonation followed by granular-activated carbon filtration. Consideration was also given to slow-sand filtration, ozonation, and replacement of the sand in the existing sand filter with activated carbon, and super chlorination/dechlorination.

* Watson Hawksley, Consulting Engineers, High Wycombe, Bucks HP13 5HA
** Ashact Ltd, Process and Environmental Management, Prestwood, Bucks HP16 ONG

EXISTING TREATMENT PLANT AND WATER DEMANDS

At the present time the camp is served by an extended-aeration activated sludge plant treating average flows of about 2 100m³/d to a 30:20 (SS:BOD) standard. To accommodate expansion within the camp and serve new developments that will discharge effluent into a common sewerage system a new treatment plant has been constructed to operate in parallel with the existing plant. The existing plant will be refurbished.

The new plant, a Pasveer ditch, will increase the total treatment capacity to 5 250m³/d. After flow balancing, the combined effluent from both plants will be filtered using conventional rapid-gravity sand filters and disinfected by chlorination.

Irrigation water demand within the camp at present is satisfied partly by the use of potable quality water and some limited and controlled use of effluent from the existing wastewater treatment plant. Surplus effluent is discharged to a nearby dry water course (wadi).

Estimates showed that if the desired quality could be achieved then 60% of the ultimate effluent flow could be used for irrigation by unrestricted means within the camp and it was expected the demand would rise further.

REGULATIONS CONTROLLING THE RE-USE AND DISPOSAL OF EFFLUENT

At the time of the study a final draft of regulations for wastewater re-use and discharge was under consideration by a government body concerned with environmental protection and conservation. In formulating the regulations it was the intention that the re-use and discharge of effluent would be considered in various degrees of priority. In summary these were:

o   Buried drip-feed system for the irrigation of ornamental trees and shrubs in areas where there should not be public exposure.

o   Controlled groundwater recharge in areas where there should not be public exposure.

o   Controlled re-use for industrial processes within a closed circuit system.

o   By controlled discharge to approved areas such as open land, wadis or water courses.

o   Irrigation by flooding, hose pipe, sprinkler or spray systems would only be permitted by special consent of the executive authority.

The new plants were designed to achieve the draft regulation standards for disposal of effluent by either drip-feed irrigation or controlled discharge to wadi. For this form of disposal the required effluent quality was to a 10:10:1 (SS:BOD:NH₃) standard with a free chlorine residual.

There are, however, substantial residential areas within the camp where irrigation by drip-feed systems are not viable by virtue of the type of planting, e.g grass, where spray irrigation would be more appropriate. Of course, irrigation by spray or hose pipe increases the chances of effluent coming into contact with the public, either through direct consumption or ingestion of aerosols by personnel ignorant or unaware of the health hazards involved. It was for these reasons that the re-use of effluent by this means would require special consent.

Although, in the sense of security, the camp is a controlled area, irrigation would be largely in an area of residential domestic accommodation. In which case it was thought most unlikely that the degree of treatment provided by the conventional process would be acceptable to the environmental authorities.

The study was initiated under principal terms of reference as follows:

o   Identify target standards for irrigation water quality taking note of proposed irrigation methods and the location of areas to be irrigated.

o   Review available processes for further treatment to achieve the required standards.

o   Review existing treatment system to ensure efficient integration of the upgrading processes and plant.

EFFLUENT QUALITY

To permit the unrestricted use of treated effluent it was proposed that the effluent should conform to a microbiological standard approaching that of drinking water. It had been suggested in WHO Scientific Group Report No 639 (1979) referring to the use of spray irrigation near populated areas that this quality is achieved when 0 (zero) E Coli per 100ml is obtained and no virus is detectable in 10 litres of sample. It was considered that in order to achieve this standard reliably an additional stage of treatment following the filtration stage would be needed.

Preliminary discussions suggested that the proposed standards would satisfy the authorities subject to an efficient level of operation and maintenance being provided. The limits of other determinands included in the draft regulations are given in Appendix 1.

REVIEW OF TREATMENT PROCESSES

The Client had specified from the outset of the project that the additional plant and processes needed to upgrade the effluent quality should not interfere with, or disrupt, the operation of the existing treatment plant. For this reason the processes considered were essentially an additional or quaternary stage of treatment which could achieve the high degree of solids removal and low turbidity to permit effective disinfection.

The processes selected for review in terms of their key elements or units were as follows:-

o   High-lime treatment.

o   Alum treatment.

o   Maturation pond-flotation treatment.

o   Ozone-activated carbon.

o   Reverse-osmosis.

A brief description of these processes is given in Table 1 and schematic diagrams are shown in Figure No 1.

Whilst all five processes reviewed were capable of achieving the desired effluent quality, none, however was without some disadvantage. The advantages and disadvantages for each process are summarised in Table 2.

Before proceeding further it is worth noting that several other treatment processes were considered, but for the reasons outlined below were not considered further.

Slow-Sand Filters:

Effluent from the activated sludge process after rapid-gravity filtration could be treated by slow-sand filters. This process was rejected for the following reasons:-

o   Slow-sand filters are costly and require a large land area.

o   In hot climates algal growth on the slow-sand filters limits run times and makes cleaning the filters very labour intensive.

o   Pre-chlorination has been used with some success in controlling algal growth but in many ways defeats the object of the slow-sand filtration process.

Ozonation and Replacement of the Sand in the Existing Rapid-Gravity Filters with Activated Carbon:

This process was rejected for the following reasons:

o   Considerable modifications to the existing plant were required.

o   Presence of solids reduces the efficiency of ozone disinfection.

o   Existing rapid gravity filters were relatively shallow and hence rather unsuited for activated carbon adsorption.

o   Presence of solids would reduce the carbon life and adsorption capacity.

Super Chlorination - Dechlorination:

After rapid-gravity filtration using a filter-aid to improve solids capture, the effluent would be super chlorinated using either gaseous chlorine plus an alkali or sodium hypochlorite (generated on-site) plus an acid for pH control. Excess chlorine would be removed using either sulphur dioxide or sodium bisulphite. The process was considered unsuitable for the following reasons:

o   With loss of nitrification in the activated sludge process chlorine doses up to, or even exceeding, 300mg/1 would be required for quite extended periods. The large chlorine dosing facilities needed were not considered particularly safe nor indeed very practical on a small treatment plant.

o   The capital costs for on-site generation of hypochlorite were high and the addition of as much as 1 500mg/1 TDS at times of peak chlorine demand would render the effluent almost unfit for re-use purposes.

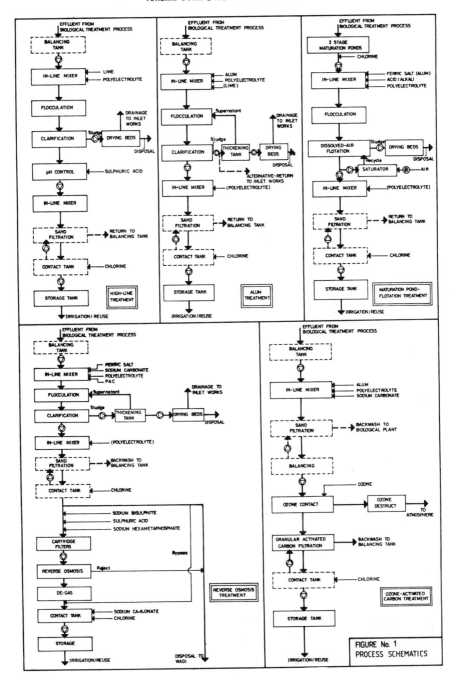

FIGURE No. 1
PROCESS SCHEMATICS

TABLE 1 - OUTLINE PROCESS DESCRIPTION

High Lime Treatment

pH control using 10% lime slurry to pH 11-12.
Flocculation - retention 20 mins, 'G' value
30-100s^{-1}.
Sedimentation - upward flow velocity 2m/h.
pH control using sulphuric acid to pH 7-7.5.
Sand filtration - existing units, filtration
rate 5m/h.
Chlorination - average chlorine dose rate -
5mg/l.
Sludge from sedimentation stage to drying
beds.
Provision for polyelectrolyte dosing to act
as flocculation and filter aid.

Ozone-Activated Carbon Treatment

Sand filtration - existing units, filtration
rate 5m/h.
Ozonation - retention 10 mins, 3 stage
process, dose rate 11mg/l.
Granular activated carbon filtration,
filtration rate 6m/h, EBCT 17.5 mins.
Chlorination - average chlorine dose rate
3mg/l.
Provision to dose alum (or ferric salt),
polyelectrolyte and sodium carbonate.

Maturation Pond/Flotation Treatment

Maturation ponds - two stage ponds, retention
7 days.
Flash mixing alum (or ferric salt), polyelectrolyte and sodium carbonate (for pH
control).
Flocculation - retention 20 mins, 'G' value
30-100s^{-1}.
Dissolved-air flotation - surface loading
4.5m^3/m^2.h.
Sand filtration - existing units, filtration
5m/h.
Chlorination - average Cl$_2$ dose rate 5mg/l.
Sludge from flotation thickener to drying
beds.
Provision to dose polyelectrolyte to act as
filter aid.

Reverse-Osmosis Treatment

Flash mixing ferric salt, sodium carbonate,
polyelectrolyte and PAC.
Flocculation/Adsorption - retention 20 mins
'G' value 30-100s.
Sedimentation - upward flow velocity 1.5m/h.
Sand filtration - existing units, filtration
rate 5m/h.
Break-point chlorination.
Dechlorination using sodium bisulphite.
Scale control using sodium hexametaphosphate.
pH control using sulphuric acid.
Micro filtration - cartridge filters, 1 micron
filters.
Reverse osmosis - spiral wound acetate
membranes.
De-gas - air strip.
Blending tank - blend with bypass flow.
Chlorination - average dose rate 2mg/l Cl$_2$.
pH control using sodium carbonate.
Provision for polyelectrolyte dosing to act as
filter aid.

Alum Treatment

Flash mixing alum, polyelectrolyte and lime
(for pH control).
Flocculation retention - 20 mins, 'G' value
30-100s^{-1}.
Sedimentation - upward flow velocity 1.5m/h.
Sand filtration - existing units, filtration
rate 5m/h.
Break-point chlorination.
Sludge from sedimentation stage to thickening
tank and then to drying beds.
Provision to dose polyelectrolyte to act as
filter aid.

TABLE 2 - SUMMARY OF ADVANTAGES AND DISADVANTAGES

High-Lime Treatment

Advantages

High pH (pH 11) inactivates most pathogenic viruses/bacteria.
Robust process. Not seriously impaired through loss of nitrification or even carbonaceous oxidation.
Reduces levels of most toxic metals.
Reduces levels of soluble carbonaceous and colour producing components.
Lime sludges dry without odour, rodent or fly nuisance.

Disadvantages

High chemical demands.
High sludge yields. Disposal of lime sludges can be difficult.
Cold lime softening process; leaves little residual buffering capacity.
Descaling (lime deposits) in sedimentation tanks and pipelines is a hard, labour intensive job.
Phosphates precipitated as hydroxyapatite, reduces fertiliser value of effluent.

Alum Treatment

Advantages

Conventional, well tried and tested water treatment process.
Claimed to be capable of removing most viruses.
Reduces toxic metal levels.

Disadvantages

High chemical demands.
Large volumes of sludge with a high moisture content produced.
Sludge not readily dewaterable. Difficult to dispose of sludge containing high aluminium levels.
Adds unwanted ions (sulphate) to water, increases potential corrosivity of water.
Break-point chlorination required.
If nitrification incomplete then chlorine demands will be high.
Dechlorination needed to prevent residual chlorine/chloramines harming plants.

Reverse-Osmosis Treatment

Advantages

Water of potable quality with low TDS content.

Disadvantages

Process is complex and costly to operate.
Wide range of chemicals have to be dosed to protect the RO membranes; these chemicals are concentrated in the reject stream. Difficult to dispose of reject stream which contains high COD/BOD and dissolved salt concentrations.
Only 50 per cent of flow recovered for re-use, remainder used to dilute reject stream.
Despite the many and varied claims of manufacturers RO processes require very careful operation if they are to prove successful, giving good water recoveries, rejection efficiency and membrane life. Sewage cannot be considered as a good feedstock.

TABLE 2 - SUMMARY OF ADVANTAGES AND DISADVANTAGES (Cont'd)

Maturation Pond - Flotation Treatment

Advantages

Natural disinfection process not dependant on chemicals. Few viruses survive storage period of seven days.
Lower chemical demands than conventional clarification processes.
Ponds balance variations in flow and effluent quality.
Some ammonia/BOD reduction in ponds.
Effluent saturated with oxygen.
Algal growth elevates pH, some toxic metals precipitated.

Disadvantages

Maturation ponds are land intensive.
Sludge from flotation process contains algae and iron compounds; algae can create odour and fly nuisance on drying beds; high proportion of iron restricts disposal outlets.
Algae can release soluble organic compounds which form complex iron or aluminium salts. These complexes can create deposition and dirty water problems in distribution systems.
pH of pond effluent can vary diurnally; careful control of chemical dosing needed.

Ozone-Activated Carbon Treatment

Advantages

Ozone good virucide/bactericide, also effective against cysts/larvae.
Ozone disinfection efficiency unaffected by ammonia content.
Ozone flocculates colloidal and finely divided solids.
Ozone oxidises some carcinogenic/mutagenic compounds. Little evidence that ozone produces pathogenic by-products.
Residual Fe/Mn oxidised and precipitated.
Ozone converts 'hard' high Mwt compounds to lower Mwt biodegradable matter.
Ozonation saturates effluent with oxygen; aids biodegradation process on carbon (extends carbon life).
Only small amounts of chemicals needed and solids (sludge) yields low.
Process easily automated.
Process plant compact, easily 'packaged', additional modules can be added to handle increased flows.
Carbon filters solids, removes residual organics, thereby reducing risk of bacterial 'aftergrowth' in distribution system.

Disadvantages

Large mechanical plant element which is complex and fairly costly to maintain.
Process power demands are high, power supply must be reliable.
For ozone to be effective turbidity levels less than 5 NTU and soluble COD 50mg/l.
Replacement carbon costs are high; carbon usage on small plants insufficient to justify thermal regeneration facilities.
Bacterial growth on carbon makes it essential to chlorinate effluent.
High oxygen demands on carbon bed may lead to deoxygenation; reaeration may be needed to ensure a stable water in distribution.

COST COMPARISON FOR SELECTED PROCESSES

Cost estimates were prepared for the five reviewed processes. These estimates included the following elements:-

o   Capital costs - civil construction, mechanical and electrical plant (M&E).

o   Annual and recurrent costs - chemicals, power, maintenance, manpower.

The processes were designed for construction in two phases, but to simplify comparison, costs have been reported for the ultimate stage plant to treat 5 250m^3/d. Apart from the process based on reverse-osmosis all other processes would provide an average in excess of 5 000m^3/d of effluent for re-use. The reverse-osmosis process would produce only about half this amount.

Costs are based on QI 1985 prices and are summarised for ready comparison in Table 3.

TABLE 3 - CAPITAL AND OPERATING COSTS - ULTIMATE PLANT
All costs in Pounds Sterling (Thousands)

Process	Capital Cost	Annual Costs				Total Annual Costs
		Chemicals	Energy	Maintenance	Labour	
High Lime	926	350	17	13	30	410
Alum Treatment	987	212	16	10	20	258
Reverse-Osmosis	1 420	473	140	105	30	748
Maturation-Flotation	1 871	177	24	10	20	231
Ozone-Activated Carbon	836	165	44	30	10	249

The study indicated that the capital costs for the high-lime, alum treatment and ozone-activated carbon processes (at least within the costing accuracy) were broadly similar. Annual running costs for the alum and ozone processes were essentially the same but the high-lime process was significantly more expensive to operate.

The non-competitiveness of the maturation pond process was mainly due to the high cost of constructing ponds on the rocky ground. With more favourable ground conditions the pond system could well have proved the lowest capital and operating cost process.

The reverse-osmosis process, particularly after due allowance is made for the lower useable water yield, was more expensive to operate than the other processes.

DISCUSSION

On the basis of the costing study there was little to choose between the alum treatment and the ozone-activated carbon processes. In operation however, the alum process used considerably greater quantities of chemicals and produced large volumes of sludge for disposal. In contrast the ozone-activated carbon process was compact, easily automated, produced little surplus sludge and could be installed without any disruption to the existing plant operation. On this basis, had there been considerable operational experience with the ozone-activated carbon process, selection would have been a simple matter.

Only fairly recently, and then almost only by accident, has the synergistic effect of combining ozone and activated carbon been recognised. This was somewhat surprising as it had been fairly widely reported that ozone breaks down complex molecules into smaller more readily biodegradable compounds. Indeed, excessive bacterial growth after ozonation has given problems in water supply systems.

The ozone-activated carbon process was first developed in Mulheim, West Germany[1] for the treatment of water from the lower part of the Ruhr. In this plant it was calculated that the oxygen consumption was about 600g oxygen/m^3 carbon/day and it was this oxygen demand associated with biological activity which increased the capacity of the carbon filters. The lower layers of the carbon bed were still satisfactory after two years' operation.

Since the development of the Mulheim process considerable attention has been focussed on the use of ozone for flocculation and biological activation of carbon in water and wastewater treatment.

In 1978 Miller and Rice[2] reviewed the use of ozone-activated carbon and subsequently Gillies[3] referred to the process as ozone enhanced biologically activated carbon (OEBAC).

Gillies stated that OEBAC had been studied and was operating for water treatment, wastewater treatment, and as part of a physico-chemical treatment scheme with no biological treatment. Also OEBAC results from a Swiss study for tertiary polishing of biologically treated wastewater showed that effluent quality after 50 weeks was still comparable to that reported from new carbon.

Gillies listed the potential advantages of OEBAC as follows:

o   More effective removal of biodegradable and non-biodegradable organics than by GAC or ozone alone.

o   Increases organic loading compared with GAC significantly.

o   Extends time between necessary carbon regeneration (periods of 1 month have been extended to more than 3 years).

o   Applicable to both water and wastewater treatment.

o   Significantly reduces capital, operating and maintenance costs of GAC systems.

o   Prevents anaerobic conditions and resulting problems.

o   Ammonia removal (biological nitrification possible).

McGreary and Snaeyinlk[4] in a review of the results obtained by Eberhardt et al[5] on a pilot plant at Bremen, West Germany reported that during the third year of operation wthout regeneration or replacement of carbon, removals of $KMnO_4$-COD were still in the order of 25 to 30 per cent, apparently entirely by biological activity.

In a later study (1984) Neukrug et al[6] reported that carbon useage could be reduced by over 50 per cent using pre-ozonation. The estimated total first year cost of the ozone-activated carbon system was more economical for TOC control than carbon alone.

Even more recently (1985) one the authors visited a pilot plant in China treating highly polluted river water by the ozone-activated carbon process. After one years operation without regeneration or replacement of the GAC the removals of $KMnO_4$-COD had remained virtually unchanged.

Whatever the precise mechanisms involved in the synergistic relationship it is quite clear that carbon can remove a substantial proportion of the biodegradable compounds released by ozonation and thereby protect the distribution system against excessive bacterial growth. Owing to the biological action it is difficult, if not impossible, to predict the life of the carbon, but for this study it was assumed that after high-level ozonation (10mg/1) carbon life would be extended to at least 6 months and could well extend to 2 or 3 years.

Concern has been expressed that bacterial flora growing on the carbon will be discharged in excessive numbers or release endotoxins. Research studies have demonstrated that a relationship exists between the level of bacteria on the carbon particle and the level of bacteria in the effluent from GAC adsorbers[7]. Frequent backwashing can to a certain extent control the accumulation of bacterial solids and thereby minimise bacterial counts in the treated water.

Examination of the carbon using electron microscopy has revealed that the heaviest bacterial concentrations are in the macropore areas. Most predominant were genus Pseudomonas and Bacillus which have no known pathogenic significance to man. Furthermore, Constantine[8] has reported that in more than 10 years experience in European water treatment plants that employ the ozone-GAC process, no problems have been reported with sudden breakthrough of either bacterial cells, bacterial enzymes or derivatives.

Whilst the authors are not aware of any studies carried out on bacterial regrowth and release from the treatment of ozonated sewage effluent on carbon, there appears to be sufficient evidence from other research to suggest that regrowth of pathogenic micro-organisms should not be a problem. However, even though coliform counts may not increase after the carbon stage, total bacterial counts will increase. Post-chlorination will be needed to reduce these counts and to protect against recontamination in the distribution system.

CONCLUSIONS AND RECOMMENDATIONS

Draft legislation effectively prohibited the unrestricted re-use of treated sewage effluent without the special permission of the controlling authority.

To satisfy the authorities that public health would not be at risk it was necessary that sewage effluent should be treated to a high microbiological quality approaching that of drinking water.

Such water would be acceptable for irrigation use and other non-consumptive uses by flood, hose, spray and sprinkler even in areas of residential and domestic accommodation.

All the processes considered could achieve the high degree of solids removal required to permit the effective disinfection that the target effluent quality demanded.

On the basis of the costing study and operational factors the process based on the use of ozone and activated carbon was preferred for the following principal reasons:

o   effluent quality could be achieved at capital and annual operating costs equal to or less than other methods;

o   its operational efficiency is less vulnerable to the loss of nitrification in the sewage treatment process;

o   it does not require the supply and handling of large quantities of hazardous chemicals;

o   it is relatively compact in terms of land use and can be readily accommodated within the available land area;

o   the quaternary stage plant can be installed and commissioned with little modification to or interruption of operation of the present plant.

If it could be accepted that the demand for water for unrestricted applications did exist and could be further developed then it was concluded that there was justification in using high quality reclaimed wastewater in order to conserve existing resources, and avoid purchasing potable quality water from the public supply system at greater cost.

The study showed that unrestricted irrigation use would demand at least up to 60% of the available high quality effluent.

The study recommended that consideration be given to the construction of a quaternary treatment stage based on the use of ozone and activated carbon filtration.

REFERENCES

1. Sonheimer H et al (1978). Journal AWWA 78 (7), 393-396.

2. Miller GW, Rice RG (1978). Civil Engineering - ASCE 78 (2), 81-83.

3. Gillies MT (ed.) (1981). Noyes Data Corporation, 158-159.

4. McGreary JJ, Snoeyinlk VL (1977). Journal AWWA 77 (8), 437-444.

5. Eberhardt M et al (1975). Gas Wasserfach Wasser/Abwasser (75), 116:245.

6. Neukrug HM et al (1984). Journal AWWA 84 (4), 158-167.

7. Cairo PR et al (1979). Journal AWWA 79 (11), 660-673.

8. Constantine TA (1982). Journal AWWA 82 (6), 310-313.

APPENDIX 1
EFFLUENT STANDARDS FOR RE-USE AND DISCHARGE OF WASTEWATER
All units as mg/l unless otherwise stated

Parameter	Limit not greater than	
	Maximum	Monthly average over any 4 weeks
Physical		
Total dissolved solids	1500	1000
Total suspended solids	15	10
Turbidity (NTU)	5	2
Chemical		
Aluminium	5	1
Ammoniacal Nitrogen (as N)	5	1
Arsenic	0.2	0.05
Barium	2	1
Beryllium	0.3	0.1
Biochemical Oxygen Demand (5 day)	15	10
Boron	2	1
Cadium	0.03	0.01
Chemical Oxygen Demand	100	50
Chloride	350	250
Chlorine, Free Residual (after 60 mins contact time)	0.5 (min)	0.5 (min)
Chromium	0.5	0.1
Cobalt	0.5	0.1
Copper	0.3	0.2
Cyanide	0.1	0.05
Dissolved Oxygen	2.0 (min)	2.0 (min)
Fluoride	2	1
Iron	5	1
Lead	0.5	0.1
Lithium	10	2.5
Magnesium	150	30
Manganese	1	0.2
Mercury	0.005	0.001
Molybdenum	0.05	0.01
Nickel	0.5	0.2
Oil and Grease	5	2
pH (pH units)	6-9	6-9
Phenols	1	0.1
Phosphorus (total as P)	30	20
Selenium	0.05	0.02
Sodium	200	70
Sulphate	400	200
Sulphide	0.1	0.05
Organic Nitrogen (Kjeldahl)	10	5
Total Nitrogen	50	30
Total Organic Carbon	50	20
Vanadium	1	0.1
Zinc	5	2
Bacteriological		
Total Coliforms (MPN/100ml)	23	2.2
Viable Pathogenic Ova and Cysts	None-detectable	None-detectable

INDEX   Author/Title/Keywords